"To preserve the economic viability of the planet must be the first law of
economics. To preserve the health of the planet must be the first
committment of the medical profession. To preserve the natural world as the
primary revelation of the divine must be the basic concern of religion. To
think that the human can benefit by a deleterious exploitation of any phase
of the structure or functioning of the Earth is an absurdity.
The well-being of the earth is primary. Human well-being is derivative."

(FROM: THE UNIVERSE STORY, BY BRIAN SWIMME AND THOMAS BERRY.
LONDON, ARKANA,PENGUIN GROUP, ISBN 0-14019472-X.)

A Low Impact Production by Source Media

In Association with Voice

Published by United Spirit Publications.

Sustainable Ireland

SOURCE BOOK 2000

Ireland's Social, Environmental and Holistic Directory

A GUIDE FOR LIVING IN THE 21ST CENTURY.

EDITED BY Caoimhín Woods & Davie Philip

PUBLISHED BY
US
UNITED SPIRIT
PUBLICATIONS

First published in 1999 by
United Spirits Publications.
166 Lower Rathmines Road.
Dublin 6.

British Library Cataloguing in Publication Data
A catalogue record for this book is available from the British Library.

This book is printed on recycled paper.

ISBN 0 9537445 0 7

The information provided in this publication is advisory. It is not meant to replace medical advice but compliment it. If you have a serious condition or are worried about a particular health issue, it is recommended that you see a medical doctor in the first instance.

Contents

Preface
Introduction
Acknowledgements

11 ENVIRONMENT editorial

INTRODUCTION
by Sean McDonagh, Colomban missionary and chair of VOICE

CONSERVATION
Catherine O'Connell from the Irish Peatland Conservation Council

POLLUTION
Iva Pocock, co-ordinator of VOICE, Voice of Irish Concern for the Environment

ENVIRONMENTAL LAW IN IRELAND
Dr. Sara Dillon of Friends of the Irish Environment

AN INTRODUCTION TO ENVIRONMENTAL EDUCATION
Billy Flynn, manager of the NEEC at Knocksink Wood, Enniskerry

listings:
Animal Rights, Environmental Groups
Environmental Consultants, Education

34 FOOD AND DRINK editorial

INTRODUCTION
by Darina Allen, author, chief from Ballymaloe Cookery School

ORGANIC BOX SCHEMES
Anne Marie Sheridan of Absolutely Organic

FOOD CO-OPS
Gerry Boland, the manager of Dublin Food Co-op.

ORGANIC WINE
Joan Casey, Director of On the Case

VEGETARIANISM AND VEGANISM
Vegetarian Society of Ireland

Genetic Engineered Food
Sabhdh O'Neil, campaigner for Genetic Concern

listings:
Wholefood Shops, Distributors and Box Schemes
Producers, Organic Butchers
Food Co-ops, Societies and Campaign Groups
Education, Organic Wine and Beers
Water, Vegetarian Restaurants, Accommodation

52 AGRICULTURE AND FORESTRY editorial

INTRODUCTION
by John Seymour, environmentalist, author and farmer.

ORGANIC PRODUCTION
Helen Scully from the Organic Trust.

BIODYNAMIC PRODUCTION
Biodynamic producer, Penney Lange.

PERMACULTURE
Marcus McCabe, permaculture designer and eco-village pioneer.

SUSTAINABILITY FORESTRY
Jacinta French, environmental consultant.

COPPICE
T Thomson & M. R. K. Jerram.

SEED SAVING
The Irish Seed Saving Association.

listings:
Organic Standards, Producers Gardens, Permaculture and Consultants, Seeds, Fertilisers and Composting, Seed Saving, Education, Trees, Bee-Keeping, Campaign Groups

72 GLOBAL AND LOCAL editorial

INTRODUCTION BY MARTIN KHOR
Director of the Third World Network in Malaysia

SUSTAINABLE DEVELOPMENT
Member of Comhar, the national Sutainable

DEVOLMENT PARTNERSHIP

MAJORITY WORLD ISSUES
Joe Murray, co-ordinator of Afri, Action from Ireland

CLIMATE CHANGE
Jim Woolridge of Earthwatch

HUMAN RIGHTS AND SUSTAINABLE DEVELOPMENT
Komene Famaa, Ogoni Solidarity Ireland

DEBT
Niamh Gaynor, co-ordinator of Jesuits for Debt Relief and Development

DEVELOPMENT EDUCATION
Thomas Tichelmann, education officer for NCDE

FAIR TRADE
Peter Gaynor of the Irish Fair Trade Network

BIOPATENTS

Contents

Dr. Ruth McGrath of VOICE

listings:
Human Rights/Development Groups, Fair Trade
Campaign Groups, Development Education,
Cross Cultural Groups

97 ENERGY AND TRANSPORT editorial

INTRODUCTION TO ENERGY
Barnie Walsh of ERDA, Environmental Research
and Design Associates

RENEWABLE ENERGY
Ewan Chalmers of the Irish Energy Centre's
renewable energy office

TRANSPORT
Graham Lightfoot, transport consultant
specialising in sustainable transport systems

listings:
Renewable Energy, Transport

110 WASTE editorial

INTRODUCTION
Michelle Hallahan, environmental consultant

RECYCLING IN IRELAND
Bernie Walsh, manager of Sunflower Recycling in
Dublin

**THE LANDFILL CRISIS AND THE
ELIMINATION OF WASTE**
Jack O'Sullivan, environmental consultant

HAZARDOUS WASTE
Anne Marie Cunningham of VOICE

WETLAND SYSTEMS
Feidhalm Harty, environmental consultant

CLEAN PRODUCTION
Beverley Thorpe of Clean Production Action,
Canada.

listings:
General Waste Groups, Recycled Paper
Wetlands, Recycling, Education

129 GREEN BUILDING AND ECOLOGICAL
DESIGN editorial:

ECOLOGICAL DESIGN
by Brian O'Brien, Solearth Ecological Architeture

BUILDINGS AND ARCHITECTURE

**SUSTAINABLE MATERIALS AND HEALTHY
BUILDINGS**

listings:
Architects and Designers, Building
Materials and Technology, Restoration

146 MONEY AND WORK editorial

INTRODUCTION TO MONEY
by Richard Douthwaite, economist and author

LETS
Julia Kemp, freelance journalist and member of
the Bantry LETS

CO-OPERATIVES
Pauric Cannon secretary of the Dublin Food
Co-op

TELE-WORKING
Riona Carroll the Executive Officer of Telework
Ireland

CREDIT UNIONS
Des Gunning, author of, The Fate of the Third
Sector in Ireland

ETHICAL INVESTMENT
Tony Weeks, ethical investment consultant

REINVENTING WORK
Mathew Fox, founder and president of the
University of Creation Spirituality in Oakland

listings:
Sustainable Economics, Co-operatives
Teleworking

165 ARTS AND LEISURE editorial

INTRODUCTION
Ben Whelan co-ordinator of Janus and
Hyperborea.

ECOTOURISM

ART AND SUSTAINABILITY

FESTIVALS

listings:
Ecotourism, Crafts, Arts, Clothing
Sustainable Party Hire

178 SUSTAINABLE EARTH FAIR REPORT

Contents

180 MEDIA editorial

HOW TO WRITE A PRESS RELEASE
George Monbiot, journalist and activist.

listings:
Print Media, Electronic Media

190 COMMUNITY AND FAMILY editorial

INTRODUCTION
Fr. Harry Bohan, chair of the Rural Resource
Development Ltd.

COMMUNITY DEVELOPMENT
Josie Fogarty of Southside Partnership.

Sustainable Rural Development
Ms. Marie O'Malley, Manager of the Rural
Development Unit, UCD.

SOCIAL ECONOMY
Tallaghat Social Economy Unit.

ECO-VILLAGES
Rob Hopkins founding Director of Baile D'Ira.

CO-HOUSING
Robert Alcock of the Dublin Co-housing group.

LOCAL AGENDA 21
member of Northern Ireland's Local Agenda 21
Advisory Group.

listings:
Community Development, Rural Development
Community Education, Eco-Village/ Sustainable
Community, Community Centres, Homeless
Children, Education, Birth and Parenting

215 HOLISTIC HEALTH MIND, BODY, SPIRIT.
editorial

INTRODUCTION TO HEALTH
by Judith Hoad, vibrational medicine
practitioner, writer and teacher

HOMOEOPATHY
Declan Hammond, Director of the Dublin school
of Homeopathy

REIKI
Gwendoline McGowen, Reiki Master and Teacher

SHIATSU
Diana Cassidy a shiatsu practitioner

AROMATHERAPY
Mary Grant of Lifespring and chair of Register of
Qualified Aromatherapists

ACUPUNCTURE
C. Harrison and M. Muldowney, acupuncture
practitioners

CRANIOSACRAL THERAPY
Marion Bellow a Craniosacral therapist

REFLEXOLOGY
Irish Reflexologist' Institute

HYPNOTHERAPY
Dr Joseph Kearney from the Irish Association of
Hypnotherapists

AN INTRODUCTION TO FENG SHUI
By Carmel O'Connor, Feng Shui Consultant

YOGA
The Irish Yoga Association

TAI CHI
Jan Golden, Tai Chi teacher and acupuncture
practitioner

SPIRITUALITY
Darra Malloy, editor of Asling magazine

listings:

Acupuncture, Aromatherapy, Counselling
Chiropody, Chiropractics, Chinese Medicine
Clinics and Healing Centres, Feng Shui
Health Products and Suppliers, Healers
Health Farms, Herbalists, Homeopathy
Hypnotherapy, Kinesiology, Massage Therapy
Meditation, Mind/Body/Spirit
Natural Vision Improvement, Nursing Homes
Osteopathy, Psychics, Reflexology
Rebirthing, Reiki, Shen, Shen Tao
Shiatsu, Tai Chi, Yoga, Women's Health, Animal Care

249 INDEX

255 SOURCE BOOK REGISTRATION FORM

While compiling a directory for environmental, social, and holistic groups and businesses we were thrown into an interconnected world where links and connections appeared at every turn. Nothing less than a hologram could hope to describe this situation adequately. We are unfortunately limited to linear text and its attendant shortcomings.

We have tried to be as complete as possible in our listings and editorials but inevitably there will be omissions and oversights. If you have a business or service that should be listed in further editions of this publication please send us your details by filling out the form at the back of the book. A CD-ROM is being developed for release later in the year 2000 and a 2001 edition of the book will be published in November 2000.

The Source Book has a valuable networking potential. To this end, we have created an e-mail bulletin that will be sent out once a month (so as not to overload your in-box!). The Sustainable Ireland e-mail bulletin will combine short editorials with a calendar of events. To subscribe to this bulletin, or if you have any relevant workshops, lectures, or publications you would like to promote, please send your details to sustainable.ireland@anu.ie

For further information on the Sustainable Ireland project, visit
http://www.sustainableireland.org

We see the Source Book as an ongoing venture which will be enhanced and developed through the opinions of all those who come across it. So if you have any ideas or criticisms you would like to share with us please send them to:

Source Media,
166 Lower Rathmines Road, Dublin 6.
Tel: 01 4911711 Fax: 01 4911710

Awareness of the need for this publication developed at the three Sustainable Earth Fairs that were organised by this book's editors and held at Maynooth University in 1997 and 1998, and at Trinity College Dublin in 1999. The Source Book was a natural follow-on from these events and is a reflection of the dynamic work being carried out in the social, environmental and holistic areas. This timely directory aims to promote sustainable activities and introduce the Irish consumer to natural, ethical and healthy products and services.

The Source Book takes us on a journey through the many exciting solution-driven businesses and services that enhance our health, promote social justice or help us to live in a more sustainable way. Most of the ideas outlined in the book have been developed over the past three decades as awareness of the effects of human activities on the environment has grown. Ideas such as eco-design and permaculture, although relatively new, have enjoyed a rapid growth mainly because of their accessibility and their community focus. Taken as a whole, this book directs you to a more sustainable lifestyle.

A sustainable lifestyle does not require a return to pre-industrial society but a new approach to the future that integrates indigenous wisdom, natural healthcare and beneficial technology. Each of the 12 chapters are introduced by a leading thinker, complemented with additional articles by organisations and individuals working in each area. This book directs you to over 1000 groups and services that can help you live in a healthier, more balanced way.

EDITORS Caoimhín Woods and Davie Philip

PUBLISHER Don Coughlan

PUBLICATION MANAGER Mette Borgstrom

ASSISTANT EDITORS Elaine Nevin and Ben Whelan

DATABASE MARKETING Geni Clarke

SALES Cléo Fenlon

MARKETING CO-ORDINATOR Sarah Murphy

DESIGN AND LAYOUT Roberta McIntyre

DEVELOPMENT TEAM Iva Pocock, Brian O'Brian,

Michelle Hallahan and Niamh Gaynor.

THE SOURCE BOOK WAS PRODUCED IN ASSOCIATION WITH voice

Acknowledgements

Thanks to all those who collaborated with us to shape, develop and produce this book. Thanks to the National Committee for Development Education and the Patagonia Fund for the initial funding to commence the project. Thanks to all the authors who kindly contributed their articles. To Foyle Basin Council in Derry for their on-line support, ENFO and to everyone who attended the Sustainable Earth Fairs.

Thanks to Felix Ford for her illustrations and photographs. Thanks to Joelle Grospelier and Fran Gibson for proof reading and typing, and researchers Chris Gambetese, Bridgit Kavanagh, Sinead O'Higgins and Karl Broughton.

A very special thanks to Don Coughlan for taking this publication on, to Iva Pocock and all at VOICE for their support throughout the production of this book.

Special thanks to Shelley and Áine for their support and tolerating our absence. And finally, thanks to everyone who is working in any way towards a sustainable Ireland.

ENVIRONMENT

page 12 **Introduction** Sean McDonagh

page 17 **Conservation** Catherine O'Connell

page 18 **Pollution** Iva Pocock

page 21 **Environmental Law in Ireland** Dr. Sara Dillon

page 22 **An Introduction to Environmental Education** Billy Flynn

ENVIRONMENT Introduction by **Sean McDonagh**, SSC

Sean McDonagh is a Columban missionary. He worked for 20 years in the Philippines with the tribal people called the T-Boli. He has written three books on ecology, development and religion including *Greening the Church*, and is presently the chair of VOICE; Voice of Irish Concern for the Environment.

Human-Earth interaction at the dawn of the new millennium is totally unsustainable.

During the 20th century, the power unleashed by the newly discovered electrical, chemical, biological and nuclear technologies have begun to inflict damage of a biological and geological order of magnitude on the fabric of life of planet earth. Despite the growing evidence of global and national environmental degradation, the leadership of most of the institutions of society - educational, industrial, commercial, religious - are unaware of the magnitude of the environmental crisis and the urgency with which it must be faced.

Destroying the Earth

I would argue that as we face into the new millennium we are called to face up to the fact that our modern industrial society is also destroying our air, water, and the life-giving quality sunlight; it is poisoning our soils and causing the extinction of a vast number of creatures. The scale of the destruction is enormous. Every part of the globe and every ecosystem on earth has been affected. The damage everywhere is grave: in some situations it is irreversible.

Land

Poor land management, overgrazing, chemical agriculture, deforestation and human population pressures have caused soil erosion and desertification on an unprecedented scale. About 3500 million hectares - an area the size of North and South America -are affected by desertification. Each year at least another six million hectares are irretrievably lost to desertification, and a further 21 million hectares are so degraded that crop production is severely affected.

Professor David Pimentel and his team at Cornell University in Ithaca, New York estimates that world-wide about 85 billion tons of soil are lost each year. Most of this damage, unfortunately, is in the Third World where between 30 and 40 tonnes per hectare are eroded each year. Such a scale of soil erosion is due mainly to deforestation, mono-cropping cash crops and farming on steep hillsides that are unsuitable for annual crops. Even in the US 17 tonnes of topsoil per hectare are eroded with each cropping. Topsoil is precious; without it no crops will grow and pasture land will not be fertile. No machine can readily create topsoil. It builds up slowly and takes between 200 and 1,000 years for 2.5 cm of topsoil to build up.

Most of the money invested in agriculture in recent decades, especially by multilateral lending agencies like The World Bank was used for mega-projects like irrigation or for farm machinery, agricultural credit and petrochemicals. This form of agriculture is extremely expensive. It benefits the oil companies, manufacturers of farm equipment, banks and the large farmers. But it has impoverished the poor, and in many parts of the world it has destroyed the fertility of the soil and is unsustainable.

Repeated research in many parts of the world has demonstrated that the most successful programmes aimed at halting desertification and soil erosion are, in fact, cheap, local, small in scale and run by those who are most intimately affected. They involve tree planting, improved farming techniques, especially small-scale organic farming and better land use. Unfortunately very little money has been made available by governments or multilateral lending agencies for such programmes.

Water

Human activity is polluting water in the oceans, rivers, aquifers and lakes. More than 97 per cent of all the water on Earth is seawater. During the UNESCO proclaimed International Year of the Ocean in 1998, it emerged that the oceans are being over-fished and polluted at an unprecedented rate. Important areas of the oceans close to the continental shelf are contaminated with human, agricultural, industrial and radioactive waste. Much of this is toxic and carcinogenic. Because we have tended to treat the oceans as sewers the Baltic, Mediterranean, Black, Caspian, Bering, Yellow and South China Sea have all been seriously damaged in recent decades. The waters of the Black Sea, once a flourishing eco-system, are now considered to be 90 per cent dead. The Aral Sea has diminished by one-third and what remains is heavily polluted.

Over-fishing is depleting the oceans and leaving them barren. It is like killing the goose that lays the golden egg. Many people feel that the oceans are so vast and the variety of fish so abundant that there would always be vast quantities of fish in the sea. We are now learning how false those assumptions are. According to a report by the UN Food and Agricultural Organisation (FAO) in 1995 over 70 per cent of the world's marine fish stocks are either "fully-to-heavily exploited, overexploited, or slowly recovering".

When only one plant becomes extinct, along with it will disappear the 20 to 40 animal and insect species that rely on it. Kenny Ausubel

Fresh Water

Only one per cent of the fresh water of the world is available for human use in either agriculture, industry or for domestic purposes. Worldwide demand for water is doubling every 21 years and access to this water is very inequitable. Supply cannot keep pace with demand as populations soar and cities explode. The situation in the Middle East and North Africa is precarious. North East China, Western and Southern India, Pakistan, much of South America and Central American countries like Mexico face water scarcity.

Water in Ireland

Ireland is blessed with a plentiful supply of rain. Nevertheless the quality of water in many Irish rivers and lakes has deteriorated in recent decades. Fish kills, unfortunately, still happen each summer. This is due to the increased levels of phosphorus entering our rivers from a variety of sources, including sewage treatment plants, factories and farms. The subsequent algal bloom depletes the supply of oxygen and causes the fish to die. The Coast Watch report for 1997 complained that the excessive use of nitrate and phosphate fertilizers was polluting Ireland's coast to a "very worrying" degree.

There is also grave concern about the quality of ground water. A March 1999 EPA Report states that 40 percent of group water schemes in rural Ireland are contaminated with the E-coli bacteria which makes the water unfit for human consumption.

The Greenhouse Effect

The atmospheric concentration of carbon dioxide, methane, CFCs and other "greenhouse" gases are expected to increase by 30 percent during the next 50 years. This build-up is likely to increase the Earth's surface temperature by between 1.5 and 4.5 degrees centigrade by the year 2030. This will cause major, and in the main, deleterious climatic changes. The changes will have major, but as yet unpredictable, effects on agriculture and natural eco-systems. As the oceans warm up and expand, sea levels will rise, leading to severe flooding over lowland areas like Bangladesh. Storms of great ferocity like hurricane Mitch that slammed into Central America in October 1998 will probably become more frequent.

In the run up to the United Nations meeting on climate change in Kyoto, Japan in December 1997, a group of almost 2000 scientists that comprise the Intergovernmental Panel on Climate Change (IPCC) called for a 60 per cent reduction in the use of fossil fuel. Unfortunately, the politicians who attended the meeting could only agree to a miserly 5 to 7 per cent reduction.

Rich nations, including Ireland, are mainly to blame for global warming. A 1993 booklet produced by the World Council of Churches (WCC) 'Signs of Peril, Test of Faith' indicates that between 1800 and 1988 rich countries emitted 83.7 per cent of all greenhouse gases while poorer countries contributed only 16.3 per cent. Ireland is set to breach the 2010 target which we signed up to at Kyoto a decade early - testimony to our fossil fuel addicted economy. We need an urgent and concerted effort to move away from fossil fuels and to promote alternative sources of energy like wind, solar and wave power.

Tropical Forests

Tropical forests once covered almost 10 per cent of the land area of the earth. This is no longer so. They are disappearing at an extraordinary rate. An area greater than the United Kingdom is cleared and destroyed each year. The forests have been cleared through logging, cattle ranching and opening up lands for agriculture. This is deemed necessary because much of the arable land in tropical countries is in the hands of a small percentage of the elite and very few governments or international development agencies are willing to promote and fund widespread land reform.

Tropical deforestation wipes out 17,000 species of plants and animals per year, that is 48 species made extinct every day or 2 per hour.
Worldwatch Institute

Effects of Tropical Deforestation

The destruction of the tropical forests has many adverse effects. Massive soil erosion results in a decrease in agricultural productivity and consequent malnutrition and even famine. Siltation also destroys the health and productivity of nearby rivers, lakes and estuaries.

The greatest tragedy of all is the mega-extinction of species which follows in the wake of the destruction of the forests. It is estimated that human activity is extinguishing species at "1,000 times the natural rate seen in evolution".

If the present rate of extinction continues fifty per cent or even more of all the life-forms on earth could be extinguished during the next few decades. This "extinction spasm" is one of the greatest set backs to life's abundance and diversity since the first flickering of life emerged almost four billion years ago.

Given the history of forest exploitation Irish people should be very sensitive to forest destruction. In 1600 over 12 percent of the country was covered in broadleaf forests. The 18th century saw a concerted attack on Irish forests. By the time the Act of Union was passed in 1800 only 2 percent of the country was covered in woodland. Since the foundation of the State the forest cover in Ireland has increased, but the bulk of the planting unfortunately is made up of Sitka Spruce rather than native broadleaf trees.

It would also seem that we Irish have learned nothing from the forest mining that marred our own country during the second half of the present millennium. We are now the largest per capita importers of tropical wood in the European Union. Imports grew a staggering 64 per cent during the decade between 1977 and 1987. Most of our tropical wood, especially iroko, comes from West Africa forests which are being logged in an unsustainable way. If the present rate of depletion continues the forests there will be gone within five years.

Waste and the Disposable Society

The unsustainability and vulnerability of our present day global industrial and commercial society is also very evident when one looks at the rubbish heaps which have continued to grow higher and higher in recent decades.

In 1998 in Ireland on average each individual generated half a tonne of waste. Between 1984 and 1995 there was a 62 per cent increase in the level of household and commercial waste. Ninety two percent of this waste ends up in landfills, but space is running out. Despite efforts by waste management groups to promote landfills or incinerators very few communities want either in their backyard.

The Irish Environment

During the past 25 years the increase in industrialisation and intensive agriculture has taken its toll on the Irish environment. The Environmental Protection Agency's (EPA) report for 1998 concedes that Ireland's environmental problems are intensifying with economic growth. Ironically, their main worry is that environmental degradation might scupper the "Celtic Tiger". They seem to forget that Ireland's economic growth has been pursued at the expense of the environment.

Summary

One could continue to pile depressing data on data, but the data I have presented above gives us a valid framework with which to begin to appreciate what is happening to our planet and happening locally in Ireland. Human industrial activity is changing the chemistry of the air and water, altering the hydrological cycles and upsetting the entire self-renewing pattern of nature that has taken billions of years to emerge. Only now are we beginning to wake up to the consequence of our activity. It is now threatening the very survival of many of the Earth's creatures, including human beings. We can only turn back the tide by pursuing fundamentally different policies across a wide range of human activities. *The Sustainable Ireland Source Book* signposts many of the necessary changes.

Conservation Catherine O'Connell Irish Peatland Conservation Council

In the last 20 years there has been increasing concern in Ireland about the loss of species and their habitats and the general depletion and exhaustion of natural resources. Humans have shaped the present landscape of Ireland. The country has been extensively deforested and is unusual in Europe (along with Scotland and Iceland) in having so much open, treeless landscape. Only tiny fragments of native forest, which once covered most of the country, survives. Ireland's abundance and diversity of living

Felix Ford

organisms (biodiversity) is naturally low, being an island outside the natural range of many continental European species, but there are unusual assemblages of species, such as in the Burren, and the island is one of the last outposts for a number of peatland types in Western Europe. Ireland is also internationally important for its seabird colonies and migratory waterfowl.

Ireland was a "late starter" in developing its conservation policies. It has the smallest area of land devoted to nature protection of any European country, and landscape protection policy is also poorly developed. In view of this fact there is a very strong network of non-governmental organisations who campaign independently, and who work with the Government to ensure the conservation of species and their habitats. They are also calling for a range of environmental policies to be put in place that will ensure the wise use of natural resources in the future.

2.5 million tons of pesticides are used globally each year. The World Health Organisation estimates that as many as 20,000 deaths occur annually from pesticide poisoning. Worldwatch Institute

Pollution

Iva Pocock co-ordinator of VOICE, voice of Irish Concern for the Environment

The dictionary definition of pollution - 'the contamination of one substance by another so that the former is unfit for its intended use' - is limited and anthropocentric. Pollution does not just affect substances which can be used by humans, it affects all of nature. It takes many forms - noise, radiation, heat, chemical - and effects land, air and water. It knows no boundaries - the wind and the rivers do not recognise political borders, nor are the oceans separate entities. Pollution now even reaches beyond planet Earth in the form of space junk.

Despite international agreements and the adoption of pollution prevention policies by governments throughout the world over the last 25 years, pollution levels are higher now than ever before. The 1999 United Nations Environment Programme (UNEP) report Geo-2000 on the global environmental crisis concluded that things are worse now than ever before and that 'postponing action is no longer an option'. Essentially, all the predictions about environmental destruction and pollution made 30 years ago are correct, except that the destruction is happening at a far faster pace than previously thought.

So what is the solution to pollution? Perhaps the first thing to realise is that pollution does not just affect the environment, it affects people. A polluted environment means polluted people. An average European woman now has over 60 persistent toxic chemicals in her breast milk, not because she chose to ingest them but because her air, food and water is polluted. As the relationship between pollution and disease is increasingly acknowledged, the impetus for creating a pollution-free life increases. The Sustainable Ireland Source Book offers practical, positive advise for making these changes. It is a small response to an overwhelmingly negative story, providing pointers for individuals in their quest for a more sustainable life.

The concept of sustainable development does imply limits- not absolute limits but limitations imposed by the present state of technology and social organisation on environmental resources and the ability of the biosphere to absorb the effects of human activities. But technology and social organisation can be both managed and improved to make way for a new era of economic growth.
Brundtland Commission

What kind of world do you want for your children?

Is it a place where our rivers continue to be used as sewers,
our soil polluted by intensive agriculture,
our biodiversity threatened by genetically engineered organisms,
our air poisoned by unseen chemicals?

Saving the earth begins at home

VOICE is working to protect your environment.

VOICE is Ireland's leading environmental organisation.

VOICE is leading the campaign for safe, clean water. We are campaigning to end chemical pollution of our rivers and seas. We are campaigning to end fluoridation of our drinking water. In 2000 we launch our river catchment awareness roadshow, which will tour nationwide.

VOICE is committed to protecting biodiversity. By leading the Irish campaign against biopatents we are opposing genetic engineering Corporations' quest to monopolise global food diversity.

We are playing a key role in the establishment of internationally recognised ecological forestry standards for Ireland and are calling for planting of native tree species.

We have forged vital partnerships with other organisations. We are supporting the publication of the Sustainable Ireland Source Book. As part of the National Waste Working Group we are bringing innovative, dynamic ideas to key decision makers who are dealing with the waste crisis.

Here's what you can do

Support VOICE by
Giving £4 a month by standing order
Details overleaf
**£4 a month is not a lot
but together we have a strong VOICE**

If you give just £4 a month then we have a regular income all year round. This means we can plan our campaigns. By supporting us you are adding your voice to the thousands who will not remain silent while the Irish environment is destroyed for our children.

If you are a supporter of the Irish environment recycle this page now. Complete the Standing Order below and send it to VOICE today.

Can you think of a better way.

VOICE STANDING ORDER FORM

Please complete Parts 1 to 4 to instruct your Bank to make a standing order payment to VOICE and then return the form to: VOICE, 7 Upper Camden Street, Dublin 2.

---

1. Please write the name and full postal address of your bank and branch:

_____

2. Name of Account Holder:

_____

3. Branch Sort Code [_____] Account Number [_____]

4. YOUR INSTRUCTIONS TO THE BANK AND SIGNATURE

_____

_____

Please pay VOICE Ltd., the sum of £4 ☐ £6 ☐ or other £ [_____]

PAYABLE EVERY MONTH.

starting on [_____] and debit my bank account.

Signature: _____

Date: _____

PLEASE RETURN YOUR COMPLETED APPLICATION FORM TO:
VOICE, 7 Upper Camden Street, Dublin 2.

Phone: 01-6618123 Fax: 01-6618114
E-mail: avoice@iol.ie Web: www.voice.buz.org

CUT HERE

Environmental Law in Ireland

Dr. Sara Dillon Friends of the Irish Environment

Many people do not realise that most of Ireland's environmental law derives from European legislation. Thus, the Irish government is under an obligation to fulfill its European law obligations, and citizens in Ireland have a right to insist on this. EC directives on the environment cover a broad range of issues, from air and water quality, through bio-diversity and environmental impact assessments.

While European environmental directives generally look impressive on paper, it can be extremely difficult to ensure that the Irish government is in full compliance with them.

Citizens have the right to bring complaints to the attention of the European Commission's Directorate General dealing with the environment. The Commission will not investigate on its own, but it will accept evidence from citizens that the Irish authorities are not honouring European law obligations. In very compelling cases, the Commission may even proceed to bring a legal action against the Irish authorities before the European Court of Justice. Such cases establish important principles for the future application of European environmental law in the Member States.

Under European law, many kinds of developments require environmental impact assessments [EIA] when they are "likely to have significant effects on the environment". This is particularly true when the project may have an effect on an area designated for nature protection or is identified as ecologically vulnerable under EU directives. Unfortunately, the planning authorities seem often to think that the filing of an impact study [Environmental Impact Statement or EIS] by the developer is the whole environmental impact assessment. However, properly understood, the environmental impact assessment must be carried out by the official decision maker in the form of a systematic analysis of the possible effects on the environment of a particular development, taking into account the comments of all the interested public. In this regard, recent attempts to restrict public participation in the planning process under proposed Irish legislation is likely to be found inconsistent with European environmental law.

While far from perfect, European environmental law grants Irish citizens, along with citizens from all the Member States, important rights to be involved in the protection of their own environment. The trend in other European countries is definitely towards a stronger role for citizens in terms of comment, objection, and ultimately rights to proceed to court to have decisions affecting the environment reviewed in the light of European law principles. Friends of the Irish Environment urges citizens in Ireland to read and study the many environmental directives that have emanated from Europe and to insist on their full and proper implementation at national level.

Cairde Chomhshaoil na hEireann Friends of the Irish Environment

European Community:
http://www.europa.eu.int

EU Dublin Information: 01-662-5113 (Research service will call you back).

Local Euro Information Centres:
Dublin 01-2695011;
Galway 091-562624;
Sligo 071-61274;
Cork 021-509044;
Limerick 061-410777;
Waterford 051-872639

EU Environmental Complaints: Environmental Directorate XI, Legal Affairs Division B.3, Rue de la Loi, 200, B-1049, Brussels, Belgium.

Friends of the Irish Environment is a network created by conservationists in Ireland in order to monitor the full implementation of European environmental law, to work for changes in the Irish planning laws, and to pursue concerns and cases in both the built and the natural environment based on the principles of sustainable community development.

[Animal] extinctions are estimated at 1,000 times the natural rate, about 27,000 a year. Kenny Ausubel

An Introduction to Environmental Education
Billy Flynn manager of the National Environmental Education Centre at Knocksink wood, Enniskerry

Environmental education is many things to many people; the environment itself is a concept notoriously difficult to define satisfactorily. Perceptions of our environment and our respective impacts thereupon have undergone several stages of evolution in recent years. From early close association with ecology and natural history, through the many interpretations of concepts such as sustainable development and 'wise use', the environment has remained an elusive subject.

For the same reasons, environmental education has eluded strict definition. The vast scope of this field, encompassing (to name a few) ecology, economics and spirituality, hardly allows for an easy fit into any textbook or curriculum. Understandably enough, educators have thus far been unwilling or unable to take on such subject matter.

The 'environment' has frequently been tied up with particular issues. In themselves, these are often broad and complex, raising questions which lack the straightforward answers readily supplied to 'conventional' problems.

Things are changing, though. From international directives to local initiatives, the notion of empowerment over the fate of our environment has become widespread. Environmentalism is no longer the sole territory of the academic or militant. The diverse ranges of pressures and impacts on the environment have necessitated this change.

The holistic nature of environmental education could thus prove to be its saving grace rather than its downfall. We must respond similarly and think not in the same old terms but across the board. We must learn to view the place of environmental education in the same way as we must view our own place and roles in the modern environment.

The responsibility we bear for educating and being educated about our environment is surely as great as that which we bear for our impact on the world around us.

Green Schools

The Green Schools Programme and Award Scheme is organised by An Taisce in co-operation with local authorities. The programme is operating in 16 European countries to encourage and acknowledge whole school action for the environment.

There are over 300 schools registered throughout the country. Schools which establish all seven steps of the programme and achieve recorded improvements in their environment can apply for a Green Schools Award, i.e. a Green Flag to display inside or outside the school. Winners also receive a certificate and a logo to use on their headed paper or on other publicity material. Three schools have been granted the Award. There are lots of other opportunities for schools to contribute to a more sustainable lifestyle.

EOLAS AR AN gCOMHSHAOL
INFORMATION ON THE ENVIRONMENT

17, St Andrew St., Dublin 2, Ireland
Tel 1890 200 191 or 01 888 3001
Fax: 01 888 3946
e-mail: info@enfo.ie
Website: www.enfo.ie

It's easy to make a difference.
Extracts from the forthcoming ENFO SUSTAINABLE LIVING GUIDE for shoppers and investers.

EU ECO-LABELLING SCHEME

Claims and symbols placed on products by manufacturers are often not substantiated and cause confusion amongst consumers. One way to be certain that a product is truly environmentally friendly is to check whether it displays a recognised eco-label. Eco-labelling is a relatively recent concept in the Irish context but, as criteria for an increasing number of product groups are agreed and as consumers become more aware of the scheme, we can expect to see more products on Irish shelves carrying the label.

WHAT IS THE PURPOSE OF THE EU ECO-LABEL SCHEME ?

The objectives of the EU eco-label scheme are:

- to promote the design, production, marketing and use of products which have a reduced environmental impact during their life-cycle, and

- to provide consumers with better information on the environmental impact of products and to encourage preferential consideration of eco-labelled products in purchasing decisions.

The EU eco-label scheme was established by the European Commission in 1992 and is one element in an overall strategy aimed at promoting environmentally friendly production and consumption. Food, drink and pharmaceuticals are the only product groups excluded under the scheme.

HOW DOES THE SCHEME WORK ?

The present Community scheme for the award of the eco-label consists of four phases:

- the selection of appropriate product groups on the basis of marketing surveys,

- the establishment of ecological criteria for product groups having regard to fitness for use considerations,

- the award of the label to products, and

- the revision of criteria.

Responsibility for establishing and revising the criteria is a matter for the European Commission, in consultation with the Member States and other interests representing consumers, industry and environmental organisations operating at European level. The award of the eco-label to products is a matter for national competent bodies (the Irish competent body is the National Standards Authority of Ireland).

WHAT ARE THE PRODUCT GROUPS FOR WHICH ECOLOGICAL CRITERIA BEEN ESTABLISHED ?

The product groups for which criteria have been established are set out in table 1. (over) Work is also ongoing in the development of criteria for further product groups including, Rubbish Bags, Tyres, Furniture, Tourist Accommodation, Televisions, Shampoos, Batteries and Floor Cleaning Products By late 1999, the number of products awarded the eco-label logo was in the region of 270.

By late 1999 ecological criteria have been set for the following product groups:

TABLE 1

PRODUCT GROUP	YEAR WHEN CRITERIA WERE ESTABLISHED OR REVISED
Washing machines	1999
Dishwashers	1998
Laundry detergents	1999
Textiles	1999
Copying paper	1999
Paints and varnishes	1999
Refrigerators	1999
Tissue paper products	1998
Soil improvers	1998
Bed Mattresses	1998
Personal Computers	1999
Footwear	1999
Dishwasher detergents	1999
Portable Computers	1999
Light bulbs	1999

HOW ARE THE ECOLOGICAL CRITERIA DETERMINED ?

The criteria are determined on the basis of a life-cycle analysis of the product group and are related to issues such as:

- reduced potential for causing pollution to air, water or soil
- economy in the use of energy, water and other resources
- production processes and re-use
- recycling
- disposal of waste.

The Commission undertakes wide consultation with interest groups representing industry, consumer organisations, environmental NGOs and trade unions.

WILL THE PROPOSED REVIEW OF THE ECO-LABEL REGULATION AFFECT THE ON-GOING OPERATION OF THE SCHEME ?

The Commission has presented proposals for the review of the scheme. The proposals involve the streamlining of procedures, clarification of relationship with national labels, such as the Blue Angel and Nordic Swan and the extension of the scheme to some service activities. The scheme will also be opened to retailers for their own brand products.

WHERE DO I GET MORE INFORMATION ?

- Competent Body in Ireland: National Standards Authority of Ireland, Glasnevin, Dublin 9.
  Telephone: 01 807 3800   **Fax:** 01 807 3838   **E-mail:** burnsw@nsai.ie

- Department of the Environment & Local Government,
  Environmental Awareness Section, Custom House, Dublin 1.
  Telephone: 01 888 2616   **Fax:** 01 888 2014
  E-mail: noel_casserly@environ.irlgov.ie

AN ROINN COMHSHAOIL AGUS RIALTAIS ÁITIÚIL
DEPARTMENT OF THE ENVIRONMENT
AND LOCAL GOVERNMENT

- **European Commission Website on eco-labelling:**
  http://europa.eu.int/en/comm/dg11/ecolabel/index.htm

ENVIRONMENT BOOKS

Gaia:
the Practical Science of Planetary
Medicine
James Lovelock
ISBN: 185675040X, 1991.

Silent Spring
Rachel Carson
ISBN: 0140273719, 1999.

Biopiracy:
the Plunder of Nature and Knowledge
Vandana Shiva
ISBN: 1870098749, 1998.

The Dream of the Earth
Thomas Berry
ISBN: 0871566222, 1990.

Woodlands
British Trust for Conservation Volunteers
Series.

Drystone Walling
British Trust for Conservation Volunteers
Series.

Footpaths
British Trust for Conservation Volunteers
Series.

Waterways and Wetlands
British Trust for Conservation Volunteers
Series.

Fencing
British Trust for Conservation Volunteers
Series.

Hedging
British Trust for Conservation Volunteers
Series.

Tool Care
British Trust for Conservation Volunteers
Series.

The Heritage Council. (1999). `Policies
and Priorities for the National Heritage:
Forestry and the National Heritage'.
Kilkenny.

Forest Service. (1996). `Growing for the
Future: A Strategic Plan for the
Development of the Forestry Sector in
Ireland'.
Government Publications, Dublin.

Higman, S. (et al). (1999). `The
Sustainable Forestry Handbook'.
Earthscan, London.

The natural step for business; wealth,
ecology, and the evolutionary corporation
Brian Natrass and Mary Altomare,
Gabriola Island, British Columbia,
Canada: New Society Publishers, 1999.
ISBN 0-86571-384-7.
See www.newsociety.com.

ENVIRONMENT WEB SITES

The International Council for Local
Environmental Initiatives
http://www.iclei.org/
WWF: http://www.worldwildlife.org/
Earthwatch Institute
http://www.earthwatch.org/
Earth Vision
http://www.earthvision.net/
Greenpeace
http://www.greenpeace.org

ENVIRONMENTAL ORGANISATIONS

AN TAISCE -
The National Trust for Ireland

Contact: The Secretary
Tailors Hall, Back Lane, Dublin 8

Tel: 01-4541786
Fax: 0-4533255
E-mail: planning@connect.ie
Website: www.antaisce.org

A voluntary organisation founded in 1948 to advance the conservation and management of Ireland's natural and built endowments in manners which are sustainable.

BURREN ACTION GROUP

Contact: Michael Miller
Clogher, Kilfenora, Co. Clare

Tel: 065-7088187
Email: burrenag@iol.ie
Website: http://www.iol.ie/~burrenag

BAG evolved in 1991 as a local response to oppose plans by the Irish National Parks and Wildlife Service to develop a large scale interpretive centre at Mullagmore in the Burren, Co. Clare, Ireland.

COLIN GLEN TRUST

Contact: John Terrington
Forest Park Centre, 163 Stewartstown Road, Belfast, Co. Antrim

Tel: 0801-232 614115
Fax: 0801-232 601694
E-mail: info@colinglentrust.org
Website: www.colinglentrust.org

A cross-community environmental organisation which aims to protect and enhance the Colin river corridor in West Belfast. The Trust manages the Colin Glen Forest Park and provides education and volunteering opportunities.

CONSERVATION VOLUNTEERS IRELAND

Contact: Melanie Hamilton
The Green, Griffith College, S.C.R, Dublin 8

Tel: 01-4547185
Fax: 01-454 6935
E-mail: info@cvi.ie
Website: www.cvi.ie

Conservation Volunteers Ireland is a leading practical environmental organisation. It provides year round opportunities for volunteers to protect and enchance the environment. Activities including weekend and weeklong working holidays one day weekend and ten day training courses.

DU GREENS SOCIETY

Contact: Chris Dardis
Box 23, Regent House, Trinity College, Dublin 2

Tel: 01-6081827
Fax: 01-6778996
Email: greens@csc.tcd.ie/~greens
Website: www.csc.tcd.ie/~greens

We are a student society who aims to inform and involve our members in green issues and activities. We hold weekly discussions, host talks and workshops and lend our support in an active way to many campaigns.

EARTHWATCH /
FRIENDS OF THE EARTH IRELAND

Contact: Tonia McMahon
7 Upper Camden Street, Dublin 2

Tel: 01-4973773 or 01-4973374
Fax: 01-4970412
Email: foeeire@iol.ie
Website: www.iol.ie/~foeeire/
Environmental Campaigning Organisation
We work actively to promote sustainable development and environmental protection based on principles of equality and public participation.

ENVIRONMENTAL PROTECTION AGENCY

Contact: Annette Cahalane
PO Box 3000, Johnstown Castle Estate, Wexford

Tel: 053-60600
Fax: 053-60697
E-mail: a.cahalane@epa.ie
Website: www.epa.ie

Independent public body established under legislation to promote improved environmental protection. The EPA has a wide range of powers and functions which include the licensing and regulation of activities with significant polluting potential.

ECOLOGY SOCIETY
NUI GALWAY

Contact: Maread Ni Chaoimh
Ecology society, Comhaltas Na Mac Leinn, NUI, Galway

Tel: 091-528140
Fax: 091-750566
E-mail: maread.nichaoimh@nuigalway.ie

To promote environmental awareness in the university through campaigns and inviting speakers in. To create a cohesive social grouping or environmentally interested students through social nights, weekends away etc. To carry out practical work such as recycling of glass, cans on campus. To publish an annual magazine "GAIA". Increase awareness around Galway generally through exhibitions and forthcoming publication "Green Guide for Galway Students" etc.

ENVIRONATURE RECOVERY ASSOCIATES

Contact: R. John Gibson
29 North Avenue, Mount Merrion, Co.Dublin
Tel: 01-2835887
Email: Gibby@iol.ie
Website: www.webpage.ca./enra

Our goals include the rehabilitation of lands and
waterways presently damaged by construction so
that these sites become natural, self-sustaining
ecosystems. We present educational and
illustrated talks demonstrating natural and
damaged stream ecosystems.

ENVIRONMENTAL ACTION ALLIANCE (EAA)

Contact: David Malone
40 St. Josephs Terrace, Portalington, Co. Offaly
Tel: 0502-23567
E-mail: davidmalone@freenet.ie

Environmental Action Alliance-Ireland works with
groups in enforcing European environmental
directives. It registers companies to European
Commission and prepares High Court actions for
groups.

FRIENDS OF THE IRISH ENVIRONMENT

Contact: Tony Lowes
Allihies, Co.Cork
Tel: 027-73025
Fax: 027-73131
Email: tony@tinet.ie
Website: http://www.anu.ie/wirl/friends/home.htm

Friends of the Irish Environment is a network
created by conservationists in Ireland in order to
monitor the full implementation of European
environmental law, to work for changes in the Irish
planning laws, and to pursue concerns and cases
in both the built and the natural environment
based on the principles of sustainable community
development.

GREEN PARTY COMHAONTAS GLAS

Ecological Politics
Contact: Stephen Dawson
5A Upper Fownes St., Dublin 2
Tel: 01-6790012
Fax: 01-6797168
E-mail: greenpar@iol.ie
Website: www.greenparty.ie

The Green Party is a political party campaigning
on environmental, social and justice issues. It is
now represented at every level of government in
Ireland - at local, national and European
Parliament level.

IRISH PEATLAND CONSERVATION COUNCIL

Contact: Peter Foss
119 Capel Street, Dublin 1

Tel: 00353-1-8722397
Fax: 00353-1-8722397
Email: ipcc@indigo.ie
Website: http://indigo.ie/~ipcc

Peatland Conservation and Education.
IPCC aim to conserve a representative sample of
bogs for future generation to enjoy. Our work
includes buying bogs, campaigning, education and
helping community initiatives.

IRISH WILDLIFE TRUST

Contact: Shirley Clerkin
107 Lower Baggot Street, Dublin 2
Tel: 01-6768588
Fax: 01-676 8601
E-mail:enquiries@iwt.ie

To conserve Ireland's wildlife and habitats (rare
and common) using campaigning, lobbying and
education.

IRISH DOCTORS ENVIRONMENTAL ASSOCIATION

Contact: Dr. P. Cullen or Elizabeth Cullen
34 Halliday Square, Stoneybatter, Dublin 7
Tel: 01-6703422
Email: idea@tinet.ie

IDEA was founded in 1997 with the intention of
highlighting the link between health and the
environment. Our concerns include pollution of air,
water and soil, possible adverse health effects
from GM food. Exploring link between electro
magnetic radiation and health, and the association
between ill health and poverty affiliated to ISDE.

IRISH WOMENS' ENVIRONMENTAL NETWORK

Contact: Jennifer Wann
Carmichael House, North Brunswick Street,
Dublin 7
Tel: 01-8732660
Fax: 01-8735737

Education, sustainable lifestyle, consumerism.
We aim to enable women and men to live a
sustainable lifestyle and work for the betterment of
our environment through the provision of
information, talks and representation.

INISHOWEN ENVIRONMENTAL GROUP CO-OPERATIVE SOCIETY LTD

Contact: Evleen Harvey
Mogheramore, Carndonagh, Co. Donegal
Tel: 077-74579
Email: jamhouse@esatclear.ie

Lobbying and public education on local, national
and global environment issues. Part of a network
of environmental groups in Donegal and Northwest
Northern Ireland. Currently working on campaigns
regarding waste management, genetically modified
organisms and justice.

KEEP IRELAND OPEN

Contact: Roger Garland
43 Butterfield Drive, Dublin 14

Tel: 01-4934239
Fax: 01-4934239
E-mail: rgarland@tinet.ie

Preservation of Rights of Access.
Preserving rights of access to the countryside
particularly natural amenity - mountains, beaches,
lakes, rivers etc. for ourselves, our children and
our children's children.

LANDSCAPE ALLIANCE IRELAND

Contact: Terry O'Regan
Old Abbey Gardens, Waterfall, Co. Cork

Tel: 021-871460
Fax: 021-872503
Email: lai.link@indigo.ie

Landscape Alliance Ireland is a partnership of
individuals, non-governmental organisations,
representative organisations, public officials
committed to quality in our shared landscape and
the view that landscape should be managed in its
totality: urban, suburban and rural rather than the
present piecemeal approach.

MACROOM DISRICT ENVIRONMENTAL GROUP

Contact: Pete Hayward
South Square, Macroom, Co. Cork

Tel: 0260-42498 (wk) 026-48208 (hm)
Fax: 026-42498
E-mail: mdeg@oceanfree.net

Environmental matters both local and global.
The group has been operating for 16 years and is
involved in seed saving for an indigenous tree
masonry, waste management, magazine
production, organic gardening and supplying
environmental information.

MOVILLE / GREENCASTLE ENVIRONMENTAL GROUP

Contact: Rose Kelly
Ballybrack, Moville Co.Donegal

Tel: 077-82950

The Moville/Greencastle is a voluntary organisation
whose members seek to protect the environment
from violation and to promote sustainable living
for individual and the community.

SAVE OUR LOUGH DERG (SOLD)

Contact: Paddy Mackey
Ballyhogan, Ballycommon, Nenagh, Co.Tipperary

Tel: 067-24315
Fax: 067-24315
Email: badoir@iol.ie

Water Quality Campaign on River Shannon.
SOLD is a representative action group dedicated

to the environmental rescue of Lough Derg and
the River Shannon. Main activities lobbying and
education.

THE WILDFOWL AND WETLANDS TRUST

Contact: James Orr
Castle Espie, Ballydrain Road, Comber Down,
NI BT23 6EA

Tel: 0801247-874146
Fax: 0801247-873857
E-mail: james.orr@wwt.org.uk

WWT exists to promote the conservation of
wetlands and their biodiversity worldwide by
concentrating on wetland birds, particularly
threatened waterfowl and their habitats. This is
carried out through research, conservation and
environmental education programmes.

TRINITY GREENS

Box 23, Regents House, TCD, Dublin 2

Tel: 087-2811985
E-mail: clnichea@tcd.ie

Trinity Greens is a student organisation which
aims to promote sustainability environmental
awareness and multicultural tolerance. We try to
tackle practical issues around campus and in the
Dublin area and to create a broad network of like-
minded people.

VOLUNTEER RESOURCE CENTRE

Contact: Sandra Velthuis
Carmichael Centre for Voluntary Groups
Coleraine House, Coleraine St., Dublin 7

Tel: 01-8722622
Fax: 01-8735737
Email: vrc@tinet.ie

Services: Information on volunteering
opportunities, database of volunteers,
matching/placement service, training programme,
fact sheets, consultancy. Library of resource
materials, help desk, meetings, talks and
presentations. (Most services are free-of-charge.)

WICKLOW PLANNING ALLIANCE

Contact: Judy Osbourne
Cronroe, Ashford, Co. Wicklow

Tel: 0404-40523
E-mail: judyosbourne@tinet.ie

The Wicklow Planning Alliance is an alliance of
organisations dedicated to the achievement of
better planning in County Wicklow, for sustainable
and balanced development achieved through an
open and inforcable planning process.

BRAADE/CARRICKEIN CONSERVATION GROUP

Contact: Michael Gillespie
Airport Rd., Braade, Kincasslagh, Co. Donegal
Tel: 075-48873
Fax: 075-43107
E-mail: birdfarm@indigo.ie

To maintain the integrity of the special area of conservation around Donegal Airport and to oppose the siting of inappropiate industry in scenic rural areas of Donegal or other special areas of conservation.

TCD ENVIRONMENTAL SOCIETY

Box 14, The Atrium, TCD, Dublin 2
E-mail: enviro@csc.tcd.ie

College society dealing with environmental issues.

VOICE

Contact: Iva Pocock
7 Upper Camden St., Dublin 2
Tel: 01–6618123
Fax: 01–6618114
E-mail: avoice@iol.ie
Website: www.voice.buz.org

Voice is Irelands leading environmental organisation founded in 1997 following the cloosure of Green Peace Ireland. A membership based organisation VOICE campaigns for positive solutions to environmental problems. For membership details see ad.

CONSERVATION VOLUNTEERS NORTHERN IRELAND

Contact: Ian Humphreys
Tel: 0044–2890645169
Fax: 0044–2890644409
E-mail: l.humphreys@btcv.org.uk
Website: www.btcv.org.uk/cvni

Conservation Volunteers Northern Ireland supports over 4000 community groups, schools, families, individuals and businesses involved in practical conservation projects - providing an advice line (0845–6030472), site visits, training and information.

ENVIRONMENTAL CONSULTANTS

ENVIRONMENTAL EFFICIENCY CONSULTANTS LTD.

Contact: Rob Suttcliffe
48 Main St., Bray, Co. Wicklow
Tel: 01-2761428
Fax: 01-2761561
E-mail: energy@iol.ie
Website:www.enivro-consult.com

Environmental efficiency consultants specialise in energy and environmental audits to help others reduce environmental impact, reduce costs and achieve best practice. Services include laboratory, implementation, feasability studies, IES, IPC applications.

ENVIRONMENTAL MANAGEMENT SERVICES

Contact: Jack O'Sullivan
Outer Courtyard, Tullynally, Castlepollard, Co. Westmeath
Tel: 044 -62222
Fax: 044-62223
Email: 100065.1471@compuserve.com

Environmental Management Service Ltd. (EMS), founded in 1981, is the longest established environmental consultancy in Ireland and specialises in providing environmental advice and assistance to local community groups, international organisations, businesses and Governments. Specialist areas of expertise include planning appeals and oral hearings, submissions to the Environmental Protection Agency, landfill site evaluations and reports, coastal resources management, aquaculture studies and reports, eco-auditing and environmental management systems, institutional strengthening and capacity building training, environmental mediation and dispute resolution, development of public participation in environmental decision-making, rural development issues, investigation of pollution by oil and other substances, environmental impact assessments and reviews of industrial and infrastructure projects, ecological surveys and baseline studies, and legal research relating to environmental issues.

COMMUNITY ENVIRONMENTAL SERVICES

Contact: Jack O'Sullivan
Outer Courtyard, Tullynally, Castlepollard, Co. Westmeath
Tel: 044-62222
Fax: 044-62223
E-mail: 100065.1471@compuserve.com

Community Environmental Services is a registered charity established in 1994 to provide advice and assistance on environmental issues at affordable rates exclusively to local citizens' groups and other voluntary organisations seeking to improve environmental quality or to prevent environmentally damaging activities.

DAVID HEALY & ASSOCIATES

Contact: David Healy
54 Evora Park, Howth, Co. Dublin
Tel: 01-8324087
Fax: 01-8324087
E-mail: verdire@eircom.net

Environmental consultant and campaigner-particularly air pollution, planning, waste, environmental law and environmental policy issues.

Consultation service provided for community groups, campaign groups, individuals and businesses.

CLEAN TECHNOLOGY CENTRE

Contact: Tadhg Coakley
Unit 1, Melbourne Business Park, Model Farm Road, Cork, Co. Cork

Tel: 021-344864
Fax: 021-344865
Email: ctc@cit.ie
Website: http://cleantech.cit.ie

Environmental consultants / advisors.
Proponents of sustainable development since 1991. Environmental consultants and adivsors to industry, local authorities, governments, European Commision etc. Environmental awareness raising, training aims and development, cleaners production and technology, promoting environmental strategy development.

SEE ENVIRONMENTAL RESOURCES MANAGEMENT P. 33

EDUCATION

ECO-UNESCO

Contact: Grainne O'Leary
26 Clare Street, Dublin 2

Tel: 01-6625491
Fax: 01-6625493
Email: ecouneso@tinet.ie

Promoting Environmental Awareness & Education. ECO is a national voluntary youth organisation aimed at the personal development of young people through environmental training and activity and the conservation of the environment. ECO promotes environmental awareness through the running of the ECO community tree nursery in Finglas and environmental projects nationwide.

NATIONAL ENVIRONMENTAL EDUCATION CENTRE (NEEC)

Contact: Billy Flynn
Knocksink Wood, National Nature Reserve, Enniskerry, Co.Wicklow

Tel:01-2866609
Fax: 01-2866610
E-mail: billy@iet.ie

The NEEC is a joint initiative of DIT and Duchas the heritage service, which provides environmental education for visiting groups of all ages and the general public. Our motto-'Bringing Environmental Science to Life'.

THE EARTH EDUCATION CENTRE

Contact: Padraig Fahy
Dromcollagher Enterprise Centre, Dromcollagher,

Co.Limerick
Tel: 063-83472

The Earth Education Centre is an established teaching institute which aims to bring the importance of the environment and nature into the classroom. We use active education techniques to teach primary organic gardening, recycling, tree cultivation and seed saving.

TIDY NORTHERN IRELAND

Contact: Peter McGaffin
35-37 Talbot Street, Belfast, Co. Antrim BT1 2LD

Tel: 0801-232 328105
Fax: 0801-232 326645
E-mail: tni@tidybritain.org.uk
Website: www.tidybritain.org.uk

To educate and enable the public to be more responsible in the disposal of waste, not litter or permit dog fouling and encourage the creation of high quality local environments.

ENFO

Contact: Odette Gormley
17St. Andrew Street, Co.Dublin

Tel: 1890-200191 or 01-8882946
Email: info@enfo.ie
Website: www.enfo.ie

Environmental Information Service
Our role is to collect and maintain up-to-date information on all aspects of the environment and to make it readily available to anyone who wants it. Our information centre provides an attractive atmosphere for school children on group outings or pursuing individual projects. It offers facilities for an in-depth study and research by third level students, researchers, consultants, journalists, environmental groups and others.

ENVIRONMENTAL EDUCATION FOR SCHOOLS AND ORGANISATIONS

Contact: Elaine Nevin MA, Hdip in Ed.
3 The Orchard, Seapoint Ave., Blackrock, Co.Dublin

Tel: 01-2301181

Elaine Nevin is qualified teacher experienced in environmental education. Involved in writing Environmental Education Packs for various environmental organisations. Issues include water, waste, recycling, development issues, etc. Available to research and compile environmental education material for use in Secondary schools and Youth groups and to prepare and give workshops on environmental and development topics.

SEE GOING FOR GREEN P 33.

THREE ROCK INSTITUTE

Contact: Goff Lawlor
Rosedale, Quinn's Road, Shankill, Co.Dublin
Tel: 01-2827331
Fax: 01-2820237
Email: tri@indigo.ie

The Three Rock Institute is a solution based organisation involved in awareness, research and education for sustainable development. Our vision is to advance socially, economically, and environmentally sustainable practices and technologies that return the power and control of our lives and environment to the individual and community. Facilitating change through dialogue, respect, co-operation, personal example and education, our aim is to maximise opportunities for individuals, organisations and communities to move towards the realisation of the sustainable vision in all areas of life. Three Rock Institute does this through sustainable skills training workshops, demonstration eco-house, round table discussions, eco-consultancy. Contact us for a schedule of events or more information.

ARMAGH CITY AND DISTRICT COUNCIL

Contact: Rachel Cooper - Education Officer,
The Palace Stables Heritage Centre
The Palace Demesne,Armagh, Northern Ireland
Tel: 0801-861 529629
Fax: 0801-861 529630
E-mail: education@armagh.gov.uk
Website: www.armagh.gov.uk

Environment education.
The education programme provides focused experimental learning opportunities on various environmental themes throughout the year. Action Grasshopper holiday clubs (7 to 12 years) have an environmental focus. For more information contact the Education Department.

SONAIRTE-THE NATIONAL ECOLOGY CENTRE

Contact: Sean McCabe
The Ninch, Laytown, Co.Meath
Tel: 041-9827572
Fax: 041-9828130
E-mail: sonairte@drogheda.edunet.ie

Environmental visitor and education centre. Centre for raising environmental awareness. Riverside nature trail, organic garden. Renewable energy park. Natural gift shop, coffee shop. Tours for schools, adult courses, open to public.

THIS WORLD SERVICES

Contact: Catherine Caulwell
Gardenfield, Drumcollogher, Limerick
E-mail: taobiol@hotmail.com

Permaculture and Group Facilitation. Empowering and informative workshops on environmental and permaculture issues with a local and global perspective. Catherine uses creative REFLECT-ACTION methods to facilitate active participation and group decision making processes.

ANIMAL RIGHTS

IRISH COUNCIL AGAINST BLOOD SPORTS

Contact: Aideen Yourell
30 Austin Friars Street, Mullingar, Co. Westmeath
Tel: 044-49848
Fax: 044-49848
Email: icabs@tinet.ie
Website: http://homepage.tinet.ie/~icabs

The Irish Council Against Blood Sports campaigns, via peaceful and legal means, for the abolition of legal blood sports in Ireland, principally hunting and killing wild animals with dogs.

ASSOCIATION OF HUNT SABOTEURS IRELAND

Contact: Colm
PO Box 4734, Dublin 1
Tel: 087-2386023
Email: huntsabs@emc23.tp
Website: www.emc23.tp/huntsabs

Campaigning demonstrations and direct legal action for hunted wildlife. We campaign directly in the fields on a weekly basis using hunting horns and fake scents to disrupt, usually, a foxhunt between October and March. Members welcome especially with transport.

BADGERWATCH IRELAND

Contact: Bernadette Barret
5 Tyrone Ave., Waterford
Tel: 051-373876
Fax: 01-373876
E-mail: barretb@indigo.ie

Environment / Wildlife Welfare.
Badgerwatch is a voluntary group trying to help badgers in practical ways. We encourage understanding, tolerance and respect. We oppose all types of badger persecution, be it legal or otherwise. Publishes "An Oroc".

DUBLIN SOCIETY FOR PREVENTION OF CRUELTY TO ANIMALS

Contact: Irene Shirley
Woodtown Cottage, Stocking Lane, Rathfarnham, Dublin 16
Tel: 01-4935502
Fax: 01-493 7674
Email: dspca@tinet.ie
Website: www.dspca.ie

Prevention of cruelty to animals and providing shelter for them. Protecting animals from cruelty since 1840. Animals who are abandoned, cruelly treated or injured are cared for at our shelter. We need your charity donation if we are to continue to help animals in need. We never say no to a call for help, please don't say no to ours.

FRIENDS OF ANIMALS (FAO)
Contact: Ann Fox
3 Fr. Griffin Ave, Galway, Co. Galway
Tel: 091-567269
Fax: 091-566251

FAO is committed to the belief that no healthy dog or cat should be destroyed, that all dogs and cats should be protected, wanted and suitably homed for life and cared for by responsible owners and that all animals should be respected. We campaign to promote pet responsibilty through neutering and spaying of dogs and cats, the licencing and control of the breeding of dogs (to alleviate the number of animals destroyed each year - because they are unwanted) and respect for animals through proper care.

IRISH ANTIVIVSECTION SOCIETY
Contact: Yvonne Smalley
P.O. Box 13, Greystones, Co. Wicklow
Tel: 01-2820154

The IAVS campaigns for the abolition of animal experiments on moral and scientific grounds. Pending this we encourage the use and development of non-animal based methodologies.

NORTHERN IRELAND ANIMAL RIGHTS CAMPAIGN (NIARC)
Contact: Beverly/Gareth
NIARC, PO Box 1115, Belfast
BT1 1AT, Co. Antrim
Tel: 0801232-687296

NIARC campaign to expose abuse ad exploitation behind all animal based industries and promote cruelty free living and vegan diet. Please send an A5 stamp addressed envelope with a donation.

SEE ALSO:

BIG GREEN ART
Promotion of environmental and social self-consciousness through public art.
Full listing: Arts and Leisure section.

PURE H2O STEAM DISTILLED WATER
Domestic and commercial steam water distillation units.
Full listing: Food and Drink section.

EARTHWATCH (MAGAZINE)
A broad based magazine discussing global issues, green politics.

Full listing: Media section
ECO-SEEDS
Workers co-op growing native wildflowers in organic peat-free media.
Full listing: Money & Work section

ENVIRONMENTAL EDUCATION

GOING FOR GREEN
Contact: Jenny Crawford
35-37 Talbot Street, Belfast, BT1 2LD, N.I.
Tel: 0801 232 245077
Fax: 0801 232 326645
E-mail: tni@tidybritain.org.uk
Website: www.gfg.iclnet.co.uk

Environmental campaign promoting the green code. Key themes are minimising waste, saving energy, travelling sensibly, saving water and biodiversity. It focuses on working with schools and community organisations. Various publications.

ENVIRONMENTAL CONSULTANT

ENVIRONMENTAL RESOURCES MANAGEMENT (ERM)
Contact: Dr. Kevin Bradley
6 Merrion Square, Dublin 2.
Tel: 01 662 0499
Fax: 01 676 9502
E-mail: kxb@ermuk.com
Website: www.erm.com

FOOD & DRINK

page 35 **Introduction** Darrina Allen

page 38 **Organic Box Schemes** Anne Marie Sheridan

page 39 **Food Co-ops** Gerry Boland

page 39 **Organic Wine** Joan Casey

page 40 **Vegitarianism and Veganism** Vegitarian Society of Ireland

page 41 **Genetically Engineered Food** Sadhbh O'Neill

FOOD/DRINK Darina Allen

Darina Allen owns and runs the Ballymaloe Cookery School with her husband Tim, in Shanagarry, Co Cork. Darina presents the 'Simply Delicious' cookery series on Irish television and has written over 10 books, many of which are bestsellers. Darina is currently on the Food Ingredients Subsidiary Board of An Bord Bia and on the Board of the Irish Organic Centre.

Ireland is a small island nation with a wonderful growing climate but despite our many natural assets the reality is - we simply cannot compete with the larger countries on economy of scale.

The way forward, it seems to me, is to capitalise on our clean green image and target the fast-growing niche market for top quality naturally produced food. We are hugely fortunate in this country to still have this clean green image, albeit somewhat tarnished. Bord Bia markets Ireland as 'Ireland the food island', so it is absolutely vital that we do not just pay lip service but absolutely understand that our future prosperity, particularly the prosperity of our farmers, food manufacturers and tourist industry depends on not merely trading on this green image, but delivering the quality produce that the image promises.

In the recent past, some sections of our society have been, to say the least, cavalier with this precious asset and consequently we are in real danger of losing this priceless marketing tool. There have been several damning articles in German and French periodicals pointing out that the reality does not match the image. Tourist figures are already reflecting this publicity as reported in the Irish Independent on Friday 2nd April. Bord Failte has described it as a 'communication challenge'!

Ireland, with its lush green grass and high percentage of fertile land, should be leading the way in Europe. Instead we are trailing behind and as our government procrastinates other countries forge ahead maintaining their environmental integrity. What we need in Ireland are some visionaries in government who realise the urgency, people who can see the potential of the organic market and value in PR terms of declaring Ireland a GMO free zone, so we can capitalise on the market for GMO-free produce, which due to consumer demand is growing daily.

As each new food scandal breaks and the demand for safe naturally produced food grows even louder, Ireland could be ideally situated to fill that demand and should be ready to do so with confidence in its integrity.

Admen know full well what it costs to create a good brand - millions and millions of pounds - Ireland's green image is worth a fortune, once lost it will be an adman's nightmare to rebuild an image despoiled.

food + drink

Nowadays it becomes more and more difficult to find food that has been non-intensively produced. The main focus of modern agriculture and agri-business is higher and higher yields, yet most of the current problems in farming are caused by over-production. Many farmers feel helpless and despondent as prices fall. The Common Agriculture Policy, which promised so much, is generally considered to be a disaster, creating false expectations and a tangled web of subsidies, much of which has been abused and wasted.

Gradually, farmers and agri-business are beginning to realise that we cannot go on indefinitely pushing animals and plants beyond their natural limits without serious repercussions. Already the results of this arrogant attitude to nature are evident for all to see - BSE, Salmonella, E-Coli and anti-biotic resistance which many scientists and doctors predict will be more serious than BSE and AIDS.

Felix Ford

All ancient cultures from time immemorial understood that they had to live in harmony with nature or disaster would ensue. How many more signs do we need before the 'powers that be' finally concede that sustainable agriculture and horticulture is the only way forward.

Those of us who are concerned about the food we eat need to seek out food that is less intensively produced, preferably chemical, pesticide and GMO free. This however is easier said than done in an age when many farmers are being forced to produce food at an uneconomic price to fulfil the unreasonable demand for cheap food which the consumers have come to expect as their right.

The direct consequence of this unrealistic expectation has been that farmers have been left with little alternative but to intensify production and cut corners to survive. Loss of quality and flavour and a build up of disease have been the result of this Catch 22 situation where there are no winners.

Eventually the public are going to have to accept the basic fact that we simply are going to have to pay more if we want healthy wholesome naturally produced food - the reality is we can't have it both ways.

Those of us who cook for other people have quite a responsibility, its not merely a question of rustling up delicious meals for family and friends. Thoughtful cooks and chefs, and I don't just mean professionals, will realise that our responsibility doesn't end there. In the current climate of food scares and changing production methods we need to inform ourselves on how our food is produced and where it comes from and armed with this information, act accordingly. For this reason I would venture to say that our food shopping is one of the most important tasks that we perform. To a great extent what we choose to put in our shopping basket will to a great extent determine the energy, vitality and well-being of those we feed.

Just a few years ago people who claimed to have a food allergy were considered to be neurotic. Nowadays an alarming number of people are complaining of allergies, the rise in the number of coeliacs, people suffering from asthma and yeast allergies is rising dramatically. People are not imagining it; the symptoms are real and many although not all is related to the food we eat. In the past year alone there has been a 50% increase in allergies to soya, one must ask why, soya was one of the first crops to be grown from GM seed. It is estimated that one third of the 1998 crop was grown from GM seed, however the US more or less refuses to segregate the ordinary soya from genetically engineered soya, so as a result a far higher percentage contains GMOs. 70-80% of processed foods contain either soya or maize. Most products are still, despite public outcry, inadequately labelled so virtually everyone will have eaten foods containing GMOs at this point in time, whether we like it or not. Consequently no epidemiological study can be done because there can be no control group, so we have no way of knowing whether the dramatic increase in allergies to soya has any connection to genetic modification.

Current nutritional advice urges us to eat more fruit and vegetables, yet most of what is available for sale is laden with pesticides, a fact that EU and national regulators feel unnecessary to point out on the label. Neither is food that has been irradiated properly labelled, despite the fact that scientific opinion is divided on the issue.

On the other hand, small artisanal producers and butchers are having an increasingly difficult time keeping up with the tidal wave of health regulations which are threatening to engulf them. Free-range chicken and pork is virtually impossible to find, there are less than a handful of producers in the entire country, so for most people intensively reared chickens and pork are the only option. Much of this has been reared on feed that contains anti-biotics and anti-depressants, bone strengthener, muscle strengthener and fat re-enforcer. The real price of an organic free-range chicken is £11-£12, a fact that many people have difficulty accepting. For economic reasons there are people who do not have the luxury of being able to make the choice, but a growing number have and for them it is a question of priorities. Often the very same people who happily spend £60-£100 a week in the pub will be shocked at the idea of spending £40-£50 more a week on food for the family. Yet, how much more important is it in terms of good health? So lets get our priorities right.

- As far as possible know the source of your food.
- Eat fresh naturally produced food in season.
- Support local producers and your local family butcher.
- Seek out organic and free-range produce. Enrol in a box system if there is one in your area.
- Best of all discover the joy of growing your own produce, even if its only some lettuce and herbs in a window box.

The World Commission on Environment and Development in their report, Our Common Future, defined sustainable development as "meeting the needs of the present without compromising the ability of future generations to meet their own needs."

Organic Box Schemes Anne Marie Sheridan (Absolutely Organic)

You've made the decision; you're going to eat organic food from now on. You find your local shop has little but the odd organic lettuce and the vegetables and fruit in the supermarket are all covered in cling film. This is a very familiar scenario. What's the alternative? One option, which is growing in popularity is the box system. This is where you buy a box of vegetables directly from the grower either at the farm gate or from a home delivery service.

The majority of the box systems focus on providing a range of seasonal vegetables which are grown locally by fully certified organic producers. The benefits to the customer are that a regular supply of organic produce is guaranteed. By eating locally produced food your diet is seasonally attuned and your body is therefore getting the nourishment it needs when it needs it. By buying directly from local producers you are supporting the local economy, encouraging the development of environmentally sound farming practices and promoting choice. The benefits to the farmer are that they have a ready and appreciative outlet for their produce. This provides security to the farming community and encourages more farmers to convert to organic methods.

Check to see if there's a box system in your area as the first step to your personal sustainability plan.

> Of the 7,000 or so types of plants that have been used by humans, only 20 species now provide 90% of the world's food. Merely 3 of these- wheat, corn and rice-account for 50%. Yet from 30,000 to 80,000 plants have some edible parts. Kenny Ausubel

Food Co-ops Gerry Boland the manager of Dublin Food Co-op

Consumer food co-operatives are trying to provide more than a place to shop. Their primary desire is not to keep improving profit, but to offer a better service to their customers and to reduce the impact of their practices on the world as a whole. These ends are achieved through member participation, education and a more holistic view of management practices. In explaining the impact of individual purchases, providing the information for the individual to make a knowledgeable choice to reduce the negative effects of consumption, and creating a community atmosphere which allows the individual to feel comfortable in their purchases. Food co-operatives give the consumer a sense of empowerment over their purchasing habits. Rather than a business where maximum gains go to the shareholders at the expense of everyone else, consumer food co-operatives are developing a business environment where consumers and suppliers, rather than adding to the world's growing problems, become participants in creating solutions.

Common principles of cooperatives worldwide

- voluntary and open membership
- democratic member control
- member economic participation
- autonomy and independence
- education, training and information
- cooperation among cooperatives
- concern for community

Organic Wine Joan Casey, Director of On the Case

Organic wines come from grapes like "normal" wines, they look and smell like "normal" wines and contain alcohol like "normal " wines. The difference is that organic wines are produced without man-made pesticides, fertilisers or flavour enhancers. This leads to fewer allergic reactions, less toxic hangovers and truer regional characters and tastes. No wonder so many organic wines win awards. They are simply wines made the age-old way, without recourse to modern chemicals.

For a wine to be deemed organic, a recognised organic certification body must approve it. In France, the top three bodies are Ecocert, Nature en Progres and Terre et Vie. Individual country organic associations in most cases recognised by IFOAM, the International Federation of Organic Agricultural Movements, carry out certification of organic wines. IFOAM is an umbrella body that co-ordinates and stringently regulates the very best organic practices.

In organic vineyards, green manures, animal manures, composts and mineral and seaweed compounds are used to improve soil fertility. This makes the vines healthier, which in turn minimises pest and disease attacks and raises resistance and recovery rates. If problems do occur, natural biodegradable sprays or biological controls are used. This "treat the cause not the symptom" approach contrasts sharply with conventional methods that draw the vines into a vicious chemical circle of dependence because their defences have not been naturally built up. Treating pest infestation organically can be simple. Some suppliers solve vine caterpillar infestation by introducing tiny wasps whose larva eat the caterpillars and ignore the vine. Another common pest and disease prevention practice is interplanting, where other plants, flowers, vegetables and herbs are introduced alongside the vines. Not only can this supply extra nitrogen to the vines but animals, birds and insects enter the environment and devour the pests as part of a vine-friendly eco-system.

The definition of "sustainable development" coined by the Brundtland Commission is open to a wide range of environmentally damaging interpretations and does not adequately recognise the intrinsic right of the environment and its living creatures to their own existence, independently of any service they may provide to humankind, i.e., it is far too anthropocentric. We need to take account of a growing awareness that human beings are not necessarily the centre of creation. (Jack O'Sullivan: Defining Sustainability; Notes for M.Sc. in Sustainable Development, DIT, 1998).

Vegetarianism and Veganism Vegetarian Society of Ireland

A vegetarian is someone who does not consume meat, fish or fowl and who aims to avoid the use and consumption of battery hen eggs and slaughterhouse by-products in food, clothing, cosmetic and household products.

A vegan is one who adopts a way of living which seeks to exclude all forms of exploitation of, and cruelty to, animals for food, clothing or any other purpose. In dietary terms veganism refers to the practice of dispensing with all animal produce - including eggs, animal milks, honey and their derivatives.

Animal farming represents a squanderous misuse of scarce natural resources and is a major contributor to environmental destruction. Vegan diets use less land, water and fuel and are gentler on the planet and its inhabitants.

A typical four ounce hamburger made from rainforest beef involves the destruction of 55 square feet of tropical rainforest
Worldwatch Institute

Genetic Engineered Food **Sabhdh O'Neil** campaigner for Genetic Concern

Genetic engineering

For many centuries, human societies have been breeding wild plants in order to confer traits that make them easier to grow or to eat. Unlike traditional breeding, genetic engineering allows scientists to cross plants in a manner that would never happen in nature. A rose would never naturally cross with the potato for example, since there are natural limits which prevent genes mixing between unrelated species.

It is now possible to isolate the genes which are responsible for certain characteristics of a plant or animal and transfer this gene into the cells of another species.

There are growing concerns about the use of this technology in food and agriculture. It has implications for animal welfare, food security in developing countries, food safety and the environment.

Animal welfare

Genes can be transferred from any living organism, including its human beings and animals, to other organisms. Salmon have been genetically modified in Scotland to grow much bigger than wild salmon, and at faster rates. Other experiments have gone disastrously wrong, resulting in deformed cattle and chickens. There is a wider question of whether it is ethically permissible to engineer animals in order, for example, to develop certain traits or get higher milk yields (using the genetically engineered BST hormone) at the expense of animal welfare.

Food security

It is argued by biotechnology companies that genetic engineering will "feed the world". However, famine is caused by many diverse factors including

Photo: Felix Ford

debt, poor food distribution, war and poverty in general, and it is too simplistic to suggest that biotechnology will solve or overcome these problems, never mind promote sustainable development.

Over 1.4 billion farmers around the world collect, save and exchange seed -a practice that would be forbidden under the licence agreements used by multinationals. There are patents pending for "Terminator Technologies" - crops engineered to produce sterile seed in a further effort to restrict the "illegal" use of seed by farmers.

Food safety

Because genetically engineered crops are treated as if they were "substantially equivalent" to conventional foods, they receive very minimal testing for food safety. Very little is known about the way in which genes function, especially in groups, when moved across species.

Genetic modification could result in the production of toxins which may provoke allergic reactions. Other concerns include the potential effects of virus and antibiotic resistance genes used during the genetic engineering process. These concerns also apply to the use of genetically modified organisms in animal feeds, since these are ultimately part of the human food chain too.

Environmental risks

Genetic engineering poses a particular threat to biodiversity, since crops designed to be resistant to herbicides can be sprayed with broad-spectrum herbicides without damaging them. This means that everything in the field dies accept the crop, including non-target plants and insects. Pollen from genetically engineered crops can cross-contaminate other related crops and related wild species. This could result in the spread of resistance to weeds, limiting farmers' weed control options in the long term.

There is emerging evidence that genetically engineered maize harms beneficial insects, including the Monarch butterfly. Other risks include horizontal gene transfer, where genes from the transgenic crop pass into soil micro-organisms, and increased resistance of insects to pesticides.

Flouride By Voice

Would you believe:

- 98% of Europe's drinking water is fluoride-free
- the fluoride added to Irish drinking water is toxic waste from the fertiliser industry
- the assertion that fluoride is good for teeth is a myth - in fact countries with the best dental health do not fluoridate their water
- there is enough fluoride in a tube of toothpaste to kill a small child.

Ireland is the only democracy in the world with compulsory nationwide water fluoridation. Most of our European neighbours banned fluoridation in the 1970s for health and environmental reasons.

International research has shown a link between fluoridation and bone cancer, arthritis, osteoporosis, hip fractures, memory loss, irritable bowel syndrome, genetic damage and immune system damage. Despite the serious health risks posed by exposure to fluoride no research has been done on the health effects of over 30 years of fluoridation in Ireland. Why do one in five Irish adults have irritable bowel syndrome? Why are more and more women in their 30s and 40s suffering from oesteoporosis? If fluoridation has been shown to increase cancer in the USA why isn't it stopped immediately?

Given the huge weight of international evidence that fluoridation is damaging to health it is scandalous that the Irish Government is extending the national fluoridation programme.

VOICE is calling for

1) an immediate halt to fluoridation of water supplies in Ireland.

2) abandonment of plans to extend fluoridation to non-fluoridated water supplies in Ireland.

3) comprehensive scientific studies into the health effects of over 30 years of fluoridation on the Irish population.

4) repeal of The Health (Fluoridation of Water Supplies) Act 1960 and related legislation as a Government health priority.

For an information video on flouradation contact VOICE (£5 incl. p&p)

food + drink

FOOD AND DRINK BOOKS

Diet for a Small Planet
Frances Moore Lappe and Marika Hahn
ISBN: 0345373669, 1991.

**Good Enough To Eat? -
How We Shop, What We Eat**
Maureen Tatlow
ISBN: 0717126978, 1998.

**Keeping Food Fresh -
old world recipes and techniques**
Terre Vivante with Elliot Coleman
ISBN: 1890132101, 1999.

**Land of Milk and Honey -
the story of traditional Irish food and drink**
Brìd Mahon
ISBN: 185371142X, 1991.

The Food We Eat
Joanna Blythman
ISBN: 0718139127, 1996.

Whole Foods Companion
Dianne L. Onstad
ISBN: 0930031830, 1996.

In Praise of Apples
Mark Rosenstein
ISBN: 1579901247, 1999.

Ripest Apples
R. Palmer
ISBN: 0952910004, 1996.

Apple Games and Customs
Geraldine Bracey
ISBN: 1870364120, 1994.

**Eat Your Genes - how genetically modified
food is entering our diet**
Stephen Nottingham
ISBN: 1856495779, 1998.

**Genetic Engineering, Food and Our
Environment: a brief guide**
Luke Anderson.
ISBN: 1870098781, 1999.

**The Permaculture Book of Ferment and
Human Nutrition**
Bill Mollison
ISBN: 0908228066, 1993.

FOOD AND DRINK WEB SITES

Genetic Engineering Network
http://www.dmac.co.uk/gen.html

One World Online
http://www.oneworld.org/guides/biotech/front.html

Greenpeace
"http://www.greenpeace.org/~usa/reports/biodiversity/roundup

Friends Of The Earth
http://www.foe.co.uk/camps/foodbio/index.htm

S.H.A.G for a better world!
http://host.envirolink.org/shag/

The Pure Food Campaign
http://purefood.org/index.html

How To Avoid GE Foods
http://wkweb4.cableinet.co.uk/pbrown/index.htm

Simon Wright's Organic Food Site
http://www.organic.dircon.co.uk/

Earth First
http://www.k2net.co.uk/ef/

Totnes Genetic Engineering Group
http://visitweb.com/totnes

Genetic Engeneering Network
http://www.dmac.co.uk/gen.html

Genetic Concern
http://www.vibrantplanet.com/geneticconcern/

WHOLEFOOD SHOPS, DISTRIBUTORS, BOX SCHEMES AND CATERERS.

WELL AND GOOD

Contact: Jill Bell
Broderick Street, Midleton, Co. Cork
Tel: 021-633499
Fax: 024-94232

Well & Good specialises in organic and standard wholefoods, bread, teas, dairy and sugar-free products. We carry a wide and expanding range of nutritional, herbal and homeopathic remedies.

Food For Thought

Contact: Paul Brogan
Lower Main Street, Buncrana, Co. Donegal

Inishowen's Health Food shop carrying a large range of alternative products. Delivery to all parts of Inishowen weekly and a full range of treatments available on our premises.

Tel: 077-63550 Fax: 077-63550

ORGANICO HEALTHFOOD SHOPS

Contact: Caroline Dare
2 Glengarriff Road, Bantry, Co. Cork
Tel: 027-31391

The largest healthfood shop in West Cork. Wherever possible we stock the organic alternative, including cheese, wine, fruit, vegetables, bread and babyfoods. Also herbal products, health information, classes, talks, books.

OTTO'S CREATIVE CATERING

Contact: Otto Kunze
Dunworley, Butlerstown, Bandon, Co.Cork
Tel: 023-40461
Fax: 023-40482
E-mail: ottokunze@tinet.ie

Growing, preparing and promoting of organic food. (veg, fruit, herbs) Organic Trust Symbol No. 97. Sourcing of organic produce and wild edibles. Catering Consultancy, cookery courses and party catering.

MEANWELL WHOLEFOODS

Contact: Roy & Tina Power
56 Henry Street, Kilrush, Co. Clare
Tel: 065-9053203
Fax: 065-9053203

Ethically sound family run wholefood business. Selling various organic wholefoods, organic fruit / vegetables, natural remedies and crafts. Box scheme in operation. Local delivery service available to customer / business on request.

KERAS WHOLEFOODS

Contact: Jacqui Hersey
Main St. Ennistymon Co. Clare
Tel: 065-7071258

Selling GMO-free, natural whole and organic foods, teas, herbs, spices and Irish Cheeses. Also homoeopathic, herbal and Bach Flower remedies, essential oils, tissue salts, nutritional supplements and reference books, etc.

THE GRAINEY

Contact: Trudy Kay and Anna Martin
Main Street, Scarriff, Co. Clare
Tel: 061-921265
Fax: 061-921271
Email: kaytrudy@hotmail.com

Wholefoods, homoeopathic remedies, herbal products, biodegradable cleaning agents, recycled paper, crafts, jewellery, cards, organic cheeses, cakes, breads, vegetables, free range eggs, honey. Emphasis on locally produced and fairly traded goods.

SIMPLE SIMON

Contact: Andrew Cape
Anderson's Yard, The Diamond, Donegal Town, Co. Donegal
Tel: 073-22687
Fax: 073-22687

North West's leading healthfood store trading in organic vegetables, farmhouse cheeses and delicious wholefood, breads and cheeses baked on the premises. Organic fruit and vegetables available. Leading suppliers of supplements on remedies.

FOOD FOR THOUGHT

Contact: Paul Brogan
Lower Main Street, Buncrana, Co. Donegal
Tel: 077-63550
Fax: 077-63550

Inisowen's Health Food shop carrying a large range of alternative products. Delivery to all parts of Inisowen weekly and a full range of treatments available on our premises.

WHOLEFOODS WHOLESALE LTD.

Contact: Brendan Clifford
Unit 2D, Kylemore Industrial Estate, Killeen Road, Dublin 10
Tel: 01-6262315
Fax: 01-6261233
Email: wfws@iol.ie

Wholefoods Wholesale distribute a very large range of health foods and health food supplements, vitamins and minerals, herbal and homoeopathic products in Ireland. Wholefoods Wholesale are the official agents for Bioforce herbal products. Quest vitamins and ESU aloe vera products.

THE HOPSACK

Contact: Erica Murray
Swan Centre, Rathmines, Dublin 6

Tel: 01-4960399
Fax: 01-4960399
Email: hopsack@iol.ie

We provide the products, advice and information you require to help you on the road to a healthier and more harmonious life.

KERAS
Wholefoods

Main St. Ennistymon Co. Clare
Tel: 065-7071258

Selling GMO-free, natural whole and organic foods, teas, herbs, spices and Irish Cheeses. Also homoeopathic, herbal and Bach Flower remedies, essential oils, tissue salts, nutritional supplements and reference books, etc.

CONTACT: JACQUI HERSEY

ABSOLUTELY ORGANIC

Contact: John Healy
38 Ormond Road, Dublin 6

Tel: 01-4968912/01-4975566
Fax: 01-4968912
email: absolorg@indigo.ie

Absolutely Organic provide a weekly delivery of organic vegetables, fruit, bread and eggs to your residence across the Dublin Area. Enjoy the benefits of organic fresh foods with regular personal service.

RAINBOW WHOLEFOODS

Contact: John Linden
North Main St., Wexford

Tel: 053-24624
Fax: 053-24624

We sell wholefoods, organic foods, organic fruit and vegetables, natural supplements, herbal supplements, essential oils, flower remedies, crystals and native American products. Information on althernative therapies, workshops diet and health.

THE GOOD FOOD STORE

Contact: Vanessa Clarke
7 Pembroke Lane (off Waterloo Rd.), Dublin 4

Tel: 01-6675656 / 087-6874367
Fax: 01-6675656
E-mail: goodfood@eircom.net

We sell a variety of foods all of which are traceable, none are GM and a large portion of which are organic. We also do catering (corporate or private), hampers & wholesale.

AN GRIANAN

Contact: Elaine Avery
An Grianan, Dykegate Lane, Dingle, Co. Kerry

Tel: 066-9151910
Fax: 066-9151910

Offering a wide range of organic foods, including fresh fruits and vegetables. Farmhouse and organic cheeses. Speciality baked goods, deli selection, nutritional supplements. Natural skincare products.

THE PANTRY

Contact: Hugo & Mimi Speytebroodt
30 Henry Street Kenmare Co. Kerry

Tel: 064-42233
Fax: 064-42233

The Pantry is the local wholefood shop. We sell local organic produce, alongside our range of other organic products, natural medicines and delicatessen. Open 6 days a week from 09.30 to 18.00 hrs.

COSGROVE & SON GOOD FOOD SHOP

Contact: Michael Cosgrove
32 Market Street, Sligo

Tel: 071-42809

Excellent selection of wholefoods, delicatessen, fine choice of cheeses, cooked meats, organic wine, large selection of dried fruits, pulses, muesli, homebrew equipment, free range eggs, a family business for over 101 years.

SEE NATURES GOLD HEALTH FOOD SHOP P.51.

BETTER BY NATURE

Contact: Bernie Maher
Market Place, Clonmel, Co. Tipperary

Tel: 052-29411
Fax: 052-35220

Modern healthstore - stocking wholefoods, organic foods, vitamins, supplements, aromatherapy, homeopathy, special dietary foods (gluten & diabetic), body natural care. Books & tapes.

THE HOPSACK

Swan Centre, Rathmines, Dublin 6

We provide the products, advice and information you require to help you on the road to a healthier and more harmonious life.

Contact: Erica Murray
Tel: 01-4960399 Fax: 01-4960399 Email: hopsack@iol.ie

PRODUCERS

NOODLE HOUSE PASTA

Curry, Co. Sligo.

Tel: 071-85589

Producers of organic pasta. As seen in the Irish Food Guide. Available in Superquinn, healthfood shops and delicatessens nationwide.

ARAN SALMON LTD

Contact: Gearoid de Brun
Cill Ronain, Inismor, Aran Islands, Co. Galway

Tel: 099-61240
Fax: 099-61410
E-mail: aransalmon@eircom.net

Suppliers of organic smoked salmon, peat smoked, graved lax, salmon with truffel, salmon with wild garlic, salmon with dill, salmon with basil, salmon with herbs de Provence. Certified organic smokers, supplying smoked organic salmon or bio salmon as it is known on the continent. Also smokers of other products; sea trout, conger eel, mackerel and other fish products.

QUALITY SEA-VEG

Contact: Manus McGonagle
Cloughglass, Burtonport, Letterkenny Co. Donegal

Tel: 075-42159
Fax: 075-42159

Quality Sea-Veg has access to large quantities of common and uncommon sea-weeds harvested from the Atlantic Ocean on the north west of Ireland supplying the food industry and various processing companies.

ORGANIC BUTCHERS

O'TOOLES ORGANIC BUTCHERS

Contact: Danny O'Toole
138 Terenure Rd. Nth., Dublin 6W

Tel: 01-4905457 01-2987940
Fax: 01-4929726

We stock full symbol organic beef, lamb, veg, fruit & eggs, free range chickens & green range pork. We can deliver to 69 destinations throughout Ireland daily. Specialising in organics since 1991.

THE ORGANIC BUTCHER, JOHN DOWNEY & SONS

Connoisseur Foods Ltd.

Contact: Mark Downey
97 Terenure Road East, Dublin 6
Tel: 01-4909239
Fax: 01-4901522

Downey's organic beef, lamb, chickens, turkey and geese. Large selection of wild game, "organically" grown meats from the rich green pastures of the Irish isles.

FOOD CO-OPERATIVES, SOCIETIES AND CAMPAIGN GROUPS

DUBLIN FOOD CO-OPERATIVE SOCIETY LTD.

Contact: Gerry Boland
12a North King Street, Dublin 7

Tel: 01-8730451
Fax: 01-8730452
E-mail: dfc@clubi.ie

A member-owned wholefood and organic food co-operative with over 1,000 active members of which almost 400 work as co-op volunteers. Open every Saturday from 9.30-3.00pm in St Andrews Resource Centre, Pearse Street. Membership open to all. Visitors Welcome.

BELFAST FOOD CO-OP

Contact: Alistair Mullan
Flat 3, 144 Antrim Road, Belfast
Co.Antrim BT15 2AH
Tel: 0801 232-740120

Distributing food to members at wholesale prices, applying ethical standards.
The co-op provides organic, fair trade, cruelty-free food at affordable prices and minimal packaging. It is aiming to develop a localised food source centred on the needs of the community rather than corporate profit.

VEGETARIAN SOCIETY OF IRELAND

Contact: Patricia Timoney
P.O Box 3010, Ballsbridge, Dublin 4
The aim of the Vegetarian Society of Ireland is to inform the people of Ireland about vegetarianism and to co-operate with other organisations promoting vegetarianism, animal welfare and animal rights.

VAVIG VEGETARIAN AND VEGAN INFORMATION GROUP

Contact: Beverly/Gareth
PO Box 1115 Belfast BT1 1AT, Co. Antrim, NI
Tel: 0801 232-687296

VAVIG campaigns to promote a cruelty free and healthier lifestyle for humans and expose abuse behind all establishments which promote animal exploitation. Send an A5 Stamp addressed envelope with donation.

MACROBIOTIC ASSOCIATION

Contact: Derek & Kathleen Halpin
Altidore Castle, Kilpeddar Co.Wicklow
Tel: 01-2811573
E-mail: grainheadz@tinet.ie

A support group which promotes a more natural and healthy lifestyle through harmonious eating habits.

GENETIC CONCERN

Contact: Jo Goldsmith or Sadhbh O'Neill
Camden House, 7 Upper Camden Street, Dublin 2
Tel: 01 4760360
Fax: 01 4760361
E-mail: geneticconcern@tinet.ie
Website: www.vibrantplanet.com/geneticconcern/

Genetic Concern is a campaigning group established in 1997 to highlight the potential risks of genetic engineering in food and agriculture. We advocate a moratorium on the release of genetically modified organisms into the environment. We carry out research, lobby government, food retailers and food agencies; we carry out supermarket tours for the public, and provide a free email information service. We receive no corporate or government funding and rely on public support and donations for our work. To subscribe to Genetwork our email service, please send your email address to geneticconcern@tinet.ie

GROWING AWARENESS

Contact: Jean Perry
Glebe Gardens, Balltimore, Skibbereen, Co.Cork
Tel: 028-20232

Growing Awareness promotes chemical free farming and safe healthy food. We campaign against genetic engineering in farming and support organic practices. Our aim is to increase public awareness of the issues involved.

EDUCATION

TEACH BAN, THE HOME OF HEALTHY LIVING

Contact: Patrick/Ann
6 Parnell Road, Harolds Cross, Dublin 12
Tel: 01-4543943

Teach Bán offers cooking classes that introduce you to a nutritional balanced diet using organic wholefoods. Also available are feng shui courses to design your home to maximise energy in all areas of your life and treat yourself to a shiatsu course to release blocked energy and allow healing power to flow through your body.

ORGANIC WINE AND BEER

ON THE CASE

Contact: Joan Casey
2 St. James Terrace, South Circular Road, Dublin 8
Tel: 01-4730156
Fax: 01-4730156
Email: onthecase@oceanfree.net

On the Case imports and distributes quality organic wines. We run Irelands only organic wine club, bringing wines direct to your home and recycling your empties. Frequent wine tastings are held.

VINCEREMOS WINES AND SPIRITS LTD.

Contact: Harriet Walsh
261 Upper Town Street, Leeds, LS13 3JT
Tel: 0044-0113-257 7545
Fax: 0044-0113-257 6906
E-mail: info@vinceremos.co.uk
Website: www.vinceremos.co.uk

Organic wine specialist with mail order catalogue of 200 wines, beers, ciders, juices and more. Organic wines from France, Italy, Spain, Germany, New Zealand, USA, Australia delivered direct or collected from pick up point at WWT, Co Down.

THE IRISH BREWING CO.

Contact: Paul Tynan
Newbridge, Co. Kildare
Tel: 045-433541 / 086-2633357
Fax: 045-435541

The Irish Brewing Company, established in 1996, brews "Number One Brew" (non additive). Pilsner lager known for its fresh natural aroma and flavour. "Number One" was the 1998 winner of the Gold medal for international lagers with The British Bottlers Institute.

WATER

SIMPLY WATER LTD.

Contact: Adrian Hamilton
Environment House, Brighton Green, Dublin 6
Tel: 01-4920414
Fax: 01-4920712
E-mail: simwater@iol.ie

Dublin based Simply Water have been developing water filter systems since 1989. Its system is ideal for both wells and town supplies as it removes bacteria, metals and chemicals.

ECOWATER-KARDEN DISTRIBUTORS

Contact: Denis Reid
30 Cooks Cove, Kircubbin, Co. Down BT22 2ST
Tel: 0801 2477-38707
Fax: 08012477-38986
Email: Denis-Reid@hotmail.com

Suppliers of a variety of systems to produce high quality water for drinking and cooking. Undersink filters, distilation and reverse osmoses. Also sun-roc filter / chilled units for offices, practices etc, in limited filtered water at fraction of cost of bottled water.

PURE H2O, STEAM DISTILLED WATER

Contact: Edmund Wall / Noreen Farrell
Cherry Lodge, Berystede, Leeson Park, Dublin 6
Tel: 01-4962784
Fax: 01-4962784

Domestic and commercial steam distillation units.

Steam distillation effectively removes all contaminents, heavy metals, inorganic minerals, chemicals, pesticides and insecticides. Including flouride, chloride, sodium and THM's. It also kills all bacteria, cysts and viruses. Leaving you with 100% pure H2O - every time.

GUIDES

THE VEGETARIAN & VEGAN GUIDE TO IRELAND

Contact: Nana Luke
East Clare Telecottage, Derg House, Connaught Road, Scarriff, Co. Clare
Tel: 061-921121
Fax: 061-921693
Email: vegguide@bealtaine.ie
Website: www.bealtaine.ie/vegguide

The Vegetarian and Vegan Guide to Ireland contains listings of hotels, hostels, guesthouses, B&B's and holistic centres in Ireland which cater for vegetarians and in most cases vegans. Also listing of events, healthfood shops and useful contacts. Published annually.

VEGETARIAN RESTAURANTS AND ACCOMODATION

LETTERCOLLUM HOUSE

Contact: Con McLoughlin & Karen Austin
Lettercollum House, Timoleague, Co. Cork

Tel: 023-46251
Fax: 023-46270
E-mail: conmc@iol.ie
Website: www.lettercollum.ie

We are a restaurant and guesthouse on 12 acres with a one-acre organic Victorian walled garden. We keep pigs, poultry (soon), and sheep. Gourmet restaurant serving modern international food. Cooking classes in the off-season.

THE NEW DELIGHT CAFE/RESTAURANT

Contact: Olga A Ireson
18 Henry St. Kenmare Co. Kerry

Tel: 064-42350
Fax: 064-84236
E-mail: newdelight@eircom.net

A family run cafe/restaurant offering our customers vegetarian, vegan and wholefood dishes. Prepared with fresh, organic and fairly traded products. All this in a relaxed and friendly atmosphere. "Enjoy".

CORNUCOPIA VEGETARIAN AND VEGAN RESTAURANT

Contact: Deirdre McCafferty
19 Wicklow Street, Dublin 2

Tel: 01-6719449 / 6777583
Fax: 01-6719449

Cornucopia has established itself as Ireland's most successful vegetarian restaurant and has been serving delicious wholefoods for fourteen years. A wide variety of tasty and healthy dishes are available, including vegetarian or muesli/ fresh fruit breakfasts, a large selection of savoury dishes, imaginative salads, tasty desserts and breads. All food is freshly prepared on the premises daily. Yeast-free, gluten-free, dairy-free, wheat-free and candida diets are catered for.

HARICOTS WHOLE FOOD RESTAURANT

Contact: Elaine Ryan
11 O'Connell Street, Waterford

Tel: 01-841299

The complete menu - from soups, starters, and main courses to deserts - is all home based without artificial additives, colourants, preservatives or flavouring. Open Mon-Fri 9am-8pm; Sat 9.30am-6pm (last orders).

VEGETARIAN / VEGAN BED & BREAKFAST

Contact: Maureen Quinn
"Saru", Tonaphubble Lane, Sligo

Tel: 071-70518

Maureen hosts a vegetarian B&B recommended by the Bridgestone Guide. She also runs wholefood cookery courses which introduce the benefits and pleasure of food to people who wish to take more responsibility for their health and well being.

UNICORN RESTAURANT

Contact: Giorgio Casari
12b Merrion Court/Merrion Row, Dublin 2

Tel: 01-6762182
Fax: 01-6624757

The Unicorn combines contemporary Italian food in delightful, friendly surroundings. Every visit whether at lunch-time or in the evening is an occasion with a sense of theatre.

LOVEBITES ORGANIC CATERERS

Contact: Deb Davis
The Old Barricks, Kappure, Manor Kilbride, Co. Wicklow

Tel: 01-4582789 / 087-2385776
Fax: 087-3385776
E-mail: JimDempsey@eircom.net

Deb Davis and Jim Dempsey are cooks as distinct from chefs, delivering from the heart. With backgrounds in Cordon Bleu, Macrobiotics, healing and mysticism, their food is experiential and tactile

THERAPEUTIC DIETITIANS

CECILIA ARMELIN

Contact: Cecilia Armelin B.Sc.,
13 Rowan House, Mespil Estate, Co. Dublin

Tel: 01-6601628

Advises adults and children: Asthma, arthritis, acne, eczema, psoriasis, candida, irritable bowel, stress, diabetes, weight control, PMT, allergies, etc. Attends Hopsack health food shop, Swan Centre, Rathmines. Alternate Saturdays, 12-3pm. Tel 01-4960399.

HEALTH STORE

NATURES GOLD

Contact: Brod kearon
1 Killincarrick road, Greystones, Co. Wicklow.

Tel: 01 287 6301
Fax: 01 287 6301
E-Mail: natgold@iol.ie

One of the original whole food stores founded in 1977. We specialise in organic products so avoiding genetically engineered foods. We also stock a wide range of premium quality vitamin and herbal supplememts.

SEE ALSO:

Bavaria House B&B

Cussens Cottage

Green Lodge

The Phoenix

All of the above provide accomodation with organic or vegetarian food.

Full listing: Eco-Tourism in Arts and Leisure Section.

ROARING WATER BAY

Harvester of seaweed and sea vegetables.

Full listing: Agiculture section.

AGRICULTURE & FORESTRY

page 53   **Introduction** John Seymour

page 55   **Organic Production** Helen Scully

page 57   **Biodynamic Production** Penney Lange

page 58   **Permaculture** Marcus McCabe

page 59   **Sustainable Forestry** Jacinta French

page 61   **Coppice** T Thomson and R, K. Jerram

page 61   **Seed Saving** The Irish Seed Saving Association

INTRODUCTION TO AGRICULTURE John Seymour

John Seymour was born in Essex, England in 1914. He has written over 40 books, including the 'Complete Book of Self Sufficiency,' and has made many films and radio programmes. He has lived and promoted natural farming practices in Ireland for over 20 years. For the last 4 years he, Angela Ash, and William Sutherland have been running courses in Self Sufficiency from their home at Killowen, New Ross. John continues to take a front line interest in environmental campaigning and during 1998 became one of the now famous Arthurstown 7 who were charged with criminal damage for destroying part of Monsanto's experimental genetically mutilated sugar beet. Most of the books written by John Seymour are available from Metanoia Press, Killowen, New Ross, Co Wexford, Ireland.

The 'owner' of a piece of land has an enormous responsibility, whether the piece is large or small. The very word 'owner' is a misnomer when applied to land. The robin that hops about your garden, and the worms that he hunts, are, in their own terms, just as much 'owners' of the land they occupy as you are. 'Trustee' would be a better word. Anyone who comes into possession, in human terms, of a piece of land, should look upon himself or herself as the trustee of that piece of land - the 'caretaker' - responsible for increasing the sum of living things on that land, holding the land just as much for the benefit of the robin, the wren and the earthworm, even the bacteria in the soil, as for himself.

Of course we have a right to use the land for our own purposes, to grow food, for example, or timber, or to make it beautiful to our eyes. We have a right - and a duty - to maintain a due order and balance among all the other forms of life on it. Mankind is part of Nature too and must take its part in the dance of Life and also of Death. If the caterpillars destroy our cabbages we have a right to sort 'em out. We do not have a right, though, to sort 'em out by using some indiscriminate poison that is going to do all other kinds of living things to death.

As well as rights, we have a positive duty with regard to land. According to the Book of Genesis, God put the Man and the Woman in the Garden to 'dress it and keep it'. Whether we look upon Genesis as divinely inspired or not, it is obvious that we should do just this. We should hand the land on to the next trustee better, more fruitful, more beautiful, and richer in living creatures than it was when we took it over. The trusteeship of land is a daunting responsibility. It is part of the Earth's surface that we are given charge of, full of living creatures other than humankind, in trust for future generations of humans as well as all other forms of life.

The reason why our land is so desperately badly husbanded now is that it is held in too large units. The loving care that a good caretaker can devote to

Agriculture + Forestry

a piece of land can only be spread so far. When one person (or company) 'owns' hundreds of acres they are forced to resort to mechanical and chemical warfare. The bulldozer and the poison spray take the place of Adam's spade and Eve's pruning shears. I am not inveighing against chemicals and machinery but simply against the thoughtless abuse of these things made necessary by over-swollen land holdings. It can be seen over and over again that a smallholding is more fruitful, more beautiful, and richer in varied life than a vast agribusiness.

This Sourcebook is not intended for the agribusinessman, but for the holder of a piece of land of a size that (s)he can really husband and cope with, and treat with the tender loving care that we should always give to the soil and its denizens. Our task is to exhort people to care well and humanely for the land in their charge, to show how it is possible to tend the land beautifully: to plant it with trees, to establish well cared-for hedges instead of wire fences, to build good timber gates instead of buying steel ones that quickly rust and become eye-sores, to drain wet places where drainage is needed and to do all the other operations that generally come under the heading of 'estate management' when applied to huge estates. If the estate management side of things is looked after, the food production part comes much more easily and will be more successful. And, further, when you come to hand over the land to the next generation, you can do so with pride.

The Sourcebook issues at a good time for I believe a new consciousness is spreading over the world. It comes in many forms and if it prevails quickly enough then maybe there is hope for the present creation, or evolution, for life on this planet. Time is desperately short. There are now a million megadeaths, poised, aimed, programmed, primed and ready, to be launched screaming across this pathetic planet at the whim of some elected fool. Only a completely new consciousness, spreading as quickly as a forest fire throughout the whole human world, can save us - and when I say us - I mean us - all terrestrial life: I mean the blue tit at my window too.

This new consciousness must purge its adherents completely and finally of the blasphemous illusion that Mankind is in any way apart from Nature or here for itself alone.

I see it being born - I see it spreading. In nearly every country now for example is an organic movement - a movement of people dedicated to finding a way of husbanding soil, crops and stock, and all wild living creatures, in a way that is not too tyrannical and destructive. Hominus extindor endeavours to destroy every living thing, vegetable or animal, on his land that is not of direct economic benefit to him. Thus a wheat agribusinessman eliminates every possible hidey-hole for wildlife in the form of hedges, woods, heathland, wild places, and douses his crop as it grows over and over again with deadly poisons - herbicides, insecticides, fungicides, bacteriocides, viricides. I cannot call him a farmer, that is an honourable title. I call him a wager of war - a chemical warfare expert of the most ruthless and destructive kind. Even worse, he may be a supporter of the new craze for genetic mutilation in the drive for profit, whatever the risks.

The real farmer works quite otherwise. They understand the wholeness of all life - and work with the life force, not against it. Far from trying to destroy all life in the soil, their constant endeavour is to increase it. They pile organic matter into the soil with the very object of encouraging the bacterial and fungal life that lives therein. They glory in the diversity of vegetable and animal life in and on the soil. Of course they exercise control over Nature. They know that in their role, they are the Caretakers. They keep fair play. They see that their own families get fed of course - it is part of Nature too. But they do not ruthlessly poison or kill every living thing that is not of immediate benefit to them.

I glory every time I hear or read of yet another country in which an organic organisation has started up!   There are groups all over the world, growing quickly, striving to protect this or that aspect of Nature from the despoilers. A cosmic battle has been joined - like the Battle of Kurukshetra, the story of which is told in the Mahabharata. It is a battle between good and evil. Maybe it is a battle that, in cosmic terms, can never finally be won. I don't know. Maybe, even in times of apparent peace, some Childe Harold has to ride up to the Dark Tower and put his slughorn to his lips and blow a blast of defiance - and a blast of affirmation that Life is still there, and ready and willing to defend itself against the forces of darkness and of death. If this book and its information can play a role in this battle then so much the better.

One out of five people does not have clean drinking water.
Worldwatch Institute

Organic Production Helen Scully the Organic Trust

What exactly is organic farming?

The popular image is of slightly backward farming systems with low output and an appreciably reduced standard of living for the organic farmer. Nothing could be further from the truth! Organic farmers and producers are forward-looking, progressive business people who employ the very latest technical developments to produce quality food. They do this while avoiding the use of soluble mineral fertilisers, herbicides and pesticides - ensuring that the systems for animal production, for example, reflect the very highest ethical and welfare standards.

If you see a vegetable producer using the latest flame or brush weeding technology, you can be certain he or she is an organic farmer. If you notice an extra emphasis on animal welfare or clover management, you can be sure an organic farmer is hard at work, making sure the food we eat is produced to the highest possible standards.

What about financial returns? The best measure of what you make from any enterprise is the bottom line. It is not the yield per cow, lambing percentage, stocking rate or production per acre. It is simply the amount of money that the producer has to spend to pay the bills, to clothe and feed children, etc. Organic farmers have as high a return as the best farmers in the country. Although stocking rates may be lower, as may yield per acre, for example, the high standard of husbandry and the small premiums which organic produce attracts, make the organic farmer's disposable income extremely inviting. All of this has resulted in organic farming developing over time into a mature market sector for Irish agriculture.

Consumption of organic fruit & vegetables has continued to rise and demand has steadily increased for organic lamb. However, one of the most explosive growth areas has been the market for organic beef, with an insatiable demand for quality Irish organic beef both at home and abroad.

This trend of increased market share for organic products of all kinds is set to continue as disposable incomes rise and consumers are prepared to spend more on the quality of their food. Consumer awareness relating to the source and conditions of production of their food is also having a huge effect on demand.

So, is it difficult to become an organic producer? Not particularly, but it does take time and planning. In order to be permitted to market any produce as 'organic' under the EU Regulation 2092/91, the prospective producer must register with an approved organic inspection/certification body such as the Organic Trust or IOFGA. A detailed plan for the conversion to organic production is submitted with the appropriate fee and the farm is inspected - an annual event thereafter. It is then up to the producer to proceed with the approved plan. The concept of traceability from field to plate originated with the stringent requirements of organic farming, so it is no surprise that record-keeping is a very important part of an organic production system.

Financial help for the two-year conversion period to organic farming, and additional help at full organic status, is available through the Department of

Agriculture & Food REPS programme under Supplementary Measure 6.

At the end of the day, however, the most important consideration for the organic producer is the marketability of organic produce. There is no point in producing vast quantities of food that the market does not want, or in a market where price is static or falling and income consequently dropping.

At present, organic farmers enjoy premium prices for their products which compensates for the lower output and yields. But more importantly they have a growing market which is still under-supplied and in which they can feel confident.

Organic production is agricultural production for the future and it is here to stay and grow!!

Biodynamic Production Penney Lange biodynamic producer
Bio-Dynamic Agriculture

The biodynamic approach to organic farming practice has as its roots a series of lectures given by the Austrian philosopher, Rudolf Steiner, at , the estate of Count and Countess Keyzerlink, in 1924.

The impulse that led to the lectures was twofold and is well worth a mention, as these same issues concern us just as much today. Firstly, the farmers of central Europe found their yields diminishing alarmingly over time, and they realised that their traditional farming methods were no longer effective. Secondly, based on his great interest in the health and future of the human being on earth, Steiner claimed that it was of utmost importance that human nutrition be based on food produced from a living soil, in harmony with the greater influence of the cosmos.

In the early years of the biodynamic movement, quite astonishing results were achieved by a small number of devoted followers. During the Second World War the movement went more or less underground, and its recovery afterwards was very slow. In the '60s and '70s many young people sought apprenticeships on Bio-dynamic farms and the biodynamic trademark, DEMETER became widely recognised. Biodynamic farmers are well known internationally for taking part in organic development, both with regard to standard making, and for the high quality of their produce.

To become a recognised biodynamic farmer, one has to abide by the standards laid down by the European Organic Regulation 2092/91 and its amendments, as well as following the International Biodynamic Guidelines for production, and most importantly becoming familiar with and using the biodynamic preparations. There are two important spray preparations, and six compost preparations, chamomile, stinging nettle, oak bark, yarrow, dandelion and valarian. The aim when using the preparations is not necessarily to increase the yield, but rather to improve the quality of crops, especially from a nutritional point of view. Instructions for making or acquiring these preparations can be got from the Biodynamic Agricultural Association of Ireland. By becoming a member of the association, one can gain contact with others working bio-dynamically, attend workshops and conferences, and receive the Irish and British BD Newsletters.

> Since 1945, pesticide use has risen 3,300%, but overall crop loss has not gone down. In fact, despite our pounding the U.S. with 2.2 billion pounds of pesticides annually, crop losses have increased by 20%
> Janine Benyus

Agriculture + Forestry

Permaculture

Marcus McCabe permaculture designer and eco-village pioneer

Permaculture is the conscious design and maintenance of agriculturally productive ecosystems with the stability and resilience of natural ecosystems. It is a design system which connects various components so that the waste of one process becomes the raw material for the next. The elements of design not only include buildings and gardens but also orchards, pasture, coppice woodlands, legal and financial structures as well as appropriate technologies and the connections. The most misunderstood aspect of permaculture design is the importance of a clear plan and an installation process which will work ecologically and financially. For the same cost an infrastructure can be set up to either generate and maintain life systems or destroy them. It is all about designing cyclic systems. Unfortunately most of the investment in land-use in the past has assisted in actually damaging the primary resources bases namely healthy soil, clean water and air.

The need to actually come up with sustainable systems is both urgent and real. Farming is in crisis. The system of lakes and rivers are in crisis. There is also a crisis in good affordable housing especially with space. Furthermore, the actual food supply is in crisis regarding quality. These are all signs of a system in collapse. In my profession I talk to agriculturalists and engineers who will privately acknowledge that this is the case. We have reached a full stop with the current system of land-use. Squeezing another increment in yield out of any enterprise is just not an option. So.... where do we go from here?

THERE IS A QUESTION OF SCALE. The aspiring permaculturalist can put a diverse system in place but will need to concentrate on a number of medium scaled systems to generate cash. Taking the hen as an example;

500 hens will generate about £300 per week if well fenced and with supplementary feed in the winter. However 50 hens are almost a nuisance. Place the hen keeper adjacent to a good market gardener, cheese maker or coppicer and suddenly the whole thing becomes more viable. These enterprises, while independent, will be supporting each other if in proximity. None of the above enterprises would be possible, however, in a landless situation and, for that matter, would be too small and intensive (in the work sense) for most farmers to consider. What is needed is a repopulation of the land in low impact primary resource generating activity. Eco-village developments, which use Permaculture design principles as the process pattern, offer this possibility.

I see it going something like this. We create revolving land funds. These funds create the land access and install permaculture systems, wild places, waterways, forests and coppices, and access for house and workshop clusters. Eco-villages which use the principles of permaculture design are likely to be the most affordable and sane alternative for the traffic weary in the future. We have a lot to learn and re-invent, but when even the conventional farmers are saying their systems do not work where else do we turn?

Permaculture is primarily about connections and solutions. Not only is a beneficial assembly of plants, animal and structures needed but a beneficial assembly of people, working bio-regionally to create ecosystems in which the human element is actively integrated in generating primary wealth. This is our direction in moving towards a revitalized and abundant society and planet.

Sustainability Forestry Jacinta French environmental consultant

Forests are amongst the Earth's most complex ecological systems, whose dynamic processes and functions we do not yet fully understand. Not only do forests produce timber for our shelter and fuel needs. They also support the largest proportion of the world's biodiversity and are an important source of food and medicines. They provide environmental services such as flood control, soil protection, carbon fixing and landscape enhancement as well as recreation and amenity facilities and socio-economic benefits. Globally, both natural and plantation forests are under threat, primarily from inappropriate management practices.

In Ireland, as elsewhere, forests have been managed for economic value, namely timber production, with little attention being given to social and environmental benefits. As a result the planting of non-native coniferous species, such as the North American Sitka spruce and lodgepole pine, has predominated because they grow faster than native hardwood species such as oak and ash. While this approach has led to a self-sufficiency in softwood production, the introduction of exotic species and even-aged, monoculture tree-farms harvested in 40-50 year cycles is, in many instances, detrimental to our wildlife, archaelogy and landscape heritage and to water and soil quality. At the same time, we are one of the largest consumers per capita of imported hardwoods, much of which comes from tropical forests where unsustainable management practices predominate. Despite recent efforts by the Forestry Service and Coillte (who manage publicly-owned forests) to minimise the negative impacts of afforestation and to increase broadleaf planting, it is doubtful that the current forest policy, which maintains a dependence on short rotation, non-native conifers, can be sustained in the long term.

Parallel concerns throughout the globe regarding the negative social and ecological impact of forestry practices has led to increased pressure for higher standards in forestry management. Efforts to establish 'sustainable forest management' (SFM) has been forestry's contribution towards sustainable development. SFM is "the process of managing forests to achieve one or more specified management objectives with regard to the production of a continuous flow of desired forest products and services without undue reduction of its inherent values and without undue undesirable effects on the physical and social integrity. While it is generally agreed that SFM should encompass environmental responsibility, social benefits and economical viability, more precise descriptions are needed to guide practices on the ground. A host of international and national agreements and standards have been developed to achieve good forest stewardship including the Forest Principals agreed at the Earth Summit, the Helsinki process in Europe, ISO 14001 and the Pro Silva method. The Forestry Service of the Department of Marine and Natural Resources are currently developing a National Forestry Standard and Coillte are also developing their own SFM system.

The most widely accepted standard and certification system internationally has been developed by the Forest Stewardship Council (FSC), a non-governmental organisation whose goal is to develop sustainable forestry by accrediting organisations which certify the quality of forest management. The specific standards used for certification are developed in each country or region. They are of high technical quality and developed through a balanced, multi-stakeholder process - a process which is currently underway in Ireland. A certified forest product carrying an FSC logo gives the buyer an assurance that the product comes from a forest that has been independently evaluated and is sustainably managed.

In order for forestry to become truly sustainable it is hoped that new standards will lead to significant changes in policy and practice. Recommended changes include a planting target of 1:1 ratio of broadleaved to conifer species, an increased mix of species in forest plantations, greater structural and spatial diversity, greater use of local Irish seed, active management to protect relict broadleaf woodlands, more education to develop broadleaved tree management skills and encouragement of local involvement at all levels of operation. In addressing these vital changes we can look forward to a better and brighter future for Irish forests.

References

1 The Heritage Council (1999). `Policies and Priorities for the National Heritage: Forestry and the National Heritage'. Kilkenny.

2 Forest Service (1996). `Growing for the Future: A Strategic Plan for the Development of the Forestry Sector in Ireland'. Government Publications, Dublin.

3 Higman, S. (et al) (1999). `The Sustainable Forestry Handbook'. Earthscan, London.

Coppice 'The Practice of silverculture' T. Thomson & M. R. K. Jerram

Coppice Systems

Coppice Systems are based on the power possessed by many broad-leaved trees, of producing shoots from the stool, stump or bole when cut over. The most important of these systems is Simple Coppice, in which the trees are cut over at ground level or near it.

With few exceptions the system is confined to broad-leaved trees, and in practice to a limited number of them. As a rule large stools do not coppice, so that the trees must not be allowed to grow too old. The system is therefore suitable for the production of small and medium sized material, not of large timber, and the rotation or period between the cuts rarely exceeds forty years and is generally much less.

Seed Saving Irish Seed Savers Association

Why should anyone save his or her own seeds year after year? Surely the big seed firms are constantly bringing out new varieties which are more disease resistant and give higher yields than anything available before? Perhaps not. When gardeners saved their own seed year after year, they automatically collected from plants which grew well in their area and could resist the diseases found there. If the diseases changed, the seeds which were saved changed also. Gradually, a wide range of different strains of most crops emerged, each well suited to the region in which it was grown. This genetic diversity insured that for the most part, pest and plant lived in balance with each other, and chemicals were not a prerequisite for crop production.

Unfortunately, most of these regional strains of crops and their inbred genetic diversity has been lost. Economic factors, including seed patenting and the monopolisation of seed production by large chemical companies, as well as an ill considered directive for the EU which actually made the sale of these unregistered seeds illegal, has greatly contributed to our diminishing genetic resources. In fact, according to the Food and Agriculture Organisation of the United Nations, 75% of the genetic diversity of agricultural crops has been lost since the beginning of the century.

In a good, healthy bit of garden wildlife habitat there will be hardly a leaf that has not had a bite taken out of it. Chris Baines

A Guide to the Techniques of Coppice Management
Mummery, Tabor and Homewood
ISBN: 0952984911, 1998.

Carrots love Tomatoes
L. Riotte.
ISBN: 1580170277, 1998.

Chicken Tractor - the Permaculture Guide to Happy Hens and Healthy Soil
Andy Lee & Pat Foreman
ISBN: 0962464864, 1997.

Earth Users Guide to Permaculture
Rosemary Morrow
ISBN: 0864175140, 1994.

Forest Gardening
Robert Hart
ISBN: 1900322021, 1996.

Four Season Harvest
Eliot Coleman.
ISBN: 1890132276, 1999.

How to Make a Forest Garden
Patrick Whitefield
ISBN: 1856230082, 1996.

Mushrooms in the Garden
Hellmut Steineck
ISBN: 091642250X, 1984.

Permaculture - A Designers Manual
Bill Mollison
ISBN: 0908228015, 1988.

Permaculture in a Nutshell
Patrick Whitefield
ISBN: 1856230031, 1993.

Permaculture One
Bill Mollison & David Holmgren
ISBN: 0908228031, 1990.

Permaculture Plot
Patrick Whitefield
ISBN: 1856230104, 1996.

Permaculture Two
Bill Mollison
ISBN: 0908228007, 1990.

Plants for a Future - edible and useful plants for a healthier world
Ken Fern
ISBN: 1856230112, 1997.

Solar Gardening
Leandre and Gretchen Poisson
ISBN: 0930031695, 1994.

Square Foot Gardening
M. Bartholomew.
ISBN: 0878573410, 1997.

**Straight-Ahead Organic; A Step-by-Step Guide to Growing Great Vegetables in a Less
Than Perfect World**
Shepherd Ogden,
ISBN: 1890132209, 1999.

**The Apple Grower -
a guide for the Organic Orchardist**
Michael Phillips
ISBN: 1890132047, 1998.

The Complete Book of Companion Gardening
Bob Flowerdew
ISBN: 1856262723, 1995.

The Flower Farmer: An Organic Grower's Guide
Lynn Bycznski,
ISBN: 0930031946, 1997.

The Forest Garden
Robert Hart
ISBN: 0948826231, 1991.

The Natural Garden Book
Peter Harper.
ISBN: 1856750566, 1995.

The New Organic Grower
Eliot Coleman
ISBN: 093003175X, 1995.

The New Seed Starters Handbook
Nancy Bubel
ISBN: 0878577521, 1988.

Agriculture + Forestry

The Seed Savers Handbook
J. Cherfas & M and J Fanton
ISBN: 1899233016, 1996.

The Soul of Soil - a Soil-Building Guide for Master Gardeners and Farmers
Joe Smillie
ISBN: 1890132314, 1999.

Travels in Dreams
Bill Mollison
ISBN: 0908228112, 1997.

Water for Every Farm
P.A. Yeomans
ISBN: 0646129546, 1993.

SUSTAINABLE AGRICULTURE WEB SITES

ORGANIC FARMING

ATTRA Publications;
http://www.attra.org/attra-pub/
Herny Doubleday Research Association;
http://www.hdra.org.uk/
National Center for Appropriate Technology;
http://www.ncat.org/
Soil Association;
http://www.earthfoods.co.uk/soil.whator.html

BIODYNAMIC FARMING

Biodynamic Farming and Gardening Association (BDA) Home Page;
http://www.biodynamics.com/

PERMACULTURE

The Fibre Resources Page;
http://www.canwine.com/fiber/index.html
Plants for a Future;
http://www.scs.leeds.ac.uk/pfaf/index.html
Permaculture Global Assistance Network;
http://www.peq.apc.org/~pqan/
Permaculture Hot Spots;
http://www.sonic.net/~lberlin/hotspots.html
Permaculture Information Services;
http://www.permaculture.co.uk/

Permaculture International;
http://www.nor.com.au/environment/perma/
Permaculture magazine;
http://www.permaculture.co.uk/pmis/menu.html
Permaculture Resources;
http://www.metalab.unc.edu/london/permaculture.html
Permaculture Visions;
http://www.ozemail.com.au/~askpv/
Welcome to Permaculture;
http://www.permaculture org/

ORGANIC STANDARDS

IOFGA (IRISH ORGANIC FARMERS & GROWERS ASSOC.)

Contact: Noreen Gibney, Operations Manager
Organic Farm Centre, Harbour Road, Kilbeggan, Co. Westmeath

Tel: 0506-32563
Fax: 0506-32063
E-mail: iofga@tinet.ie
Website: www.irishorganic.ie

Promotion and development of organic farming. IOFGA run an inspection and certificate programme. The journal of IOFGA, 'Organic Matters' is published every two months.

ORGANIC TRUST LTD.

Contact: Helen Scully
Vernon House, 2 Vernon Avenue, Clontarf
Dublin 3

Tel: 01-8530271
Fax: 01-8530271
E-mail: organic@iol.ie
Website: http://ireland.iol.ie/~organic

The Organic Trust Ltd are a Dept. of Agriculture & EU approved organic inspection and certification body who offer services complying with DoA and REPS requirements. Producers, proccesors and traders who wish to obtain certification can rely on a top class efficient and user-friendly service from the Organic Trust Ltd. The Organic Trust Ltd is a non-profit making voluntary organisation who operate an Organic Symbol Scheme of the highest integrity to meet statutory, membership and ancillary requirements through the implementation of the best possible practices, procedures and operating standards relating to the certification of the integrity of the organic enterprises marketed under its symbol. Marketing initiatives have achieved sales of organic products in most major supermarkets in Ireland together with a number of organic export initiatives. Additional services include advice, education, training and a quarterly magazine titled Clover Magazine.

DEMETER STANDARDS LTD.

Biodynamic Agricultural Association in Ireland

Contact: Anja Terpstra
Watergarden, Thomastown, Co. Kilkenny

Tel: 056-54214
Fax: 056-54214
E-mail: bdaai@indigo.ie
Website: http://www.kihe.com/demeter and www.demeter.net

Organic Inspection Body. Demeter standards is authorised to carry out inspections for biodynamic and organic farms and enterprises. The biodynamic agriculture association seek to promote biodynamic methods inaugurated by Rudolf Steiner.

PRODUCERS

NORTH WEST ORGANIC AND PRODUCERS GROUP (NWOPG)

Contact: Stan McWilliams
Colpey, Muff, Co. Donegal

Tel: 077-84107
Fax: 077-84238
E-mail: stan@erda.iol.ie

The NWOPG is a cross-border group of organic farmers and growers established during 1999, with the general aim to develop and promote organic production in the North West through promotion support and advice, from visits, marketing and demonstration.

GREENCASTLE ORGANIC FARM & DEMONSTRATION NO DIG VEGETABLE GARDEN

Contact: Patrick McCartney
Carrowhugh, Greencastle, Co. Donegal

Tel: 077-81244

High quality organic food producer supplying local restaurants, box schemes and markets with full range of vegetables, soft fruits and herbs, some organic meat production too.

DONEGAL ORGANIC FARM PRODUCE

Contact: Thomas Becht
Doorian Glenties Co. Donegal

Tel: 075-51286
Fax: 075-51286
e-mail: tbecht@ie.packardbell.org

Organic Agriculture, Demeter-Symbol, forestry and ECO Tourism based on sustainable systems on approx. 800 acres

NEANTOG ORGANIC FARM

Contact: Gaby & Hans Wieland
Ballincastle, Cliffoney, Sligo

Tel: 071-66399
E-mail: neantog@indigo.ie

At Neantog we produce goats-cheese, vegetables, herbs, provide self-catering accommodation in 2 stone cottages, and give courses in our hedge-school in cheese making, bread baking, growing and using herbs, also reflexology and reiki.

EDEN PLANTS

Contact: Rod Alston
Eden, Rossinver, Co. Leitrim

Tel: 072-54122
Fax: 072-54122

Eden Plants is a small organic farm established over 20 years ago. The herb nursery produces 180 varieties of plants, cut herb and vegetables supplied to selected local shops and restaurants.

DENIS HEALY

Talbotstown, Kiltegan, Co. Wicklow

Tel: 0508-73193 / 087-2485826
Fax: 0506-73193

Farming on fifty-five acres, twenty acres outdoor vegetables from salads-potatoes, cabbage to tomatoes. Selling at farm Temple bar market and through organic foods Lucan. Organic trust no. 35.

THE HERB GARDEN

Contact: Denise Dunne
Ford-de-Fyne, Naul, Co. Dublin

Tel: 01-8413907
Fax: 01-8413907
E-mail: herbs@indigo.ie

Specialist organic herb nursery, growing a wide range of culinary, medicinal, fragrant and decorative herbs. Herb garden consultation and design service. Visitors welcome by appointment. Organic trust licence no.140

GARRISTOWN ORGANICS

Contact: Willie Browne
Ashfield, The Green, Garristown, Co. Dublin

Tel: 088-2753129 / 01-8354527

Fresh organic fruit and vegetables available in season. Training courses, evening classes and farm walks organized for groups. Official I.O.F.G.A (Dublin Meath) area representative. All telephone enquiries welcome. Evenings/weekends.

BIA ARANN

Contact: Dermot Carey
Killeany, Inismor Aran Islands Co. Galway

Tel: 087-2286145

Organic vegetables & herbs. Bia Arann provides organic, island grown produce to Inis Mor's seven restaurants, shop, residents and visitors. The farm, specializing in salad crops, uses the traditional island method of spreading seaweed.

VEGAN VEG

Contact: Jenny / Richard
Ballyroe, Lackaroe, Youghal, Co. Cork

Tel: 024-97366
Fax: 024-97366

Organic Horticulture.
We grow a wide range of organic vegetables without any animal inputs. Home delivery to the Lismore, Cappoquin, Tallow, Ardmore, Dungarvan, Youghal, Midleton areas. Visitors welcome; phone for directions.

FRUIT HILL FARM

Contact: Manfred Wandel,
Trawlebawn, Bantry, Co. Cork

Tel: 027-50710
Fax: 027-51894
E-mail: fhf@esatclear.ie

Environment friendly farm, garden and household supplies. Organic fertilizers, compost, crop protection nettings, tools, flameweeders, poly-tunnels, irrigation, biological pest control, green manure seeds, onion sets, seed potatoes. Compost bins, laundry discs etc.

NARMADA ORGANICS

Contact: Jonathan Daig/Julia Foden
Upper Froe, Roscarbery Co. Cork

Tel: 023-48552

Our produce is sold from March to October in Fields' Supervalu and Yin Yang Skibbereen, and Scallys' Supervalu Clonakilty. We have the Organic Trust symbol no.27. No farm-gate sales.

CLONMEL ORGANIC GROWERS

Contact: Peter Binder
Abbeystreet, C/o Honeypot Clonmel Co. Tipperary

Tel: 051-647207

Organic Veg. & Fruit. Clonmel Organic Growers est. 1986 as a co-operative (now run by grower-member) to retail wide range of seasonal organic vegetables all year. Saturdays 9.30am - 2pm, Abbeystreet (behind "Honeypot"), Clonmel.

BOYTONRATH ORGANIC FARM (CERTIFIED)

Contact: Vincent & Teresa Kelly
New Inn, Cashel, Co. Tipperary

Tel: 052-62492

55 acres are farmed to produce organic beef, lamb and vegetables. Self-contained accommodation available in a restored stone cottage in the 200 year old farmyard. Camping also. An atmosphere worth experiencing.

GORTBRACK ORGANIC FARM

Contact: Ian McGrigor
Gortbrack, Ballseedy, Tralee, Co. Kerry

Tel: 066-37042

Ten acre small holding vegetables, fruit, bees, cows, ducks, trees, ponds. Open days and classes. Residential building in progress.

CAHER FRUITS

Contact: Klaus Hauschild,
Caher, Kilgarven, Co.Kerry

Tel: 064-85573

Provide organic fruits (a wide selection with many 'unusuals') to local market as an alternative to specializing and high-energy transport. Also supporting the local economy and independence. Last but not least it's fun to produce on small-scale.

NINE ACRE ORGANIC FARM

Contact: Nicole Blum / Jonathan Carr
Ringlestown, Kilmeffen, Co. Meath

Tel: 046 26270
Fax: : 046 26270
Email: nineacres@esatclear.ie

Producers of fine vegetabes and flowers, specialising in high quality salad mix, including rocket, aisian greens and lettuces. All mixed vegetables and soft fruits. Those interested in work experience on an organic farm please call us. Supply restaurants and caterers mainly.

GORTRUA ORGANIC FARM

Contact: Michael Hickey & Ute Brinker
New Inn, Tipperary

Tel: 062-72223

Gortrua is a 100 acre organic farm on the banks of the river Suir supplying high quality organic meat. We also offer a self-contained chalet (double bedroom, kitchen, sitting rooms, bathroom). Gortrua is a beautiful place.

GARDENS

IRISH GARDEN PLANT SOCIETY

Contact: Honorary Secretary
C/O National Botanical Gardens, Glasnevin, Dublin 9

Horticulture. Aims of Society: Conservation of garden plants and gardens. The society researches, locates and propogates garden plants especially those raised in Ireland. The society also takes a strong interest in garden history.

PERMACULTURE AND CONSULTANTS

LAGAN VALLEY PERMACULTURE

Contact: Philip Allen
998 Crumlin Road, Belfast, Co. Antrim BT14 8FH

Tel: 0801-232 716200
Fax: 0801-232 716200

Permaculture Centre. Run workshops / courses on permaculture including design of gardens, eco tours, networking. Small-scale vegetable garden / seed saving, plant sales and green book library - sit in.

LIVING LANDSCAPES

Contact: Dominic Waldron
Cariglas, Glanlough West, Bantry, Co. Cork

Tel: 027-61497

Fax: 027-61497
E-mail: livinglandscapes@tinet.ie

Focussing on edible landscapes and wildlife / wildflower gardens, Living Landscapes is dedicated to designing and evolving practical systems for meeting local needs from the sustainable productive capacity of the bioregion.
Workshops / courses & co-design: Permaculture, wildlife / wildflower, constructed habitats.

KEALAMINE ORGANIC FARM

Contact: John D'hondt & Madia Wolfs
Kealanine, Bantry, West Cork

Tel: 028-31686
E-mail: dhondt@tinet.ie

Experimental ecological organic permaculture. We produce 14 different animal species and 70 different vegetable, some near unique. Courses in self-sufficiency / survival techniques considered interesting in starting food-club.

JASON HARRIS DESIGN SERVICES

Contact: Jason Harris
"Sanctoir", Lotamore, Glanmire, Co.Cork

Tel: 021-504617

Comprehensive permaculture design for any site, rural or urban. May include: dwellings, e.g planning permission / self-build. Waste disposal, e.g reed beds / compost toilets, general landscape planting plans etc.

DESIGN BY NATURE-IRISH WILDFLOWERS

Contact: Sandro Cafolla
Monavea Cross, Crettyard, Co. Carlow

Tel: 056-42526
Fax: 056-42722
Email: wildflow@indigo.ie

Wild flower grower, seed and plant producer. Sustainable permaculture designs to government local authorities and all. To conserve and utilise Ireland's native flora. Produce wildflower seed, plants and ecosystems. Quality conservation grade native seeds. Inspire the public to use wildflowers.

MERLIN AGRI-ENVIRONMENTAL CONSULTANCY

Contact: Ute Bohnsacr
Sailchearnach, Clogher, Kilfenora, Co. Clare

Tel: 065-7088187
E-mail: sustag@eircom.net
Website:
http://homepage.eircom.net/~merlyn/sustag.html

Agri-environmental consultancy (include. REPS planning); permaculture design. English-German-English translations in the fields of agriculture, nature, conservation, regional planning, environmental tourism, natural/cultural heritage.

SEE ALSO

Marcus McCabe, Burdautien Eco Village
Rob Hopkins, The Hollies Eco Village
Slí An Uisce in Eco-Village in Community and Family
Richard Webb- Green Building and Eco-Design
This World Services in Environment

FEEDS, FERTILISERS AND COMPOSTING

IRISH EARTHWORM COMPANY

Contact: Michael Lynch & Jackie Fitzgibbon
Farnivane, Bandon, Co. Cork
Tel: 023-43645
Fax: 023-43645
E-mail: iew@tinet.ie
Website: www.ireaearthworm.com

Vermicomposting, waste management. We breed and supply worms and related goods for vermicomposting (worm composting). We advise on all aspects of composting for the home or business and offer free advice to anyone interested.

GROW GREEN PRODUCTS

Contact: Paddy Macaulay
Manor, Kilbride, Blessington, Co.Wicklow
Tel: 01-4582261
Fax: 01-4582591

Garden shredders, composting systems, wormeries, weed burners, poultry housing, dovecotes, poultry feeders and drinkers, incubators, brooders, hatchers, commercial chippers.

ARRAMARA TEORANTA

Contact: Anne Marie Tierney & Seamus McGarvey
Kilkieran, Carna, Connemara Co. Galway
Tel: 095-33404
Fax: 095-33494
E-mail: atierney@arramara.ie
Website: www.arramara.ie

Seaweed Processing. Seaweed is harvested by hand in a manner which will sustain future regeneration of the crop. The seaweed is carefully dried to protect the many trace elements and vitamins. The end product is seaweed meal, used in animal feeding, fertilizers and alginates.

ROARING WATER BAY

Contact: Diana Pitcher
PO Box 7, Skibbereen, Co. Cork
Tel: 028-2838483
Fax: 028-2838485
E-mail: sales@dwn.com

Harvester of seaweed and sea vegetables.
Roaring Water Bay Co-op harvest seaweed and sea vegetables from the Grade A waters by ecological and sustainable means. The seaweeds and sea vegetables we harvest can be supplied in large quantities.

IRISH SEAWEED INDUSTRY ORGANISATION

Contact: Lorna Kelly
Martin Ryan Institute, National University Ireland, Galway
Tel: 091-512022
Fax: 091-750539
E-mail: lorna.kelly@seaweed.nuigalway.ie
Website: http://seaweed.nuigalway.ie/isio/

Seaweed processing, applied seaweed research, information dissemination.
The organisation is composed of 17 industry members. We partake in applied seaweed research, promoting the use of seaweed in all applications, disseminate seaweed information to general public and represent seaweed industries at various levels including local and national.

BEOFS BIO ENERGY AND ORGANIC FERTILISERS SERVICES

Contact: Christoph Eusterbrock
c/o Camphill Community, Ballytobin Callan
Co. Kilkenny
Tel: 056-25114
Fax: 056-25849
E-mail: beofs.ballytobin@camphill.ie
Website: www.camphill.ie/beofs.htm

Renewable Energy from Farm Waste. BEOFS, a project of the Camphill Community, Ballytobin, Callan, Co. Kilkenny is an agricultural based anaerobic digested plant, planned to produce biogas (methane) from farm and waste.
The system will take in cattle slurry from three neighbouring farms and food industry wastes from a local creamery and brewery, for processing in its anaerobic digester plant. The extracted gas will be burned in a CHP (combined heat and power plant) to create heat and electricity for the community. The digested slurry will be processed through a separator; the liquid fraction will be returned to the supplying farmers as an enhanced and environmentally friendly fertilizer. The solids will be composted and marketed as garden peat-free soil improver and fertiliser.

BIO-CARA LTD.

Contact: Christina Isensee
68 Morehampton Road, Dublin 4
Tel: 01-6687016
Fax: 01-6687019
E-mail: biocara@tinet.ie

Distribution of organic products for the environment.
Bio-cara Ltd provides the Plocher Energy System with the PENAC range of products for the treatment of manure, living and polluted water. (Not on the basis of bacterial digestion.) Organic

food supplements for poultry, pig, cattle and horse breeding helps nature to regenerate itself. Reduces harmful gases in slurry and manure. Liquidises solids in pig and cattle slurry. Minimises environmental pollution and the level of nitrates in ground water.

SEED SAVING

IRISH SEED SAVERS ASSOCIATION

Contact: Anita Hayes & Bridget Carlin
Capparoe, Scariff, Co. Clare

Tel: 061-921866
Website: www.catalase.com/issa.htm

Seed saving / preservation of native Irish apple trees / brassicae / potatoes / grain. The location and preservation of traditional varieties of fruit and vegetables. The maintenance of a seed bank to distribute seed of non-commercially available vegetables and heritage potatoes to members.

EDUCATION

AN T-IONAD GLAS, CENTRE FOR ORGANIC EDUCATION,

Contact: Jim McNamara
Community College, Dromcollogher,
Co. Limerick

Tel: 063-83604
Fax: 063-83042
E-mail: ionadglas.ias@tinet.ie

Education, support and promotion of organic farmers, growers and services.
"The organic college is a peoples learning centre which affirms the right of farmers and growers to grow organically and in a sustainable way. We provide courses support and linkage with the organic and environmental movements."

ORGANIC CENTRE

Contact: Roisin McDermott
Rossinver, Co.Leitrim

Tel: 072-54338
Fax: 072-54343
E-mail: organiccentre@tinet.ie

The centre has been open since 1997 offering a range of training courses and educational opportunities for those interested in gaining knowledge and skills in organic gardening. Demonstration gardens illustrating organic methods of food production. Sells organic gardening supplies.

AN TAIRSEACH "DOMINICAN FARM AND ECOLOGY CENTRE"

Contact: Julie Newman
Dominican Farm and Ecology Centre, Wicklow Town, Co.Wicklow

Tel: 0404-61833 or 0872880508
Fax: 0404-61833

Earth education / sustainable farming. "An Tairseach" consists of a biodynamic farm and ecology centre near Wicklow town. It aims to farm in a sustainable way, preserve wild life habitats and provide earth education courses.

INISHOWEN COMMUNITY ORGANIC FARM CO-OP. SOCIETY LTD

Contact: Laurie McGee
Drung Quigleys Point Co. Donegal

Tel: 077-83043
E-mail: lauriemcgee@esatclear.ie

Centre for organic farming training and environmental education in Inishowen. Includes demonstration gardens with polytunnels and composting section. Offering a range of courses and informative seminars. Allotments to rent.

THE RURAL INNOVATION CENTRE

Contact: Brendan O'Neill
St Patricks Agricultural College
Poplar Vale, Co. Monaghan

Tel: 047-81102
Fax: 047-84815

The Rural Innovation Centre has been established as a productive means of meeting the education and training needs of all rural dwellers, in particular, those for whom participation has been restricted in the past.

TREES

CRANN

Contact: Sean Donohoe
Crank House, Banagher, Co Offaly

Tel: 0509-51718
Fax: 0509-51938

Crann is a voluntary, non-profit organisation dedicated to planting trees and protecting Ireland's woodlands. Releafing Ireland is the quarterly magazine of Crann.

CRANN (DUBLIN & EAST BRANCH)

Contact: Stephen Coyne
107 Lower Baggot St., Dublin 2

Tel: 01-4550374
E-mail: stephen-coyne@yahoo.co.uk

Crann is a voluntary organisation set up to promote & assist in the planting of broadleaf trees and the restoration of hedgerows and to promote sustainability in forests.

THE TREE COUNCIL OF IRELAND

Contact: Patricia Flanagan
Cabinteely House, Cabinteely, Co. Dublin

Tel: 01-2849211
Fax: 01-2849197
E-mail: trees@treecouncil.ie
Website: www.treecouncil.ie

Promotion of the planting, care and conservation of trees. The Tree Council of Ireland is a non-governmental organisation, which promotes the planting, care and conservation of trees in town and country. Acts as an umbrella body for 37 voluntary, trade, professional and public service bodies concerned with trees. It organises events such as National Tree Week, National Tree Day, various projects, seminars and educational initiatives.

JUST FORESTS

Contact: Tom Roche
Bury Quay, Tullamore, Co. Offaly

Tel: 0506-23557
Fax: 0506-23557
E-mail: woodlife@justforests.org
Website: www.iol.ie/~woodlife/

Forest & timber education awareness. Forest Stewardship Council (FSC).
Working for the just development of the world's forests and their dependents.

FUTURE FORESTS LTD.

Contact: Mike Collard
Kealkil, Bantry, Co. Cork

Tel: 027-66176
Fax: 027-66046
E-mail: futureforests@tinet.ie
Website: http://www.futureforests.net

Natural Tree & Shrub Nursery. For trees, shrubs, hedging, fruit, flowers. Over 1,000 varieties in stock, many unusual. Mail order catalogue available. Visitors welcome. We aspire to share knowledge on all aspects of growing plants and woodlands.

COFORD

Contact: Eugene Hendrick
Agriculture Building, UCD Belfield Dublin 4

Tel: 01-7067700
Fax: 01-7061180
E-mail: eugene.hendrick@coford.ie
Website: http://www.coford.ie

Forest Research.
COFORD aims to stimulate appropriate and cost effective research to secure long-term industrial viability and optimise environmental and social aspects associated with forestry.

MUINTIR NA COILLTE/THE COPPICE ASSOCIATION OF IRELAND

Contact: Joe Gowran & Mark Wilson
Drumcliff South, Sligo

Tel: 061-927456
Fax: 071-45504
E-mail: joegowran@ireland.com

Promoting coppice management systems and related products. Rustic products and projects. Woodland / coppice advice and planning. Demonstrations and workshops undertaken. Promoting ecologically sustainable forest management. Co-operating with other ecological traders and source providers.

BEEKEEPING

WEST CORK BEEKEEPERS ASSOCIATION

Contact: Maureen Courtney
Ardnageehy Beg, Bantry, Co. Cork

Tel: 027-50778

Our activities include winter lectures and summer practical demonstrations for members of the general public passing on information to members regarding any new beekeeping developments.

INISHOWEN BEEKEEPERS ASSOCIATION

Contact: Joan Barker
Roseberry Cottage, Lowertown, Malin, Inishowen, Co. Donegal

Tel: 077-70845

The Inishowen BKA aims to undertake all possible measures to promote good beekeeping husbandry within one area by making available information and providing assistance to promote good practice.

DUNAMAISE BEEKEEPERS ASSOCIATION

Contact: Margaret McEvoy
Graiguenahoun, Abbeyleix, Co. Laois

Tel: 0502-33408

Beekeeping & Honey Production. Beekeeping is an ancient craft which should be preserved and maintained. Bees are a necessary insect in pollinating flowers and crops and are capable of turning nector and pollen which they gather into a consumable product "honey", which is much sought after for healthy living.

FINGAL NORTH DUBLIN BEEKEEPERS ASSOCIATION

Contact: John McMullan
34 Ard na Mara Crescent, Malahide, Co. Dublin
Tel: 01-8450193

The Associations' primary purpose is the promotion of good beekeeping practice amongst its members and it also aims to improve the understanding and appreciation for bees within the community.

THE FEDERATION OF IRISH BEEKEEPERS ASSOCIATION (FIBKA)

Contact: Michael G. Gleeson
Ballinakill, Enfield, Meath

Tel: 0405-41433

Promotes efficient beekeeping, honey production and marketing. Runs an annual summer course and honey show. Holds examinations to improve beekeeping standards. Publishes monthly journal 'An Beachaine', also informative leaflets and booklets.

CAMPAIGN GROUPS

COMPASSION IN WORLD FARMING

Contact: Mary Anne Bartlett, Aoife Ni Fhearghaill
Salmon Weir, Hanover Street, Cork City

Tel: 021-272441
Fax: 021-274984
E-mail: ciwf@indigo.ie
Website: http://indigo.ie/~ciwf

This is the Irish branch of the highly respected international organisation which campaigns for improved welfare conditions for farms animals. CIWF campaigns only in a peaceful and legal way. Campaigning methods are based on raising public awareness through events and education and pressing for change in legislation where necessary. A CIWF Irish newsletter is published quarterly. http://indigo.ie/~ciwf

THE PESTICIDES TRUST

Contact: David Allen
Units 16-18, Eurolink Centre, 49 Effra Rd.
London SW2 1BZ, UK

Tel: 0044-171 2748895
Fax: 0044-171 2749084
E-mail: pesttrust@gn.apc.org
Website: http://www.gn.apc.org/pesticidestrust

An independent charity addressing the health and environmental problems of pesticides and working for a sustainable future.

SEE ALSO

GENETIC CONCERN

Group campaigning against genetic engineering in food and agriculture in Ireland.

Full listing: Food and Drink section.

GORTRUA ORGANIC FARM

100 acre organic farm producing high quality organic meat.

Full listing: Eco-tourism in Arts and Leisure section.

NATURAL INSTINCTS

Organic clothing using organic wool and cotton.

Full listing: Eco-tourism in Arts and Leisure section.

ECOSEEDS

Workers co-op growing native wildflowers in organic peat-free media.

Full listing: Money and Work section.

HARVEY PAPER ANIMAL BEDDING

Animal paper bedding suitable for horses, cattle, poultry and pigs.

Full listing: Waste section.

INEKE AND THEO PETERESE

Organic farming, eco-camping, apartments.

Full listing: Eco-tourism in Arts and Leisure section.

THE EARTH EDUCATION CENTRE

Education in organic gardening, seed saving and tree cultivation.

Full listing in Environment section/Education.

ORGANIC FARM

BALLYBRADO ORGANIC FARM

Contact: Richard Auler
Cahir, Co. Tipperary.

Tel: 052 66477
Fax: 052 66477
E-mail: ballybrado@tinet.ie

GLOBAL & LOCAL

page 73 **Introduction** Martin Khor.

page 77 **Sustainable Development** Sadhbh O'Neil

page 79 **Majoriy World Issues** Joe Murray

page 80 **Climate Change** Jim Woolridge

page 81 **Human Rights and Sustainable Development**

page 82 **Debt** Niamh Gaynor

page 83 **Development Education** Thomas Tichelmann

page 84 **Fair Trade** Peter Gaynor

page 85 **Biopatents** Dr Ruth McGrath

Martin Khor is the director of the Third World Network, coordinator of the World Rainforest Movement, and Vice President of Friends of the Earth, Malaysia. He was the winner of the 1988 Right Livelihood Award.

Facing up to power and greed - the challenge of the next century.

The world at the end of the 20th century is not as peaceful or just or nice as we may have thought it would be when the Cold War ended.

Indeed, the past few years have witnessed increasing economic turbulence, widening social inequalities and widespread feelings of insecurity and helplessness.

The latest sign of the times is the outbreak of the East Asian financial crisis. Nations that had only a short while ago been hailed as economic miracles have had their currencies depreciated, millions thrown out of jobs as their economies sink as fast as the Titanic, and their poverty rates exploding together with social and political upheaval.

The countries affected were furious with powerful currency speculators and hedge funds for taking on the Central Banks and depreciating their currencies, and at the Northern countries' investment funds for all at once pulling their capital out - events that triggered off the tragedy of East Asia.

Avoiding any responsibility, the G-7 nations and the International Monetary Fund instead tried to explain away the crisis by vilifying the affected countries for having the wrong policies and economic structures. As part of the conditions for the rescue packages for Thailand, Indonesia, and South Korea, they insisted that the governments slash their budgets, raised interest rates, remove subsidies for essential items, and insisted that the economies be reformed to enable foreign companies to enter and take over whatever assets, companies and sectors they wanted.

But the crisis spread to more and more Asian countries. And then currency speculators shifted their attack to other regions. Russia, South Africa, East Europe, Latin America are now under threat.

Countries in the developing world are no longer able to have control over their currencies and financial systems. The destabilisation that this causes is undermining their trade, investment and development prospects.
These latest events are only part of a series of developments that have combined to make the developing countries poor, dependent and helpless.

Much of Africa and Latin America have had two "lost decades" in which declining commodity prices and the external debt trap had bled their

global + local

countries of resources and reduced them to status of beggars.

The "structural adjustment" programmes, drawn up in Washington and imposed on the 80 or more indebted countries, were designed to make these countries repay the international banks as fully as possible, at the cost of people's incomes and government's social budgets. And the consequences of that strategy are now evident in the increased poverty, unemployment, social ills and conflicts.

The world is getting more and more into an apartheid-like situation, with the rich grabbing more wealth and the majority becoming poorer. The UNDP Human Development Report 1992 estimated that 20% of the world's population in the developed countries receive 83% of world income, whilst the 20% of people in the poorest countries receive only 1.4%. In 1989, the average income of the richest 20% of people was 60 times that of the poorest 20%: this has doubled from 30 times in 1950.

The UNDP's 1996 Report showed that over the past three decades only 15 countries enjoyed high growth whilst 89 countries are worse off than 10 or more years ago. In 70 developing countries, the present income levels are less than in the 1960s and 1970s. And now, even some of the hitherto toasted East Asian countries have fallen: in Indonesia the poverty rate is rising from 20 to 50 percent in a year and the GNP will fall by up to 20 percent this year.

This is the ugly face of "globalisation". It is a term used by the international establishment as a clarion call to everyone to join in the materialistic rat-race, promoting the myth that free markets and unregulated corporations will interconnect countries and people of the world, for everyone's mutual benefit.

The reality of globalisation-cum-liberalisation is the financial turbulence, great divisions of wealth and income between and within nations, and persistent poverty that we witness today.

If we were to honestly examine what has led to this state of affairs, we would have to conclude that it can be summed up in two words - power and greed.

Particularly after the Cold War ended, a great triumphalism pervaded the Western world. Those who wielded financial and corporate power worked through their governments and the international agencies to push even harder for policies and treaties that would remove remaining barriers to their ability to capture markets and natural resources to expand their empires and profits.

What the rich saw as "barriers" were in fact defence mechanisms (such as tariffs, or regulations and conditions on the entry and operations of foreign companies, or rules controlling the free inflow and outflow of funds) set up by local communities and poorer countries to protect themselves from predatory foreign companies and financial operators.

The large corporations lobby the Northern governments to break down these defences so that they and their products and services can move at will into and out of developing countries.

Those governments made use of all instruments they had or that they could fashion. Domestic instruments (such as conditions in bilateral aid and in the case of the United States the dreaded Super 301 unilateral trade retaliation weapon) were used to expand markets for their companies.

More devastatingly, international agencies such as the IMF, the World Bank, the GATT and later the World Trade Organisation were used to change the nature and structure of Third World economies, reducing their self-reliance and opening their territories for foreign products, foreign firms and banks. Third World countries that had got trapped in debt had to submit, through the IMF-World Bank structural adjustment programmes, in order to stay just a little above the default level (at optimal level from the viewpoint of those who want to continue to exert "leverage" over these countries).

Other developing countries have also been drawn into the "liberalisation-globalisation" web through the rules of the WTO, which was set up following the Uruguay Round that had expanded the powers of the old GATT.

Through new agreements, the WTO is opening up the agriculture and services sectors of the developing world (in addition to the industrial sector in the previous rules). This will have a profound and negative impact on the small and medium-sized farms and firms in developing countries, most of which (having lost their defence mechanisms) will be unable to withstand the competition from transnationals.

In addition, the WTO will also discipline Third World countries to introduce high-standard intellectual property laws that disallow their people from developing technologies in use in the rich countries. Thus the WTO will be enforcing a system of protectionism for the TNC owners of technology, which is counter to its supposed creed of "free trade". These laws will also allow transnational companies to patent life, including genetic materials, crops and animals that are genetically engineered. This will facilitate "biopiracy", by which the age-old knowledge of Southern communities in using biological resources is patented by transnationals of the North to boost sales and monopolistic high prices of their biotech products.

Moreover, the TNCs have also pressed their governments to introduce a multilateral agreement on investment at both the OECD and the WTO, that would allow foreign investors the right to enter and operate in any treaty country with minimal regulations, and be treated as well or better than local investors. Many developing countries have voiced their opposition, but it is uncertain how strong their resistance can be.

Meanwhile, the influence and authority of the United Nations and its agencies have been eroding, as the G7 countries led a process to transfer their social and economic policy functions to the Bretton Woods institutions and the WTO. The declarations of heads of state at the many UN world conferences (on environment, social development, women, habitat, etc.) have many idealistic aims and positive practical proposals, but remain rather lifeless for lack of implementation.

The greed of those controlling the large corporations, the intense competition between them, and their obsession for profits, are driving the Northern governments and the international organisations to place the opening of Third World markets (for goods, services, investments and financial operations) at the top of the global agenda.

The people's right to development, to self-determination, to fulfil their basic human needs, to a sustainable environment, are relegated to secondary or even irrelevant status.

However, the situation is not all grim. There is a growing backlash against the globalisation-liberalisation process, not only in the South but also among citizens of the North, many of whom are themselves victims rather than beneficiaries.

There are strong national groups of citizens either existing or emerging that are combating the social effects of the market (which today is a monopoly-controlled rather than a genuinely free market of many small producers and traders), or that are fighting to protect the rights of communities to control their own land and resources, that campaign against the patenting of life, and are rallying against the MAI and the undemocratic processes and negative effects of the WTO. Some of these groups have formed networks at national, regional and international levels to increase their outreach and influence.

One key objective is to make the corporations, the banks, funds and financial operators, the G7 and the OECD, the IMF, World Bank and the WTO, more accountable to people, communities and the vast majority of states that now have little say in their policies and processes.

Dozens of groups in the North have worked with groups in the South to pressure the World Bank and the IMF to be more transparent and more socially responsible in their policies and projects. The Jubilee Campaign is making big waves in its campaign to cancel the debt of poor countries. Many citizen groups have joined the campaigns against patenting of life forms and against genetic engineering of crops. A global network of groups opposing the MAI have made a visible impact in making their views heard, even though they may not be able to stop the process. Thousands of groups across the Earth are promoting environmentally sound and socially just ways of production, consumption and living.

These efforts by ordinary people, their communities and organisations, are the building blocks of a different world where markets and technology are to be used to serve humanity, and not the other way round. And where the interests of community and the satisfaction of human needs (instead of materialistic greed and the drive for individual or corporate power) are the driving forces and the sources of fulfilment.

(Martin Khor can be contacted at 228 Macalister Road, Penang, Malayasia, or fax 604-2264505, e-mail: twn@igc.apc.org)

This we know; the Earth does not belong to humanity; people belong to the Earth, this we know. All things are connected. Whatever befalls the Earth, befalls the people of the Earth. We do not weave the web of life, we are merely a part of it. Whatever we do to the web, we do to ourselves. Chief Seattle

Sustainable Development

Sadhbh O'Neill worked with Earthwatch / Friends of the Earth and is now a member of Comhar, the national Sutainable Devolpment Partnership.

Sustainable development is no longer a new concept, having first been introduced in 1987 by Gro Harlem Brundtland as chair of the UN Commission on Environment and Development. Then it was defined as development which meets the needs of the present generation without compromising the ability of future generations to meet their own needs.

Early advocates of sustainable development argued for improved environmental management without inhibiting the growth strategies for developing countries. Indeed, sustainable development was ultimately viewed as a way to extend the Northern growth model to the South without making the same 'mistakes', and with the benefit of new and cleaner technologies.

For others, particularly environmental organisations, sustainability can only be properly defined in strict ecological terms, according to levels of consumption and production that improve quality of life and that do not deplete the carrying capacity of the earth's ecological systems. For example, in the Friends of the Earth model, sustainability is defined in terms of 'environmental space'. This is the amount of non-renewable resources available per capita for key materials such as wood and metals for everyone on the planet. In other words, if there is a total 'budget' of an important but non-renewable material such as aluminium or CO_2 emissions available it should be divided equally between North and South, and equitably within nations. The environmental space available globally per capita for most materials is up to around 80% lower than current levels of consumption - targets that would require drastic cuts in current energy and materials use.

Other views of sustainable development focus on integrating environmental, social and economic perspectives, and achieving a social consensus between various critical factors. This approach suggests that the success of strategies for sustainable development depends on the full participation of civil society and various interests coming together, as well as the linking of measures such as anti-poverty strategies with environmental goals, so as to fully integrate environmental and social concerns with economic development. In this model, process is as important as outcome, and the outcome is driven by negotiation rather than by target setting. This path recognises the huge power of large and transnational corporations, and sometimes aims to galvanise this influence in the direction of sustainability. Environmental organisations are sceptical of approaches which rely on voluntary industry efforts and market incentives rather than government regulation and firm targets.

Institutions too play an important role in bringing about social change, and in some countries localised Agenda 21 programmes have been successfully initiated by local authorities and civil society in order to map out a local or regional sustainability agenda. These programmes cover anything from health services to public parks, recycling and spatial planning.

In Ireland, the first national sustainability plan was introduced in 1997, with chapters covering key sectors such as industry, forestry, agriculture, tourism and transport. Virtually no progress has been made in initiating local Agenda 21s here despite the publication of a set of guidelines for local authorities in 1995. The extent to which environmental policies and goals are integrated into other sectors is limited, and is made all the more difficult by deregulation and concerns that environmental measures could affect Ireland's competitiveness in a global economy. Although government efforts remain modest, many organisations and bodies in both the public and private sector have adopted sustainability as an objective, including Coillte, the state-owned forestry company (though not without criticism from the environmental community).

In terms of its global dimensions, however, every trend suggests we are moving further and further away from sustainability rather than towards it. As Richard Sandbrook put it at the Earth Summit in 1997, 'what we need is the environmental equivalent of money'.

Majority World Issues

Joe Murray the co-ordinator of Afri, Action from Ireland

The publication of this Sustainable Ireland Resource book is a welcome development. It is good to have a comprehensive record of the practical initiatives, products and services that promote sustainable development in Ireland. It is also important that the book contains a 'Majority World' perspective, given that the impact of many of the unsustainable policies pursued in Ireland and in other parts of the Northern Hemisphere is often most keenly felt in countries of the Southern Hemisphere.

We are in an era when a New World order is being constructed. Dominant interests in the leading industrialised nations, especially the United States and Europe, are driving this construction. The agenda is one in which the interests of rich sections of rich countries are paramount. It is based on the imposition of a model of development, which is more about expanding capitalism and creating markets for multinational corporations than about concern for the people or environment of poorer countries.

The rape of the resources of Majority World countries continues, stockpiling an excess of consumer products on the shelves of western supermarkets and leaving the cupboards bare in the contributing countries. Despite the very effective Jubilee 2000 campaign, G8 countries have made only a feeble gesture at relieving the stranglehold of debt on the most heavily burdened countries. Human Rights violations abound and arms traders provide ever more sophisticated means of killing and oppression. Despite this bleak scenario, countless people throughout the world continue to struggle for their rights - and, with support, they can still record victories.

Ireland can play a critical role in the issues that confront countries of the Majority World today. Our history and our geographic location leave us ideally placed to stand in solidarity with the world's most exploited countries and peoples. We can do this best by maintaining an independent voice on foreign policy issues and by staying out of NATO and its surrogate, 'Partnership for Peace', which would ally us to those very dominant interests which shape the emerging world order.

The last thing the world needs at this critical juncture is another contributor to the international arms trade. We must intensify our opposition to the arms trade and to all forms of exploitation, whether through debt collection

global + local

or unfair trade. We must intensify our efforts to create a world order in which human rights and the environment are respected and an economic system is promoted that more justly distributes the finite resources of this wonderful planet.

Climate Change Jim Woolridge of Earthwatch

Causes

Modern lifestyles and population levels have lead to significant changes in the composition of the earth's atmosphere, e.g. carbon dioxide previously has been at 270 parts per million of the atmosphere; it is now at 364 ppm. As a result of such changes more solar heat is being retained in the atmosphere and global temperatures have climbed by 0.6 degrees in the last century.

The increased levels of the 'greenhouse gases' (carbon dioxide; methane; nitrous oxide; CFCs; HFCs; PFCs and sulphur hexafluoride) are due to the burning of coal, oil and gas and the clearing and burning of forests. Certain industrial processes and intensive agriculture are also implicated. In brief, modern industrial society has caused climate change.

It now looks as though climate change is accelerating. For example damage from climate related disasters for ten months of 1998 exceeded that for the whole decade of the '80s. As heat levels build up long established patterns can crumble into chaotic confusion, with rapidly escalating danger of catastrophic outcomes such as major sea level rise, loss of the Gulf Stream, major growth of deserts.

Kyoto

The UN's Kyoto Protocol (1997) decrees that the industrialised nations shall reduce their emissions of greenhouse gases by 5.2% between 2008 and 2012. The Protocol was an uneasy compromise between industry demands and scientific forecasts – according to the UN's own expert studies 5.2% is far too little; immediate cuts of 60-80% are actually needed to protect climate.

Cures

Stop burning fossil fuels; stop clearing and burning forests; clean up our industrial processes; move away from intensive agriculture; change to renewable energies; move towards sustainable levels of population and economic activity. All of the preceding are not only possible but good in themselves and capable of moving society towards sustainability and prosperity for all.

Human Rights and Sustainable Development

Komene Famaa of Ogoni Solidarity Ireland

Last year marked the 50th anniversary of the UN Declaration of Human Rights, which was proclaimed on December 10th, 1948. The rights and freedoms crucial to human dignity were stated as being the common benchmark for achievement of all people and nations.

This declaration contains several components or related rights. Most of them constitute the right to people-centred human development where people and their well-being come first, ahead of all other development objectives and priorities. Human rights and the right to development have also been reiterated and further elaborated on - largely by consensus - at the UN Conference on Human Rights (Vienna), the International Conference on Population and Development (Cairo), the World Summit on Social Development (Copenhagen) and the Fourth Conference on Women (Beijing).

I have noticed two perspectives or emphases regarding the above concept. Western democracies consider human rights to be revolving around individuals, contrary to "developing democracies". Furthermore, as Dr. Chandra Muzaffer succinctly states, "Western governments, with their liberal-democratic ideologies, policies and practices, have helped create the erroneous belief that human rights are essentially political freedom and civil liberties".

On the other hand, the developing economies of Asia, Africa and Latin America view Human Rights as applying to collectivity, community and the nation. The concept of collectivism is so inextricably intertwined with society that one finds it extremely difficult to separate it from human dignity, the environment, politics and social justice. In fact, the rights that matter most to the majority of humanity are the collective rights to food, health, clothing, shelter, education, employment and of course the environment, all of which are fundamental to their very survival and existence.

The following quote from the Habitat Agenda document is an example of the relationship between human rights and sustainable development: "...sustainable development... combines economic development, social development and environmental protection, with full respect for all human rights and fundamental freedoms, including the right to development, and offers a means of achieving a world of greater stability and peace, built on ethical and spiritual vision. Democracy, respect for human rights, transparent, representative and accountable government... in all sectors of society, as well as effective participation by civil society, are indispensable

global + local

foundations for the realisation of sustainable development...".

Today our right to a better and clean environment is threatened with the pollution of our air and water, global warming and the release of dangerous gases, chemicals and the indiscriminate dumping of toxic wastes. The major culprits are the transnational corporations in collusion with governments who are repressing human rights either for the sake of national profit or in the name of infrastructure initiatives for the "public good". Their modus operandi has not only been exploitative but also (environmentally) racist, with double standards, as observed when one makes a comparison between the ways multinationals operate in the developed and the developing worlds. There is a total disregard for human rights to a better environment. The environmental injustice practiced by Shell on the minority Ogoni people of Nigeria is a case in point, where production is also linked to people being imprisoned, killed or even hanged. We as people must query the products we consume.

Human rights should be a key element in sustainable development, by adopting a bottom-up approach and by encouraging active participation, capacity-building, empowerment, gender balance and respect in decision-making. Without such essential key elements, sustainability will be evasive. I believe that human rights and sustainable development should be part of a global revolution in human efforts towards organising life better for the whole of humanity.

We confuse ourselves into thinking we are producing oil, when what we are really doing is digging it and burning it. Amory Lovins

Debt

Niamh Gaynor co-ordinator of Jesuits for Debt Relief and Development

Debt is an economic problem with a distinctly human face. Rooted in actions taken by leaders in both the North and the South in the early '70s, its crippling impacts are most severely felt by ordinary citizens in the South, in particular the poor. Diverting scarce resources away from social sector spending, debt leaves them without immunisation against fatal, but easily preventable diseases, and without treatment for readily curable ones. It condemns them to a life without education, threatens their livelihoods, their environment, and perpetuates the vicious cycle of poverty to which they are born. Sub-Saharan Africa, for example, spends more on servicing its $200 billion debt than on the health and education of its 306 million children (1) whilst Zambia's debt servicing last year was greater than spending on all social sectors combined (2).

This system is economically unsustainable. There is clear evidence that investment in health and education is one of the best ways to promote economic growth. It is also clear that an economy cannot develop from a depleted natural resource base. However the impact of the debt burden goes far beyond economics. A system which demands that the poor repay the debts of the rich, with their jobs, their education, their environment, and their lives, clearly must change. Moreover, those most deeply affected by the current system must have a strong voice in defining and implementing this change.

The present economic system works well for select groups in select countries – witness the Celtic Tiger roaring loudly here in Ireland for some. Yet this is at the expense of too many. A sustainable solution to the present debt crisis will involve redressing this system, both economically and politically. It will require cancellation of sums greater than the $102 billion offered by G7 governments in their most recent debt relief package (3) and it will require the development of structures whereby the needs and rights of all peoples, rich and poor alike, receive fair and adequate representation.

1 *The Progress of Nations* 1999, UNICEF, New York
2 *Zambia's Current Socio-Economic Situation*, March 1999, Pete Henriot
3 This was announced in Cologne in June 1999. Jubilee 2000 UK has estimated the debts of the world's poorest countries to be worth approximately $300 billion. Whilst cancellation of this sum would make a critical difference to the lives of hundreds of millions, it is a tiny amount on the international stage – less than the amount earned by rich countries in three days.

Development Education

Thomas Tichelmann Education Officer, for the National Committee for Development Education

The United Nations defines Development Education as seeking to "enable people to participate in the development of their community, their nation and the world as a whole. Such participation implies a critical awareness of local, national and international situations based on an understanding of social economic and political process". In Ireland the National Committee for Development Education, established by Irish Aid at the Department of Foreign Affairs, has defined Development Education as:

• an educational process aimed at increasing awareness and understanding of the rapidly changing, interdependent and unequal world we live in;

• being based on an educational and development model which has at the centre the participants' own situations, opportunities and problems with regard to development. This model employs holistic, participative learner-centred strategies and has at its core the principles of justice and equality;

- seeking to engage people in analysis, reflection and action for local and global citizenship and participation;

- supporting people in understanding and acting to transform the social, cultural, political and economic structures which affect their lives at personal, community, national and international levels;

- incorporating a local as well as a global dimension, as one is incomplete without the other;

- seeking to develop the appropriate skills and attitudes which promote action for global justice, human rights and sustainable development for all people;

- not seeking to create a single definition of nor approach to development, as there is great cultural, economic, political, ideological, geographical, and environmental diversity in the world.

Development Education is not passive knowledge about development issues; rather it is knowledge applied through action to bring about justice, human rights and sustainable development. Development education is a multi-faceted and complex process which explores many distinct yet complimentary perspectives and visions as well as approaches.

Fair Trade Peter Gaynor of the Irish Fair Trade Network

Fair Trade – Guarantees a Better Deal for Third World Producers – (something you can buy into today)

The people of the Third World have nothing? Wrong! They supply us with a lot of the food we eat and usually they receive very little of the value of the products we buy from them. Commodities like coffee, tea, cocoa, and bananas are all grown in Third World countries.

Some Third World countries like Uganda depend on coffee and tea for over 90% of their total exports earnings. For these countries their dependence on one or two commodities means they are subject both to the whims of commodity markets, where prices fluctuate viciously, and to the power of multinational companies, a handful of which control the trade in most agricultural products. Sitting on top of this are international trade agreements that favour rich countries and corporations.

In real terms, i.e. what you can buy for what you earn, the prices paid to producer countries have not risen in over forty years while the costs of importing machinery and agricultural inputs have risen continuously. For millions of marginalised producers this means that they often receive less for their crops than it costs to grow them. They have to work harder, for longer, to earn less.

Fairtrade - It does exactly what it says on the label!

Alternative trade organisations like Oxfam began importing craft products about forty years ago, and this kind of alternative trade grew to a point where there are now over 3000 'World Shops' in Europe selling a wide range of craft and food products.

About ten years ago in Holland the first Fairtrade Label was launched as an independent guarantee to people shopping in supermarkets that products (coffee initially) carrying the label had been traded fairly. In its first year coffee sales doubled the sales levels of all Fairtrade products sold in Holland. Currently bananas with a Fairtrade Mark account for 15% of the total Swiss banana market and Fairtrade Labelling organisations now exist in seventeen countries.

An increasing range of coffee, tea, and chocolate products carrying the Fairtrade Mark are available through supermarkets. If they are not on the shelves just ask the manager. Coffee products in particular are increasingly being used in bars, hotels, canteens, universities and cookery schools - Ballymaloe!

For more information see Fairtrade Mark Ireland.

Suicide Seeds: Biopatents, TRIPs, and the Developing World.

Ruth McGrath Voice 315

Did You Know

- An estimated 30,000 plant species have edible parts, but just 3, wheat, maize, and rice, supply more than half of the worlds food.

- As these staple foods are genetically engineered and patented, the grip of Multinational Corporations (MNCs) on the world's food supply is tightening.

- 80% of patents on GM foods are owned by only 13 MNCs.

- The genetic makeup of the biopatented seed is the property of the corporation; the farmer cannot own it, merely lease it. The farmer's practice of saving seed for next year's crop is a thing of the past for patented crops.

- Patents on crop species threaten the 1.4 billion farmers in the developing world who currently depend on saved seed for the following years crop.

Why is this drive to gain control of the world's food supply taking place now? In 1995, the TRIPs agreement, (a satellite agreement of the World Trade Organisation), allowed patents on biological resources such as plants and animals for the first time on a global scale. Major MNCs were not slow to seize their opportunity to gain control over the genetic resources that form the basis of agriculture. The TRIPs agreement, and the biopatenting and biopiracy that it legalises, will affect the access of developing countries to basic needs such as biological resources for food and medicine, key elements of equitable and sustainable development. So far, countries have had the choice of prohibiting patents on plants and animals, under Article 27.3(b) of the TRIPs agreement. However, this Article is under review during 1999, and the next round of WTO negotiations will be starting in November of this year. Without concerted opposition, rich and powerful countries such as the US will seek patenting of animals and crops in all countries in this new round of negotiations. VOICE and other groups worldwide are campaigning to ensure this does not happen.

GLOBAL AND LOCAL BOOKS

Debt Boomerang:
How Third World Debt Harms Us All
Susan George
ISBN: 0745305946, 1997.

Discordant Harmonies: A New Ecology for
the Twenty-First Century
Daniel B. Botkin,
ISBN: 0195074696, 1992.

A Sustainable World
Thaddeus C. Trzyna
ISBN: 1853832677, 1995.

Approaches to Sustainable Development
Richard M. Auty and Katrina Brown
ISBN: 1855674394, 1997.

75: 25 - Ireland in an Increasingly
Unequal World
Congood, 1991.

Education for Development: A teachers'
resource for global learning
Unicef, 1995.

Global Teacher, Global Learner:
A handbook for teachers -
Global Education Project, 1988.

A Tale of Two Cities:
A photopack on life in London and Calcutta
WWF/Birmingham DEC.

Kids Like Us - A pack for primary schools
on life in Kenya and Ireland
Actionaid Ireland, 1995.

Fufu and Light Soup: A pack for primary
schools on food and culture in
Ghana and Ireland - Interculture, 1995.

Teaching About Localities: A handbook for
teachers on teaching about other places
Oxfam, 1998.

Development Education and Human Rights
Education in Scotland, Wales,
England and Ireland
80:20/Birmingham DEC, 1998.

All Different All Equal :
A handbook for anti-racism training

NYCI, 1997.

The Trade Trap: poverty and the global
commodity markets
Oxfam, 1992

The Oxfam Poverty Report
Oxfam, 1999.

Words into Action: basic rights and the
campaign against world poverty
Oxfam, 1999.

GLOBAL AND LOCAL WEB SITES

UN Commission on Sustainable
Development
http://www.un.org/esa/sustdev/csd.htm
The Earth Council
http://www.ecouncil.ac.cr/
World Wide Web Virtual Library,
Sustainable Development
http://www.ulb.ac.be/ceese/meta/sustvl.h
tml
Amnesty International
http://www.amnesty.org/
One World
http://www.oneworld.net/
A Seed
http://www.antenna.nl/aseed/

global + local

Pressures on the Global Environment

Since 1950

- World population has more than doubled while the economy, the global output of goods and services, has grown nearly sixfold
- Carbon dioxide emissions, mainly from fossil fuel burning, has increased fivefold thereby contributing to global warming - the 13 warmest years since record keeping began in 1866 occurred since 1979
- Water use has tripled -over pumping is causing water tables to fall in all continents
- Timber use has tripled - paper use has increased sixfold, firewood use has soared, all of which have contributed to deforestation
- Air and water pollutants have increased several fold
- 20% of the world's population consume 80% of the world's natural resources
- World grain stocks are declining
- Nearly all oceanic fisheries are being fished at or beyond capacity
- Plant and animal species are disappearing, e.g. 1,100 of the 4,400 species of mammals are threatened with extinction
- 60% of people in developing countries lack sanitation - 30% have no clean water
- Municipal Solid Waste, of which packaging forms up to 33%, continues to grow.

Pressures on the Irish Environment

This high level of consumption is not just a global problem - it is happening here in Ireland too. A preliminary study, based on four criteria, i.e. fossil fuels, built up land, food and forestry, concluded that Ireland's "ecological footprint" is at least one and one quarter times its ideal size and is growing.

The ecological footprint is an indicator developed to illustrate human impact on this finite planet. A footprint represents the area of productive land and waters required to meet the needs of a particular population at a particular standard of living.

In other words . . .

We are using up more than our fair share of the Earth's available resources.

EOLAS AR AN gCOMHSHAOL
INFORMATION ON THE ENVIRONMENT
17, St Andrew St., Dublin 2, Ireland
Tel 1890 200 191 or 01 888 3001
Fax: 01 888 3946
e-mail: info@enfo.ie
Website: www.enfo.ie

It's easy to make a difference.
Extracts from the forthcoming ENFO SUSTAINABLE LIVING GUIDE for shoppers and investers.

HUMAN RIGHTS / DEVELOPMENT GROUPS

ACTIONAID IRELAND

Contact: Caroline Maxwell
Unity Buildings,16/17 Lr. O' Connell Street,
Dublin 1

Tel: 01-8787911
Fax: 01-878 6245
Email: actionaidireland@tinet.ie

Actionaid Ireland is dedicated to improving the lot
of people in developing countries. We do this
through programmes that help local communities
achieve long-term, sustainable development.
Giving to Actionaid is not just giving - it's
investing.

ARASI

Association of Refugees and Asylum Seekers

Contact: Mohamed Haji
213 North Circular Road, Dublin

Tel: 01-8381142
Fax: 01-8381143
Email: arasi@indigo.ie

ARASI provides information and support services
to refugees and asylum seekers. Also educational
work with the Irish public through talks and
workshops to schools and community groups and
the organisation of cultural events.

BANULACHT

Contact: Eileen Smith
20 Lower Dominick Street, Dublin 1

Tel: 01-8726952
Fax: 01-8724183
Email: banulach@iol.ie

Banulacht is a network of women working to
promote awareness of the links between
development issues that affect people locally and
globally. We work from a gender perspective that
entails analysing unequal effects of development
on women and men.

BETWEEN

Contact: Criostoir de Baroid
8 North Mall, Cork

Tel: 021-393572/021-961375
Fax: 021-393537
Email: between@eircom.net

The promotion of reconciliation, human relations
and rights with and between Northern Irish
communities.

CARMICHAEL CENTRE FOR VOLUNTARY GROUPS

Contact: Kate O' Sullivan
Carmichael House,North Brunswick Street,
Dublin 6

Tel: 01-8735702
Fax: 01-8735737
E-mail: carmichaelcentre@eircom.com

Carmichael Centre provides accommodation,
administrative services, training and support to
small voluntary organisations, enabling them to
achieve their objectives in a cost effective manner.

CHERNOBYL CHILDREN'S PROJECT

Contact: Adi Roche,
2 Camden Place, Camden Quay, Cork City

Tel: 021-506411
Fax: 021-551544
E-mail: adiroche@indigo.ie
Website: www.adiccp.org

International Humanitarian Aid Charity. The
Chernobyl Children's Project is a registered charity
founded in 1991 by Adi Roche to help alleviate
the suffering of the 3-4 million children the
United Nations estimates have been affected by
the worlds worst nuclear disaster at Chernobyl in
1986.

COMHLAMH

Contact: Conaill O Caoimh
10 Upper Camden Street, Dublin 2

Tel: 01-4783490
Fax: 01-4783738
Email: comhlamh@iol.ie

The association of returned development workers.
Comhlamh is an organisation whose members work
in global solidarity promoting a just and
sustainable world and a multi-cultural Ireland. Its
activities include education courses, public
awareness, campaigns, lobbying and social
activities.

DEBT AND DEVELOPMENT COALITION IRELAND

Contact: Jean Somers
All Hallows, Grace Park Road,
Drumcondra, Dublin 9

Tel: 01-8571828
Fax: 01-8571828
Email: ddc@connect.ie

A coalition of development, religious solidarity and
other organisations in Ireland campaigning for
developing country debt cancellation. Co-ordinates
Jubilee 2000 Ireland. Campaigns in Ireland and at
international level.

EL SALVADOR AWARENESS

Contact: Fr. Peter Coleman
Romero Centre, 101 Harolds Cross Road,
Dublin 6

Tel: 01-4964138
Fax: 01-4964138
E-mail: romero@connect.ie

LISTINGS

El Salvador Awareness is a voluntary network of people and groups to promote justice and peace. The Romero Centre has development education programmes with art, craft, awareness and newsletter.

GLENCREE RECONCILIATION CENTRE

Contact: Ian White
Glencree, Enniskerry,Co. Wicklow
Tel: 01-2829711
Fax: 01-2766085
Email: info@glencree-cfr.ie
Website: www.glencreecfr.ie

Glencree Centre for Reconciliation is an autonomous organisation which seeks to work together with all who are trying to build peace in whatever area of society.

GOAL

P.O Box 19, Dun Laoghaire, Co. Dublin
Tel: 01-2809779
Fax: 01-2809215
Email: info@goal.ie
Website: www.goal.ie

Goal targets resources towards the poorest of the poor, primarily in developing world. Goal responds to humanitarian emergencies and implements development programmes which include primary health care, caring for street children etc.

GORTA

The Freedom From Hunger Council of Ireland
Contact: Jim Coughlan
12 Herbert Street, Dublin 2
Tel: 01-6615522
Fax: 01-6612627
Email: admin@gorta.ie
Website: www.gorta.ie

Gorta is an NGO that funds long-term self-help agricultural projects in developing countries around the world.

IRISH MEXICO GROUP

Contact: Mark Connolly
LASC, Merrion Row,
Dublin 2
Tel: 01-6760435
Fax: 01-6621784
Email: lasc@iol.ie
Website:http://flag.blackened.net/revolt/mexico.html

Supports struggles for justice in Mexico and Ireland sending human rights observers to Zapatista communities in Chiapas. Bringing Mexican activists here. Raising funds. Raising hell! Solidarity, liberty, justice, democracy.

IRISH AID ADVISORY COMMITTEE

Contact: Emer O'Brien
25 Herbert Place,
Dublin 2
Tel: 01-6760112
Fax:01-6760118
Email: iaac@indigo.ie

The Irish Aid Advisory Committee offers expert advice to the Minister for Foreign Affairs and the Minister of State, with responsibility for overseas development. Assistance in matters relating to Ireland's development co-operation programme, through research it undertakes.

IRISH COUNCIL FOR CIVIL LIBERTIES

Contact: Judy Welsh
Dominick Court, 41 Lower Dominick Street,
Dublin 1
Tel: 01-8783136
Fax: 01-8783109
Email: iccl@iol.ie www.iccl.ie

ICCL is an independent voluntary organisation that works to defend and promote human rights and civil liberties. It monitors potential human rights violations and mounts public campaigns.

JESUITS FOR DEBT RELIEF
AND DEVELOPMENT (JDRAD)

Contact: Niamh Gaynor
26 Upper Sherrard Street, Dublin 1
Tel: 01-8556814
Fax: 01-8364377
Email: cfj@s-j.ie
Website: http://www.jesuit.ie/jdrad

JDRAD is an international network of Jesuit and non-Jesuit organisations and individuals committed to human development. Analysis and action on specific issues is informed by the experiences of members.

OXFAM IRELAND

Contact: Michael O'Brien
9 Burgh Quay, Dublin 2
Tel: 01-6727662
Fax: 01-6727680
Email: oxireland@oxfam.ie
Website: www.oxfamireland.org

Oxfam Ireland promotes sustainable livelihood among the world's poorest people through long-term development programmes and commitment to fair and ethical trading. Creating the political will and human action necessary to successfully tackle poverty is the focus of Oxfam's campaigns and advocacy work.

OGONI SOLIDARITY IRELAND (OSI)

Contact: Frank Kirwan
73 Windmill Park, Crumlin, Dublin 12
Tel: 01-4553066
Email: frank-kirwan@hotmail.com

OSI is committed to raising awareness of the political and economic marginalisation of the Ogoni ethnic minority in Nigeria. OSI focuses also on the environmental damage caused by the Shell Oil Company and their collusion in human rights abuses.

SELF HELP DEVELOPMENT INTERNATIONAL

Contact: Ann Murphy
Hacketstown, Co. Carlow
Tel: 0508-71175
Fax: 0508-71292
Email: info@selfhelpintl.ie
Website: www.selfhelpintl.ie

A Third World development agency aimed to assist locals become self sufficient by helping them to develop their own land.

TCD ONE WORLD SOCIETY

Contact: Rory Hearne
Box 25, Reagent House, Trinity House, Dublin 2
Tel: 01-6082351
Email: oneworld@csc.tcd.ie

We aim to raise awareness among the student body and the wider public about issues that affect the developing world, e.g. international trade, Third World debt, fair trade and the arms industry.

TOOLS FOR SOLIDARITY

Contact: Stephen Wood,
Unit 181 Edenderry Ind. Estate,
326 Crumlin Road, Belfast, Co.Antrim
Tel: 0801-232 747473
Fax: 0801-232 742283

To support sustainable development and raise awareness of interdependence by collecting and refurbishing basic hand tools and machines for communities, co-operatives and villages in Africa, particularly in Tanzania.

TROCAIRE

Contact: Caoimhe de Barra
169 Booterstown Ave., Blackrock, Co. Dublin
Tel: 01-2885385 01-2836022 / 2883577
Email: campaigns@trocaire.ie
Website: www.trocaire.org

Trocaire is a development agency committed to tackling the causes of poverty and injustice in developing countries through community projects in almost 50 countries. Trocaire is also committed to education and campaigning in Ireland, on key issues such as debt, trade, human rights, land

rights, conflict, refugees and slavery.

VOLUNTARY SERVICE INTERNATIONAL

Contact: Tom Ryder
30 Mountjoy Square, Dublin 1
Tel: 01-8551011
Fax: 01-8551012
Email: vsi@iol.ie
Website: www.homepages.iol.ie/~vsi

VSI works for peace, international understanding and social justice through the medium of voluntary and community work in Ireland and 50 countries world-wide, development education programme, programme for young people (16 plus) from disadvantaged areas.

WORLD DEVELOPMENT CENTRE

Contact: Lucy Whittle
3 Vulcan Street, Waterford
Tel: 051-873064
Fax: 051-853979
Email: wdcentre@tinet.ie

The World Development Centre is a development education and resource centre and a fair trade shop. Our aim is to raise awareness on issues of justice, human dignity and the environment.

JESUIT CENTRE FOR FAITH AND JUSTICE

Contact: Bill Toner
26 Upper Sherrard Street, Dublin 1
Tel: 01-8556814
Fax: 01-8364377
E-mail: cfj@s-j.ie

The CFJ engages in action and reflection to counter injustice in Ireland. Through social analysis the CFJ endeavours to work for changes that will benefit the vulnerable in society. Current issues of concern to the CFJ include homelessness, mental illness, crime and punishment and asylum seekers. Check our our journal working notes on our WEB site.

SEE ALSO

Development Education in this section / Columban Mission / Amnesty International / LASC

FAIR TRADE

ALL THAT'S GREEN

Contact: Dominick & Grace Donnelly
27 Pearse St.,Kinsale, Co. Cork
Tel: 021-773814
Fax: 021-773815
Email: info@allthatsgreen.ie
Website: www.allthatsgreen.ie

Ireland's first environmentally-friendly one-stop shop. Mail order catalogue. Natural paints and wood finishes, solar-powered lighting and fountains, solar-powered battery rechargers, cotton and eco-disposable nappies, organic baby clothes, fairly-traded cotton clothes, recycled stationery, worm composting, books on green issues, organic and fairly-traded food, natural toiletries, biodegradable cleaning products, green gadgets and much more...

FAIRTRADE MARK (IRE)

Contact: Peter Gaynor
 7 Upper Camden Street, Dublin 2
Tel: 01-475 3515
Fax: 01-475 3515
E-mail: fair.mark@pobox.com

Insist on the Fairtrade Mark.
The Fairtrade Mark is an independent consumer guarantee that provides a powerful and positive link between consumers and Third World producers. It empowers marginalised producers to take more control over their lives through the fair deal it guarantees. It also helps consumers to understand and take responsibiltiy for the role they play when buying products form the Third World. Fairtrade Mark coffees are available for both retail and catering markets. Ask for 'Bewleys Direct', 'Cafedirect', Tiki Caffe from Muttner Alcie.

TRAIDCRAFT

Contact: Patricia Norrington
30 Bryansglen Ave., Bangor, Co. Down BT20 3RU
Tel: 0801-247 465817
Email: susan@traidcraft.co.uk
Website: www.traidcraft.co.uk

Traidcraft markets fairly traded foods, crafts, clothes, recycled paper and cards from developing countries. Fair trade helps rather than exploits people and protects the environment on which we all depend.

WAR ON WANT NI

Contact: Shirelle Steward
1 Rugby Avenue
Belfast, Co. Antrim
Tel: 0044-2890 232064 / 0801-232 232064

War on Want NI is a local independent development agency which works in partnership with small grass roots organisations in their struggle against poverty. We campaign to ensure the voice of the worlds poorest is kept firmly on the national and international agenda. Retail or campaign on Fair Trade.

THE TRAID

Contact: Jorg Schmidt
167 Capel Street, Dublin 1
We aim to improve the situation of producers in developing countries by selling as many Fair Trade

goods as possible. To raise awareness about Fair Trade goods and the issues connected with them.

SEE ALSO
Oxfam Ireland / World Development Centre

CAMPAIGN GROUPS

AFAN
(ATLANTIS FOUNDATION ACTION NETWORK)

Contact: Mary Kelly
Burtonport, Co. Donegal
Tel: 075-42304

A community of activists (50% teenagers) working with extreme urgency - AFAN for the abolition of nuclear weapons, protection of the environment, human rights, Irish neutrality and independence. Our roots are in therapy and self-sufficiency. We are currently restoring a 55ft wooden sailing boat so that we can campaign at sea. Visitors welcome.

AMNESTY INTERNATIONAL IRISH SECTION

Contact: Mary Lawler
Sean MacBride House, 48 Fleet Street, Dublin 2
Tel: 01-6776361
Fax: 01-6776392
Email: info@amnesty.iol.ie
Website: www.amnesty.ie

Amnesty International is an independent worldwide human rights movement. It promotes the observance throughout the world of human rights as set out in the Universal Declaration of Human Rights through impartial action and the international solidarity of a worldwide movement of people. The Irish section, which was founded in 1961, now has over 12,000 members and donors, 43 local groups and 160 school and youth groups.

BABY MILK ACTION

Contact: Gill Ryan
10 Upper Camden St., Dublin 2
Tel: 01-4622026
Email: babymilkaction@tinet.ie
Website: www.babymilkaction.org

Campaign group for ethical marketing of babymilk, multinational accountability, protection of parents rights to informed infant feeding choices. Infant health through safe infant feeding and adequate support for breastfeeding mothers and babies.

CUBA SOLIDARITY CULTURAL COMMITTEE

Contact: Bernie Dwyer
20 Seaview Terrace, Howth, Co. Dublin
Tel: 01- 8324169
Fax: 01- 8324169

Campaigning for human rights in Cuba.

global + local

EAST TIMOR SOLIDARITY GROUP

Contact: Tom Hyland
Room 13, 24-26 Dame Street, Dublin 2

Tel / Fax: 01-6719207
Email: etisc@indigo.ie

East Timor Solidarity Group campaign for human rights and democracy in East Timor.

ESPERANTO-ASOCIO DE IRLANDO

Contact: Maire Mullarney
The Mill House, Whitechurch Rd., Rathfarnham, Dublin 14

Tel: 01-4931219
Email: esper@indigo.ie

We try to inform Irish people that it is possible for people in any part of the world to talk and write to each other easily, not in English.

LATIN AMERICA SOLIDARITY CENTRE (LASC)

Contact: Colette Spears & Claire Prendeville
5 Merrion Row, Dublin 2

Tel: 01-6760435
Fax: 01-6621784
Email: lasc@iol.ie
Website: latinamericasolidarity.freeservers.com//index.htm

LASC works to promote mutual solidarity between those working progressive change in Ireland and Latin America, raise awareness and campaign on issues relating to Latin America, and celebrate their cultures and peoples.

COURSES IN DEVELOPMENT STUDIES

FULL-TIME AND PART-TIME OPTIONS

MA in Development Studies (day-time)

Graduate Diploma in Development Studies (day-time)

National Diploma in Development Studies (day-time)

Understanding Development (eve)

Environment and Development (eve)

Since 1974, the Centre has given an opportunity to people to enhance their understanding of global development issues and to acquire new skills. All courses are accredited by the National Council for Education Awards (NCEA). People can attend individual subjects on a part-time basis and obtain academic credits leading to an internationally recognised qualification.

FOR A COURSE PROSPECTUS AND FURTHER INFORMATION CONTACT:

The Applications Office,
DEVELOPMENT STUDIES CENTRE,
Kimmage Manor, Whitehall Road, Dublin 12.

**Tel: (01) 4064386 / 4064380 Fax: (01) 4560089
E-mail: apply@dsckim.iol.ie**

PEACE & NEUTRALITY ALLIANCE

Contact: Roger Cole
52 Silchester Park, Glenageary, Co. Dublin

Tel: 01-2806878 / 087-2611597
Email: silchester@tinet.ie

PANA seeks to promote a policy of Irish independence, neutrality & support for the United Nations. We oppose the transformation of the EU into a federal superstate armed with nuclear weapons.

SEE ALSO
TROCAIRE / ENVIRONMENT SECTION

DEVELOPMENT EDUCATION

COLUMBAN MISSION EDUCATION/JUSTICE/PEACE DEPARTMENT

Contact: Pat Raleigh / Michael O'Sullivan
St. Colomban's Park, Dalgan Park,
Navan, Co. Meath

Tel: 046-21525
Fax: 046-22799
Email: colomban@indigo.ie
Website: www.colomban.com

The Columban Mission Education / Justice/Peace Department offers workshops relating to justice (particularly on world debt), ecology and dialogue between people of different faiths. It also runs a visitor centre which is open to the public. It produces, quarterly, a Columban Justice/Peace newsletter "Voices For Justice".

DEFY

(Development Education For Youth and One World Week)

Contact: Grainne O'Byrne / Liam Wegimont
17 Upper Stephen Street, Dublin 8

Tel: 01-4751826
Fax: 01-4751970
Email: defy@iol.ie

Defy is a partnership coalition of Irish NGOs and Irish Youth organisation. DEFY's purpose is to promote and co-ordinate development education in the youth sector. Through development education with young people, Defy aims to foster action in solidarity with developing world and public awareness raising in Ireland.

DEVELOPMENT STUDIES CENTRE

Contact: Tom Campbell
Kimmage Manor, Whitehall Road, Dublin 12

Tel: 01-4064386 / 01-4064380
Fax: 01-4560089
Email: apply@dsckim.iol.ie
Website: www.iol.ie/~dsckim

Education and training for development workers / practitioners, provide NCEA accredited courses in

COMHAR

THE NATIONAL SUSTAINABLE DEVELOPMENT PARTNERSHIP

Comhar seeks to work in partnership to encourage sustainable development across Irish economy and society, and to advise Government on policies which support and promote sustainable development.

Comhar is a representative advisory body, chaired by Dr. John Bowman, which was established by Government in February 1999. Its terms of reference are to advance the national agenda for sustainable development, to evaluate progress in this regard, to assist in devising suitable mechanisms and advising on their implementation, and to contribute to the formation of a national consensus in these regards.

FURTHER INFORMATION, INCLUDING COPIES OF COMHAR'S WORK PROGRAMME FOR THE PERIOD 1999-2002, ARE AVAILABLE FROM:

Comhar Secretariat
17 St. Andrew Street, Dublin 2

Telephone: (01) 888 3990 or (LoCall)1890 - 200 327
Fax: (01) 888 3999 **E-mail:** comhar@environ.irlgov.ie

global + local

development studies at national diploma, post grad' and MA level. Also run a number of evening courses - Environment and Development, Understanding Development and Demystifying Development Economics.

DEVELOPMENT STUDIES LIBRARY

Contact: Sally Corcoran
University College Dublin, Belfield, Dublin 4 ,
Tel: 01-7067560
Fax: 01- 7061148
E-mail: sally.corcoran@ucd.ie
Website: www.ucd.ie

Books and journals on developing countries and issues such as development, debt, environment, agriculture, rural development, politics, aid, women, history, sustainability etc. Open to the public. Please phone first to visit the library.

GALWAY ONE WORLD CENTRE

Contact: Heike Vornhagen & Vicky Donnelly,
The Small Crane, William Street West,
Galway, Co. Galway
Tel: 091-581688
Fax: 091-581694
E-mail: gowc@iol.ie
Website: http://homepages.iol.ie/~node

The Galway One World Centre is a development education resource centre providing books, magazines and videos on development issues. Main areas of work are anti-racism, refugee and asylum human rights and globalisation. For details of workshops please contact us.

INTERNATIONAL CENTRE FOR DEVELOPMENT STUDIES

Contact: Anne Dolan
NUI, Galway
Tel: 091-750475
Fax: 091-750567
Email: anne.dolan@nuigalway.ie

The International Centre for Development Studies is an interdisciplinary facility involving a range of departments with an interest in development. The centre makes a practical contribution to local regional and international development through its research programmes, training courses and consultancy service. Specialist interests within the centre include community and rural development, adult education and regional planning.

MIDLAND DEVELOPMENT EDUCATION PROJECT

Contact: Rory Murphy
79 Main St., Portlaoise, Co. Laois
Tel: 0502-61185
Fax: 0502-61590
Email: admin@mdep.iol.ie
Website: hompages.iol.ie/~mdep

The Midland Development Education Project receives state funding to employ a number of people on a part-time basis. We are committed to raising awareness of social, politicial and economic issues both locally and globally. We aim to increase understanding of the developing world by promoting solidarity with those who suffer inequalities, hunger abandonment and powerlessness and consequently highlight the wealth of tradition, culture and diversity of both ancient and contemporary civilisations.

NATIONAL COMMITTEE FOR DEVELOPMENT EDUCATION

Contact: Barbara Wilson
16-20 South Cumberland Street, Dublin 2
Tel: 01-6620866
Fax: 01-6620808
Email: ncde@eircom.net

NCDE under the auspices of Irish Aid at the Department of Foreign Affairs, seeks to promote development education in all sectors of Irish society. It works in collaboration with other organisations to promote and support best practice in development education. NCDE administers a funding scheme and has a resource centre which is open to the public.

NODE NETWORK

Contact: Owen McCarney
10 Upper Camden Street, Dublin 2
Tel: 01-4751998
Fax: 01-4783738
Email: Node@iol.ie
Website: homepages.iol.ie/~node/

NODE is a network of twelve grassroots development education centres and groups throughout Ireland. Its primary aim is to raise awareness of the causes and effects of poverty and inequality at local, national and international levels.

ONE WORLD CENTRE FOR NORTHERN IRELAND

Contact: Stephen McCloskey
4 Lower Crescent, Belfast, Co. Antrim BT7 1NR
Tel: 0801-232 241879
Fax: 0801-232 241879
Email: belfastdec@gn.apc.org

A resource base/library for global and developing world studies which offers a range of education materials on development issues. We provide outreach services in the formal and non-formal education sectors and produce publications on sustainable development themes.

TULLAMORE ONE WORLD GROUP

Contact: Therese Kinahan-Sayer
Bridge Street, Tullamore, Co.Offaly

Tel: 0506-52361
Fax: 0506-52073

Aims to increase awareness of development education issues through our resource library. We operate educational events for schools, groups/organisations. One World week and African arts and culture, Third World debt.

SEE ALSO
Trocaire / African Cultural Project / World Development Centre / Comhlamh

CROSS-CULTURAL GROUPS

AFRICAN CULTURAL PROJECT

Contact: Adekunle Gomez
Ulster Bank Chambers,
4 Lower O'Connell Street, Dublin 1

Tel: 01-8780613
Fax: 01-8780615

Established as a cultural and educational organisation, the African Cultural Project co-ordinates a multi-disciplinary programme of arts and educational events, including the African Festival. It works in partnership with a network of various bodies throughout Ireland, including major cultural institutions and county arts officers.

INTERCULTURE

Contact: Kerry Lawless
10A Lr. Camden Street, Dublin 2

Tel: 01-4782046
Fax: 01-4780614
Email: infa@afs.org
Website: www.afs.org

Interculture was founded in 1976 by AFS International programmes. We are a voluntary non-profit making organisation working to promote tolerance and understanding and combat prejudice and injustice through intercultural programmes and international exchange.

PARTNERSHIP IRELAND-AFRICA

Contact: Brid McAuley,
Clogher, Westport, Co. Mayo

Tel: 098-26409
Email: bmcauley@anu.ie
Partnership Ireland-Africa aims to foster friendship and understanding between communities in the west of Ireland and in Africa at grassroots level. Activities include education conferences and awareness-raising events.

FOR FURTHER INFORMATION ON MORE GROUPS SEE ALSO ENVIRONMENT SECTION.

page 98 **Introduction** to transport Barnie Walsh

page 100 **Renewable Energy** Ewan Chalmers

page 103 **Transport** Graham Lightfoot

ENERGY AND TECHNOLOGY Barnie Walsh

Barney Walsh is a Landscape Architect and Environmentalist with wide experience in design, construction and installation of green energy systems. Born in Waterford, he has spent many years abroad in Europe and the United States. He now runs ERDA, Environmental Research and Design Associates, a green energy consultancy in Gleneely, Co. Donegal.

Whatever the answers turn out to be in our current debates over the major issues of today, such as climate change, genetically modified foods, agribusiness, or our continuing predilection for making war upon each other, it will be seen, if time allows, that energy usage is at the heart of all these matters. For better or worse we are now, right across our planet, an energy-dependent species. When we say energy, we mean fossil fuel derived energy, or more ominously, nuclear energy. We know, quite without question, that although this energy is apparently end-of-pipe cheap like never before, it has inherently high costs with respect to our health, climate and social sustainability.

Today we require energy for every facet of our lifestyle: for manufacturing, transport, communications, research and development, the maintenance of our knowledge repositories, educational systems, households, health delivery, food production, commerce, retailing, leisure pursuits, and other activities without which life would be unimaginable. Energy supply is at the heart of our services infrastructure: our municipal, judicial, governmental, defence, and life support maintenance for clean water, clean air and waste evacuation. Energy is our species' lifeblood and our consumption rate is climbing exponentially.

This emergence of homo sapiens as an Energy-dependent species is not necessarily a bad thing. We shall never turn back - barring catastrophe - to lower rates of energy consumption again. What we can turn to is clean energy, which is alternative or renewable energy, in order to replace our dangerous and mounting dependence on current toxic supplies.

As our energy habit steepens we look at 4 possibilities for the future:

• We can go on as we are: not a viable option.

• We can arrest the climb of our energy consumption: clearly this is impossible and anathema to a global economic growth philosophy.

• We can hope for a silver bullet, a breakthrough technological fix, a *deus ex machina*: this would seem to be an irresponsible expectation.

• We can invest in renewable energy from solar through wind, wave, tidal, hydro, biomass and geothermal. This means investment on a

Energy + transport

global scale, where the potential returns are of a magnitude matching current corporate expectations: large scale infrastructural and regional plant, high technology and extensive, meaningful job creation. This would involve good traditional economic practice.

The thinking here is quite orthodox now. What is radical is the prospect of implementation. Just as we can realistically only approach part solving of 'Globalist' problems by acting positively in our own backyards, so also is the idea of regional self-sufficiency in energy supply and management a key factor in sustainability. This will necessarily mean local and community participation in, and management of, energy matters which directly affect the life of our regions. For practical sustainability, the goal will have to be, as in food production and waste treatment for example, regionally self-sufficient.

This agenda is most easily approached in today's economic climate through innovative harnessing of renewable sources such as wind, hydro, solar and biomass. These energy sources can be easily appreciated as communal or 'heritage' resources. The legal and political mechanisms for community development of renewables and public holding of equity in the economic benefit and management of renewable energy have yet to be put in place. This is a really practical direction for us to move in since it not only serves us environmentally in the production of clean energy, but also nurtures technical and management skills which are valuable in economic terms. Furthermore, it is a movement with social benefit. These callings towards self-sufficiency and self-reliance are fundamental to our sense of confidence and self-determination in the maintenance of our social structures.

For any real shot at sustainability for our species across this planet we need to act seriously in terms of energy procurement. Energy is the central tenet of our human, environmental and economic concerns. Renewable energy, alternative to fossil supplies, is the only practical future reality. Community, or citizen, participation in the energy business is our business, and renewable energy is good business.

> **Sustainable development seeks to improve the quality of human life without undermining the quality of our natural environment. It therefore embraces social, economic and environmental issues and recognises that none should be in conflict with the other.** English Nature, position statement on sustainable development

Renewable energy sources

Ewan Chambers, the Irish Energy Centre's renewable energy office

Why and what elements of the current system are unsustainable

Modern societies consume huge amounts of energy - to heat homes and offices, fuel transport systems, power industry and generate electricity. Ireland is no exception; and as our economy grows, so does our demand for energy.

Today, most of this energy is produced using fossil fuels such as gas, oil, coal and peat. We now know that large-scale use of fossil fuels is unsustainable in the long term. They are finite resources -which will one day run out. Burning them releases vast quantities of carbon dioxide, a potent greenhouse gas, into the atmosphere. Other emissions released in fossil fuel combustion cause acid rain. Ireland now imports over 85% of the fuel required for energy production, which is clearly insecure if not unsustainable.

What would be more sustainable

Renewable energy resources, on the other hand, are constantly replenished through the cycles of nature. The sun, wind, running water, organic materials like wood, and even wastes from domestic and agricultural activities, are all potential sources of energy. Their supply will never be exhausted.

Ireland is richly endowed with renewable energy resources. They offer a sustainable alternative for our energy supply. Renewable sources of energy currently contribute just two percent of Ireland's total energy requirement - a fraction of the potential of the resources available.

We can't just switch from fossil fuels immediately. But a gradual shift towards renewable energy would mean reduced CO_2 emissions, cleaner, less polluting energy production, secure and stable energy supply for the long term, reduced reliance on fuel imports as well as investment and employment in indigenous renewable energy projects.

Suggestions on how we can move to the more sustainable option

Several renewable energy technologies are now commercially viable and could make a much greater contribution to sustainability in our energy supply. Renewables with the greatest immediate potential in Ireland are wind and biomass energy for electricity generation and biomass, geothermal and solar energy for heating and process heat.

Electricity from renewables

Renewables currently provide around six percent of Ireland's electricity capacity. More than two thirds of this is in large-scale hydropower stations operated by the ESB.

Wind energy could make a far larger contribution to our electricity supply. Ireland has one of the best wind resources in Europe. The technology is well proven as safe, reliable and cost-effective. Modern turbines are also much quieter than common wisdom suggests. A single 1 MW wind turbine produces enough electricity for 650 homes. Since early 1999 there were ten wind farms in Ireland with a combined capacity of 63 MW.

Biomass (e.g. wood and waste) can be burned or processed to provide heat and power on both large and small scale. There is great potential to use forestry, agricultural and domestic wastes for large-scale electricity generation in Ireland. Energy crops and short-rotation forestry offer further potential for the future. Another form of biomass, decomposing municipal waste, produces landfill gas which in 1999 provides around 15 MW of electricity - enough for over 19,000 homes. There is potential to expand to this capacity.

Heat from renewables

The use of renewables to provide sustainable heating (and cooling) in commercial and residential buildings could also be greatly increased. Passive solar design, which uses orientation, materials and good building design principles to ensure that solar gains are maximised is a mature and well-established design technology. Just by facing a house south to capture the maximum sunlight, energy bills can be reduced by ten percent. With additional measures this saving can be trebled.
Using wood fuel to heat our homes is also a sustainable choice. Wood is 'CO2 neutral', absorbing as much CO_2 when it grows as is released when it burns, and takes just 5-20 years to grow. Modern, highly efficient stoves and fireplace inserts make wood fuel a far more practical option for today's lifestyle.

Heat pumps offer an ideal solution for heating and cooling in homes and commercial buildings in Ireland. Ground source heat pumps use a small amount of electricity to collect and concentrate geothermal energy stored in the ground to provide space and water heating, or to dispel heat for air conditioning. Installation costs are similar to those of conventional heating systems; running costs are much lower.

Active solar heating systems can provide economical hot water and space heating. In Ireland, solar panels can provide around 60 percent of the annual hot water requirements for homes and buildings. This is a well-established technology, commercially available across Europe and equipment costs are falling all the time. Solar resources in Ireland are considerable (comparable to those in the Netherlands and Austria) and yet remain undeveloped to a large extent.

> **"Pond scum" may be a synonym for "primitive", but the tiny organisms that compose it easily beat the human state of the art when it comes to capturing energy from the sun. Some purple bacteria answering to that unflattering description use light energy with almost 95% efficiency-more than four times that of the best man-made solar cells.** University of Southern California

Energy Consumption

Energy use can be reduced by:

- purchasing energy efficient appliances and equipment - look for the energy label.
- purchasing low energy CFL light bulbs instead of the tungsten filament type
- buying a lagging jacket for your hot water tank, or, if the old one is too light or does not cover the entire surface area of the tank, replacing it
- buying rechargeable batteries (and a charger), particularly for high drain products which are used frequently, such as personal tape or CD players and some motorised toys
- buying a car with a more fuel efficient engine
- enquiring as to insulation standards when buying a home - typically a house built today will use only 40% of the heating energy required by a pre-1979 home; timber framed homes are highly energy efficient with heating costs up to 50% lower than standard masonry built houses
- choosing a location for a new house close to public transport to work, shops and schools to minimise private transport use.

EOLAS AR AN gCOMHSHAOL
INFORMATION ON THE ENVIRONMENT

YOU CAN CONTACT THE IRISH ENERGY CENTRE AT 01 836 9080
FOR FURTHER INFORMATION ON ENERGY ISSUES

17, St Andrew St., Dublin 2, Ireland
Tel 1890 200 191 or 01 888 3001
Fax: 01 888 3946
e-mail: info@enfo.ie
Website: www.enfo.ie

It's easy to make a difference.
Extracts from the forthcoming ENFO SUSTAINABLE LIVING GUIDE for shoppers and investers.

Energy + transport

Transport

Graham Lightfoot, consultant specialising in sustainable transport systems

We've become dependent on the car...or so we're told. That's amazing, really, when the majority of us don't drive; we walk, cycle, use public transport and travel in a car as a passenger or don't travel at all. In Dublin, only one person in three owns a car, and in the rural areas it's an even lower percentage. Even so, access to places of employment, education, training, shopping and recreation has become increasingly difficult without use of a car. It seems that planning for the car has taken precedence over planning for other modes. Our level of car ownership is still much lower than most other EU countries, but car owners in Ireland make far more journeys by car than in many other EU countries. Public transport is considered to be for losers and poor people. The hullabaloo about the introduction of the Stillorgan Quality Bus Corridor concentrated on the problems it will cause for car users (the people who cause traffic congestion), not on the benefits to the bus user, the cyclist and the pedestrian (the people who suffer from traffic congestion).

What was that bump?

Adbusters www.adbusters.org

The Dublin Transportation Initiative and plans elsewhere have shown that it is possible to move away from a car-centred approach towards a more sustainable approach, one in which public transport, cycling and walking take precedence. Surely, this is a more sensible approach; one in which the undoubted benefits of the car can best be seen...as a mode of transport to be used when it is not appropriate or suitable to use the other modes. Our planners should therefore be planning for the majority by supporting developments, which do not require people to travel long distances to access facilities and services. They need to recognise the relationship between land use strategies and transport provision. Public transport and the provision of facilities for public transport users, cyclists and pedestrians must be seen as part of the infrastructural investment for a sustainable future, so that we can follow a decision chain, which goes... can I walk there, wheel myself there, be pushed there; cycle there; get there on public transport or by taxi; have to use the car to get there; and to follow such a decision chain even if we are a car owner.

Energy + transport

ENERGY BOOKS

Y2k and Y-O-U - the sane person's home-preparation guide
Dermot McGuigan
SBN: 1890132268, 1999.

Wind Energy Basics - a guide to small and micro wind systems
Paul Gipe
ISBN: 1890132071, 1999.

Solar Water Heating
P. Trimby
ISBN: 0951450468, 1996.

Windpower Workshop:
Building Your Own Wind Turbines
Hugh Piggott
ISBN: 1898049203, 1997.

Off the Grid
P. Allen and R. Todd
ISBN: 1898049092, 1999.

Solar Living Sourcebook 10th ed. - The Complete Guide to Renewable Energy Technologies and Sustainable Living
John Schaeffer and Doug Pratt
ISBN: 0916571033, 1999.

Going With The Flow; Small Scale Water Power Made Simple
Curtis, Langley & Ramsey
ISBN: 1898049181, 1999.

TRANSPORT BOOKS

Road Transport: the Environment and Sustainable Development
Institution of Highways & Transportation
ISBN: 0902933205, 1996.

The Sustainable City Part III:
Transport and Public Places
Fabio Maria Ciuffini
ISBN: 9282749215, 1996.

Transport for a Sustainable Future
John Whitelegg
ISBN: 1852931450, 1993.

ENERGY WEB SITES

Irish Energy Centre, renewable energy
http://www.irish-energy.ie/reio.htm
Department of Public Enterprise
http://www.irlgov.ie/tec/energy/energy.html
Irish Wind Energy Association
http://www.iwea.com
Energy Research Group, UCD
http://erg.ucd.ie/
Renewable energy picture library
http://www.renewablenergy-images.org/
EU Commission Directorate-General XVII (Energy)
http://europa.eu.int/en/comm/dg17/dg17 home.htm
Centre for Alternative Technology, Wales:
http://www.cat.org.uk
Appropriate Technology for Sustainable Living:
http://www.jademountain.com/index.html
Real Goods Trading Corporation:
http://www.realgoods.com/
Solar Ovens:
http://www.solar-ovens.com

TRANSPORT WEB SITES

10 Steps to Sustainable Transport;
http://www.greenfleet.com.au/Html/transport.html
Sustainable Transportation for a World Beyond Oil;
http://www.ecotopia.com/webpress/wre4/index.html
Sustainable Transportation in the 21st Century;
http://transweb.sjsu.edu/symposium/curri cg1.htm

RENEWABLE ENERGY

IRISH ENERGY CENTRE
RENEWABLE ENERGY INFORMATION OFFICE
Contact: David Taylor
Glasnevin, Dublin 9
Tel: 01-8369080
Fax: 01-8372848
E-mail: info'irish-energy.ie
Website: www.irish-energy.ie/reio.htm

Promotion of energy efficiency and renewable energy. The Irish Energy Centre is an EU funded initiative of the Department of Public Enterprise with a mission to promote the development of a sustainable natural energy economy.

MAYO ENERGY AGENCY

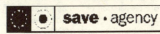 save · agency

- DOMESTIC & SMALL BUSINESS ENERGY ADVICE

- ELECTRICITY LOAD MONITORING & TARIFF ANALYSIS

- RENEWABLE ENERGY SYSTEM DESIGN

Roger Adair - Agency Manager
Cathedral Road, Ballina, Co. Mayo.
Tel: 096 74034 Fax 096 70711

RENEWABLE ENERGY INFORMATION OFFICE
Contact: Ewan Chalmers
Shinagh House, Bandon Co. Cork
Tel: 023-42193
Fax: 023-41304
E-mail: renewables@reio.ie
Website: www.irish-energy.ie

Renewable Energy Information. REIO is a service of the Irish Energy Centre established to promote the use of renewable energy resources and provide independent advice and information on financial, social and technical issues relating to renewable energy development.

CORK CITY ENERGY AGENCY
Contact: Fiona Duggan
Lord Mayor's Pavillon, Fitzgerald's Park, Mardyke Walk, Cork
Tel: 021-363749
Fax: 021-363749
E-mail: corknrg@iol.ie
Website: http://www.corknrg.com

Energy Efficiency & Conservation. Cork City Energy Agency promotes renewable energy and the use of renewable energy in Cork City. Information and advice is available free of charge.

CORK COUNTY ENERGY AGENCY
Contant: Pat Walsh
Spa House, Mallow, Co. Cork
Tel: 022-43610
Fax: 022-43678
E-mail: mallowre@indigo.ie

Energy Conservation and renewable energy: Public Office, information dissemination, domestic/industrial/farming sectors, independent, EU energy projects.

ENERGY ENGINEERING GROUP
Contant: Chris Gibbons
Dept. of Mechanical & Manufacturing Engineering, Cork
Tel: 021-326224 / 311803
Fax: 021-345244
E-mail: cgibbons@cit.ie

To develop and encourage sustainable energy technologies and related appropriate technologies through research, training and promotional activities, at a local and national level (especially Solar thermal and electrical, geothermal, wind, energy management)

IRISH WIND ENERGY ASSOCIATION
Contact: Lawrence Staudt
Kellystown, Slane Co. Meath
Tel: 041-982 6787
Fax: 041-982 6787
E-mail: staudt@iol.ie
Website: www.iwea.com

The Irish Wind Energy Association promotes the development and use of wind energy in Ireland.

EAST CONNACHT ENERGY AGENCY(ECEA)
Contact: Michael Layden
King House, Boyle, Co. Roscommon
Tel: 079-64048 / 1800-461100
Fax: 079-64049
E-mail: info@ecea.ie
Website: www.iol.ie/~ecea1

Energy efficiency, renewable energy (Sligo, Leitrim, Roscommon). ECEA is a public service, operated by Roscommon Country Council, to promote energy awareness, conservation and efficiency measures and the use of renewable energy, in Leitrim, Roscommon and Sligo.

TIPPERARY ENERGY AGENCY LTD.

Contact: Seamus Hoyne
Education Centre, Church Street,
Cahir, Co. Tipperary
Tel: 052-43090
Fax: 052-43012
E-mail: tippenergy@tinet.ie

Local Energy Agency promoting energy conservation and renewable energy through involvement in projects, provision of services and information dissemination, across all sectors in Tipperary, one of the twelve agencies in Ireland.

GALWAY ENERGY AGENCY LTD.

Contact: Peter Keavney
City Hall, College Road, Galway
Tel: 091-566954
Fax: 091-567493
E-mail: pkeavney@galwaycorp.ie

Promoting energy conservation, providing training and professional services in energy management, and facilitating alternative energy resources commensurate with the sustainable development of the region of Galway.

MAYO ENERGY AGENCY

Contact: Roger Adair
Cathedral Road, Ballina, Co. Mayo
Tel: 096-74034
Fax: 096-70711
E-mail: mayonrg@tinet.ie
Website: http://homepage.tinet.ie/~mayonrg

The agency carries out energy audits, electrical demand monitoring and feasibility studies for renewable energy projects. It provides technical consultancy and training courses, exhibitions and talks for schools.

DONEGAL ENERGY ACTION TEAM

Contact: Patrick Mangan
Three Rivers Centre, Lifford, Co. Donegal
Tel: 074-72471
Fax: 074-41367
E-mail: deat@donegalcoco.ie
Website: www.renewableenergyimages.org

Energy agency & local energy advice centre. DEAT aims to promote sustainable development through waste reduction, energy conservation and the application of renewable energy resources. We provide information to the local community through local energy advice centres.

CITY OF DUBLIN ENERGY MANAGEMENT AGENCY (CODEMA)

Contact: Dr. Gerry Wardell / Claire Bourke
Paradigm House, Dundrum Office Park, Dublin 14
Tel: 01 2964072
Fax: 01 2962484
E-mail: codema@iol.ie
Website: http://www.iol.ie/~codema/

Promoting and advising on the rational use of energy including renewables there by contributing to sustainable development in the city set up in January 1997 as a Dublin Corporation EU initiative.

HOEY ENVIRONMENTAL

Contact: John Hoey
81 Upper Georges Street,
Dun Laoghaire, Co. Dublin
Tel: 01-2802921
Fax: 01-2805544
E-mail: hoeyenv@indigo.ie

Development of wind farms - assessment and design of site preparation of EIS and planning applications. Selection of wind turbines and financial evaluation. Gas Leak Detection and Monitoring.

BEULAH PLUMBING & HEATING & SOLAR SERVICES

Contact: Roy Shannon
5 Abbeydale Gardens, Belfast
BT14 7HG, Co. Antrim
Tel: 0801-232-719974
Fax: 0801-232 -719974

Energy efficiency and solar heating.
The solar water heating specialist - we are the approved, registered agent for thermomax, solar systems, providing installations, maintenance and servicing - a free no-obligation demonstration and survey is available.

DUNSTAR LTD.

Contact: Paul Sikora
1 Kent Street, Clonakilty, Co. Cork
Tel: 023-35165
Fax: 023-35174
E-mail: dunstar@tinet.ie

Renewable energy, heat pumping, heat recovery. Dunstar's expertise and experience are concentrated in providing practical and economical solutions to problems involving thermal energy transformation primarily by innovative application of renewable and sustainable energy technology.

FUTURE WIND PARTNERSHIP LTD.

Contact: Brian Hurley
63 Greenlawns, Skerries, Co. Dublin

Tel: 01-8490396
Fax: 01-8490438
E-mail: bfhurley@iol.ie
Website: http://www.iol.ie/~bfhurley/futurewind.htm

Future Wind Partnership is a leading Irish
Company in developing the Irish wind energy
resource. What can Future Wind Partnership do?
We can work with landowners to help them
develop the wind energy potential of their property.
We can work with builders of wind power plants by
providing low cost finance. We can work with
electricity consumers giving them a green source
of electricity.

SOLARIS

Contact: Fritz Raake
Kilnarovanagh, Toames, Macroom, Co. Cork

Tel: 026-46312
E-mail: solaris@tinet.ie

Thermal Solar Systems. We supply and install,
when required, thermal solar systems to provide
hot water and supplement space heating – cost-
effectively and eco-friendly for private homes,
guesthouses, hotels or public buildings.

NATIONAL WINDPOWER IRELAND LTD.

Contact: David Fitzgerald
Ballysimon House, Ballysimon, Co.Limerick

Tel: 061-330010
Fax: 061-332060
E-mail: natwind@indigo.ie

Development and management of wind farms, also
solar energy sourcing of sites and assessment of
potential of such sites.

NICERT (NORTHERN IRELAND CENTRE FOR ENERGY RESEARCH AND TECHNOLOGY).

Contact: Dr David McIlveen-Wright
University of Ulster, Cromore Road, Coleraine
Londonderry BT52 1LT

Tel: 0801-265-324477
Fax: 0801-265-324900
E-mail: dr.mcilveen-wright@ulst.ac.uk
Website: http://www.ulst.ac.uk/faculty/science/nicert/

R&D in energy: Advanced power cycles;
refrigeration; energy efficiency; education.
Contract research on European, national and cross-
border programmes in energy-related projects on:
advanced power cycles, clean coal technologies;
energy from biomass or wastes; CFC replacements;
refrigerations; heat pump.

MIKE HALL ELECTRONICS

Contact: Mike Hall
West End, Inchigeela, Macroom, Co. Cork

Tel: 026-49367
Fax: 026-49367
E-mail: mikehall@tinet.ie

Wind, water and solar power complete installations
by experienced professional engineer equipment
and advice supplied for DIY DC (battery) and/or
230VAC supplies agent for most makes of quality
hardware. All work and equipment fully
guaranteed.

WIND TOWER MANUFACTURING LTD.

Contact: Finbar Tymon
Ross, Kilmeadon, Co. Waterford

Tel: 051-384303
Fax: 051-384277
E-mail: ftymon@iol.ie

Wind tower manufacturing and wind farm
developers. Complete services for wind farm
projects. Site evaluation. Wind measuring and
resource assessment. Sales and servicing of wind
energy equipment.

E. F. ENERGY (DEVELOPMENTS) LTD.

Contact: Patrick Healy, Antares House,
Carrignavar, Co. Cork

Tel: 021-307490
Fax: 021-880341
E-mail: efenergy@iol.ie

E.F. Energy is an Irish owned renewable energy
company, with specialist expertise in wind energy.
Core activities include feasibility studies, planning
applications, financing and building of wind
powered projects.

ERDA: ENERGY RESEARCH AND DESIGN

Contact: Barney Walsh
Gleneely, Carndonagh, Co.Donegal

Tel: 077-67321
Fax: 077-67348
E-mail: info@erda.iol.ie
Website: www.iol.ie/~erda

Environmental consultancy, renewable energy
projects. ERDA is a consultancy with regional and
European experience in energy matters. We have
run to EU sponsored regional energy agency for
Donegal and undertaken a broad spectrum of
energy related work. Our work involves planning,
education, green tourism and community. Private
sector partnerships for energy projects, ERDA is
effective in practical renewable energy projects in
design and application.

AIROGEN LTD.

Contact: James Kelly
Carrowbeg, Kilkelly, Co. Mayo

Tel: 094-67505
E-mail: airogen@tinet.ie

Wind farm development & maintenance. Hydro electric & small wind systems.
AIROGEN Ltd. provide a range of services for the renewable energy industry in Ireland. Wind farm operation and maintenance, hydroelectric and the supply of wind systems for domestic use.

B9 ENERGY (O&M) LTD.

Contact: Sacha Workman
Willowbank Road, Larne, Belfast,
Co. Antrim BT40 2SF

Tel: 048 28 263900
Fax: 048 28 263901

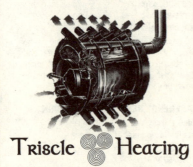
E-mail: s.workman@b9energy.co.uk
Website: www.b9energy.co.uk

Development and operation of wind and wood energy projects. The reduction of carbon dioxide and other polluting emmissions through the development of renewable energy supplier of "eco-energy" to N.I.

WIND WATER SOLAR ENERGY SYSTEMS

Contact: Gerry Cunnane
Kilgarvan, Co. Kerry

Tel: 064-85460
Fax: 064-85460

Supply and install renewable energy systems for domestic and commercial customers. Agent for Thermomax Solar Water Heaters, Proven Wind Turbines. High head Pelton hydro turbines manufactured to order. Site surveys.

PETER SCHNEIDER SOLAR ENERGY

Contact: Peter Schneider
Toberscarden, Tobercurry, Sligo

Tel: 071-85595
Fax: 071-85595

Energy Conservation surveys. Supply and installation of: Solar electric(=photovoltaic) systems, solar water heating (flat plate+vacuum) water turbines, wind generation (pipe).

LAGERWAY THE WINDMASTER

Contact: Joe O'Mahony
Ballyfair, Curragh, Co. Kildare

Tel: 045-441775
Fax: 045-441775
E-mail: jnd@tinet.ie

Irish representative for Dutch wind turbine manufacturer. Lagerway the Windmaster which has been manufacturing since 1978. Supplier of Australian Southern Cross water pumping and land drainage windmills. Manufacturing since 1870.

ALL@SEA

Contact: Paul Barrett
Ballyward, Oldcourt, Blessington, Co. Wicklow

Tel: 087-2597010 / 01-4582030
Fax: 01-4582018
E-mail: all@sea.oceanwave.org
Website: http://www.oceanwave.org

All@Sea supply and install high quality wind turbines built to exacting standards by Air Marine USA. Deep cycle/leisure batteries and precision inverters(240 volt from 12 volt) also available.

SURE ENGINEERING (EUROPE) LTD.

Contact: T.D. Hannevig,
29 Lr. Leeson St., Dublin

Tel: 01-6622099
Fax: 01-6622280
Sure Engineering provide consultancy services to the renewable energy sector. From February 2000, Sure Engineering expect to be able to offer alternative road fuels and electricity from renewable resources.

BEALTAINE LTD.

Contact: Graham Lightfoot / Nanu Luke / Martina Minogue
Derg house, Connaught Road, Scarriff, Co.Clare

Tel: 061-921121
Fax: 061-921693
E-mail: bealtaine@bealtaine.ie
Website: www.bealtaine.ie

Telecottage, teleworking, training, transport consultancy.
East Clare Telecottage provides office services, design and printing, translation, computer training, website design and hosting,internet access. Taylor Lightfoot Transport Consultants are specialists in passenger and sustainable transport operations.

ENERGY ACTION LTD

Contact: Charles Roarty Unit 14, Newmarket, Dublin 8

Tel: 01-4545464
Fax: 01-4549797
E-mail: info@energyaction.ie

The charity addresses fuel poverty by insulating the homes of older and needy people. The service is delivered by long term-unemployed who are trainged to certification standards in work that is creative, sustainable and ecologically sound.

TRISCLE HEATING

Contact: Stephen Schmeitz
Kittyplace Carriganimmac, Macroom, Cork

Tel: 026-44110
E-mail: triscle@esatclear.ie
Website: http://www.triscleheating.com

The Bullerjan Stove runs at an efficiency up to 75% by constantly and almost completely burning wood, spreading a cosy warmth all over the room very evenly and quickly.

FOYLE REGIONAL ENERGY AGENCY, ENERGY ADVICE CENTRE

Contact: Dr Peter McCallion
Foyle Arts Centre, Lawrence Hill, Derry

Tel: 0044-2871-373430 / 0801504-373430
Fax: 0044-2871-363166
E-mail: info@foyleenergy.org
Website: www.foyleenergy.org

Save over £100 p.a on household fuel bills through energy efficient measures. FREA provide FREE and impartial advice on low cost, no cost, grant aided cash back domestic energy efficiency measures.

ENVIRONMENTAL EFFICIENCY CONSUSTANTS (IRELAND) LTD.

Contact: Bob Sutcliffe
48 Main street, Bray Co.Wicklow

Tel: 01-2761428

Fax: 01-2761561
Email: energy@iol.ie
Website: www.enviro-consult.com

Consultants in environmental and energy issues. Areas of expertise are environmental audit, IPC licence applications, compliance audits, environmental management systems, energy audits and energy efficiency training.

TRANSPORT

CORK CYCLING CAMPAIGN

Contact: Cathi Llewellyn
17 Mount Eden, Model Farm Rd., Cork

Tel: 021-272441
Fax: 021-347198
E-mail: nllewellyn@cit.ie
Website; http://aoife.indigo.ie/~woz/ccc

Cork cycling campaign offers a voice to cyclists around the Cork area. Through regular meetings with the Corporation, education and awareness projects we aim to make Cork a cycle-friendly city.

DUBLIN CYCLING CAMPAIGN

Contact: Kieran Byrne
12 Millmount Grove, Windy Arbour, Dublin 14

Tel: 01-7000312

The Dublin Cycling Campaign represents the interests of everyday cyclists and is working with the four Dublin Local Authorities and Public Transport operators to provide improved cycle facilities in the city.

SQUARE WHEEL CYCLEWORKS

Contact: Kieran Byrne
Temple Lane, Temple Bar, Dublin 2

Tel: 01 679 0838

Cycle Repair / Engineering Workshop, Specialised Bicycle Sales. Square Wheel Cycle Works offer an expert cycle repair service and bicycle park, sell a variety of specialised bicycles, tricycles and trailers to suit specific needs and organise occasional cycling holidays.

RAILWAY AHEAD

Contact: Dan J.J. Kahn
137 Norwich Row, Parkhill Sheffield South Yorkshire, UK

Tel; 0044 -7970928198
Fax: 0044-11 42725828
Website: http://www.members.tripod.com/~wolfetones

A new Irish forum for promoting the need to re-open disused railways and upgrade existing railways and upgrade existing rail routes as an alternative to environmentally unsound by-passes and other road construction projects. **Irish address:** Ballyre Cottage, Killeagh, Co. Cork

WASTE

page 111 **Introduction** Michelle Hallahan

page 115 **Recycling in Ireland** Bernie Walsh

page 117 **The Landfill Crisis** Jack O'Sullivan

page 120 **Hazardous Waste** Anne Marie Cunningham

page 121 **Wetland Systems** Feidhalm Harty

page 121 **Clean Production** Beverly Thorpe

WASTE Michelle Hallahan

Michelle has provided Ecological Wastewater Treatment consultation both in Ireland
and California. She worked closely with the internationally acclaimed ecological
designer, Dr. John Todd, for a number of years in California. Michele lived and taught
at the Northern California Institute of Permaculture in 1998. She has studied with Jay
Baldwin, former editor of 'Whole Earth' magazine, and erstwhile protégé of
Buckminster Fuller, at Sonoma State University. Michele is an active member of the
Integrated Solutions Panel of Ireland, a voluntary group which offers solution-based
environmental advice to all sectors of society. She is a member of the Environmental
Science Association of Ireland, and is a current member of the Environmental
Committee in Dublin Chamber of Commerce.

Waste management (or waste 'disposal' as it used to be called, before it
was realised that we couldn't throw it away without it coming back to haunt
us) is arguably the most emotive environmental topic in Ireland today.
Many dumps are reaching capacity and/or falling under rigorous controls.
Local Authorities are desperately seeking solutions to the problem of waste
disposal, the scale of which is reaching crisis level. Plans to site 'super
landfills' around the country are provoking widespread opposition, yet
alternatives to landfilling have their own problems - incineration is
considered a dirty word; recycling gets a limp response; composting evokes
notions of a smelly, festering pile in the corner of the garden. So where do
we put the rubbish that society generates?

There are many alternatives to landfilling: gassification and/or pyrolysis
(both consist of generating heat/ electricity from waste) combined with
recycling and composting offer a solution which can result in highly
reduced landfill volumes. Incineration also offers a major reduction in
volume, but the toxicity of emissions to the air from incinerator stacks is of
grave concern to many.

One partial solution is source separation and 'recycling' - a service already
provided in parts of Dublin by Kerbside Recycling. Householders are asked
to keep aside recyclables such as bottles, cans, cartons and plastics for
separate collection. These are sorted and resold as raw materials to the
respective manufacturers of bottles, cans and plastics.
However, as a waste solution recycling pales by comparison to reuse
because the energy costs of breaking down a material and resmelting/
remoulding it can be prohibitive. Reuse only went out of fashion less than
20 years ago.

Growing up in Athlone, I remember returning milk bottles, lemonade
bottles and egg cartons to our local VG foodstore, and relishing the 5 or 10
pence I got in return. Reuse is an attractive option with no health hazards
attached, but unfortunately the possibility to reuse items has seriously
diminished as products are designed for throwing away and not reusing.

Hence the three R's - reduce, reuse and recycle - are not enough to prevent the immediate need to dispose; landfill is still required to deal with the undesirable objects thrown out each week by industry, society and householders. It is not enough that the waste stream is reduced.

The problem lies with the fact that industry is allowed to have the word 'disposable' in its lexicon. The word 'disposable' comes into direct conflict with the word 'sustainable'. As long as society insists on clinging to this new trend (have a chat with your parents or grandparents - they never used the word 'disposable' before the 1950s) of throw-away objects, we will have a waste management problem on our hands.

It is interesting that Nature, which has been designing its own 'waste disposal' solutions for millions of years (compare this to our paltry one hundred years or so...) has no such thing as waste. Consider the tree outside your window: it 'disposes' of its leaves in the autumn. In the human world this would be considered 'waste' and would be raked up and bagged to go to a landfill. Not so with Nature - the soil welcomes its once-yearly feeding each autumn and sets to, breaking down the leaves to nourish itself. Observe how in Nature waste becomes food, or 'one organism's poison is another one's pleasure'.

This principle needs to be applied to all processes throughout industry, agriculture and the home. Most packaging (which makes up about 50% by volume of the solid waste stream) should be composed of organic material. In this way, a discarded wrapper would not become litter on the street; it would compost to become soil. There is no need for shampoo bottles, drinks containers and equipment packaging to last centuries longer than their contents. Industry needs to address the issue of lifecycle in all their products. Maybe business could sell the services of the manufacturer. For instance, an electronics company in Japan produced the first 'immortal' television two years ago. Rather than selling the product, it is leased to the customer on a lifetime warranty and the manufacturer covers repairs. Because the manufacturer owns the television, sturdy, durable materials are used in the making of the product. The less parts they have to replace, the more money they stand to save.

Similarly, Xerox Corporation developed the first ever 95% recyclable/reusable photocopier two years ago. It is traded under the slogan "Xero(tm) Landfill". The machine was developed to be long-lasting and highly reparable. At the end of its lifecycle, it is collected by Xerox and returned to the factory where it is dismantled into its component parts, and rebuilt into another machine, which can be resold as a brand new product.

These are really examples of efficiency. The more you get from your raw materials, the less waste you produce. This approach is being hailed as the new Industrial Revolution. But efficiency is not a new idea - over 2,000 years ago, the Chinese philosopher Lao Tzu said "A sound man is good at salvage, at seeing nothing lost". Henry Ford's entire empire was steeped in eco-efficiency. As far back as the 1920s, the Ford plant recycled, reused materials, packaged minimally and used timesaving devices. Ford himself said "You must get the most out of the power, out of the material...". Clearly, Ford thought that the waste which left his factories was wasted money.

Getting back to Ireland, waste management is not solely the responsibility of the local authority but is also that of the waste producer. That includes industry which apart from 'landfill' waste, produced 313,000 tons of hazardous waste in 1998 alone.

Industry, in recognising its responsibility, has begun to subscribe to a packaging reduction scheme called REPAK, which recovers packaging materials for reuse.

Eco-efficiency is catching on in Ireland - this is evident from the success of the Cleaner Production Pilot Demonstration Programme, supported by the Environmental Protection Agency. Fifteen Irish companies participated in the programme. They discovered that as well as generating less waste from production processes, in many cases they also reduced production costs. Noel Dempsey, Minister for the Environment, in addressing a REPAK conference stated that "failure is not an option" when it comes to meeting national targets for waste reduction, and warned that regulations would be introduced if industry did not comply.

The remaining sources of waste production are commerce, street cleaning, agriculture (responsible for 31 million tons of waste per annum, most of which is reused) and individuals. We each produce an average of 400 kg of waste per year - that is a total of 44 million tons every year. Ninety per cent of domestic and commercial waste goes to landfill each year. This is clearly not sustainable.

As an island nation, it has become evident with accelerated awareness, that the amount of land we are willing to devote to storing piles of rubbish is limited. This is good. We shouldn't be storing rubbish. It leaks down into the water table and contaminates our drinking water. It smells. It attracts vermin. It rots for a hundred years, and still parts of it will not be broken down, even on a geological timescale. But if this all sounds hopeless, here is the beauty of the situation - you can help to solve the problem starting right now: read the article about recycling; don't use plastic shopping bags and most of all, exercise your consumer power, both as a householder and as an employee/employer. You could start by refusing to purchase over-packaged goods. Manufacturers will soon get the message.

waste

Packaging

Up to 33% of the Municipal Solid Waste going to landfill in Ireland is packaging. While some packaging is necessary for hygiene, product protection and control, much current packaging is concerned with marketing and image.

• When shopping, refuse a bag unless purchasing a large number of items.

• Bring your own shopping bag or container, e.g. plastic or cotton bag, cardboard or plastic box.

• Re-use the plastic bags from a previous shopping trip.

• Ask for other containers, e.g. cardboard boxes, which otherwise would be thrown out, to bring home your shopping.

• Avoid products with unnecessary packaging, particularly at Easter and Christmas time. You can leave the excess with the retailer.

• If you have to accept packaging you should try to choose that which is capable of being refilled or reused, either for its original purpose, e.g. milk or beer bottles, or as a container for other items.

• The next best choice should be for packaging which has a high recycled material content or which is capable of being recycled to help stimulate and support the market for recycled products.

• Materials which are more commonly recycled include glass, cardboard, PET, HDPE, LDPE, PVC and aluminium.

• Try to avoid packaging which is composed of a number of inseparable materials which would make it difficult to recycle. Compare the volumes of packaging for fast food with more traditional meals. Is the level of packaging necessary? Could you refuse some of it? How much is recycled by the retailer?

• Try to buy in bulk or economy sizes as generally these give rise to less packaging - could you share with family or friends?.

• Choose concentrated products e.g. detergents.

• Look for products with the EU Eco - label.

ENFO

EOLAS AR AN gCOMHSHAOL
INFORMATION ON THE ENVIRONMENT

17, St Andrew St., Dublin 2, Ireland
Tel 1890 200 191 or 01 888 3001
Fax: 01 888 3946
e-mail: info@enfo.ie
Website: www.enfo.ie

It's easy to make a difference.
Extracts from the forthcoming ENFO SUSTAINABLE LIVING GUIDE for shoppers and investers.

waste

Recycling in Ireland

Bernie Walsh manager of Sunflower Recycling in Dublin

It is within living memory that we recycled almost everything in our homes. People in their forties will remember returning lemonade bottles and jam jars for payment. Newspapers and magazines were valued pocket money for children who collected them. Small pig farms within the city collected kitchen and vegetable waste for feeding the animals. Furniture was always recycled by giving it to couples starting a home or to families who had many children and could not afford to buy new items. This also applied to clothes and footwear. Restaurants, hospitals and all industrial kitchens used refillable tableware. Everything was bought in bulk and refilled on a daily basis. We were a lot better at waste management then. Our landfill sites were small and only used for end products of which there were few.

The situation today is far different, only in a very small percentage of homes is it possible to recycle all that is recyclable. Restaurants, hospitals, schools etc now buy all of their daily requirements of sugar, butter, salt, vinegar and even milk in prepacked individual containers which all add to the landfill and are not recyclable. We have become a throwaway society and the way in which we deal with our waste is not only unsustainable but also unmanageable. We need to find other ways of dealing with the problem and to find solutions which are sustainable and worthwhile.

In the home

This is where it is most important for us as individuals to be aware of how much waste we each accumulate. By looking at the weekly waste collection we can assume a reduction of at least 40% when we REDUCE, REUSE, RECYCLE.

So how do we do it?

We all shop for food, clothing and household goods. The largest amount of packaging comes on our food. Even our fresh vegetables and fruit is often now presented pre-packed, offering an easy way to reduce packaging. Buy all fruit and veg loose and when you are shopping in the supermarket leave behind any unnecessary packaging. Where possible buy products in large packs which have minimal packaging or refillable containers. Say no to plastic bags and bring a cloth one yourself - if you average seven bags of groceries per week this will allow you to save 364 plastic bags annually.

Glass

Return all bottles and jars to bottle banks. If there is none in your neighbourhood then try to organise some by asking the local supermarket if they would house one. If not, you could organise a collection day with

waste

some like-minded people.

Paper

Most people feel really bad about the amount of newspaper magazines and cardboard they waste. Once again see if there is a collection point near you, if not try to set one up. Ask at the local school and youth groups if they need paper for projects, etc. Sell all old books to bookshops, including school books and paperbacks.

Clothes and shoes

Old clothes and shoes can also be recycled. If there are no clothes banks near your home then bring them to your local charity shop.

Composting

If you have a garden it is possible to compost very cheaply. There is no need to buy fancy equipment. Once you have an area of the garden or a plastic container in which you can punch holes for ventilation then you can compost. The main thing to remember is that it should be turned every couple of days.

These are just a few hint on things you can do yourself in your home. Now try looking at your workplace and see if you can apply any of these rules to the work situation. Try talking to your neighbours, colleagues and your employer about these issues and who knows, you may even influence other people!

Action speaks louder than words Reduce Reuse Recycle

On average every householder generates over 1 tonne of waste each year. That is 400kgs of waste per head of population and it is growing at a rate of 3% per year. A recent survey has shown that the composition of household waste is approximately

- **34%** food and garden waste
- **25%** paper and packaging waste
- **12%** plastic waste
- **6%** glass waste
- **7%** textile waste
- **4%** metal waste
- **12%** other unclassified find waste/special waste

At present 92% of this is taken to landfills, only 8% is recycled.

waste

> The principle of waste equalling food encourages the elimination of the concept of waste in industrial design. We need to design every process so that the products themselves, as well as leftover chemicals, materials and effluents, can become "food" for other processes.
> Paul Hawkin

The landfill crisis and the elimination of waste

Jack O'Sullivan an environmental consultant with Environmental Management Services

The goal of environmentally sustainable development requires, as a basic principle, that human communities must behave like natural ones, living comfortably within the natural flow of energy from the sun and plants, producing no wastes which cannot be recycled back into the Earth's systems, and guided by new economic values which are in harmony with personal and ecological values. In nature, the waste products of every living organism and the remains of dead organisms serve as raw materials to be transformed by other living creatures, they assist in the functioning of the Earth as a whole, or they may benefit the planet in other ways. Our policies and our actions must be changed so as to mirror and integrate with this ecological reality, if we are to become truly sustainable.

Waste Generation and Disposal in Ireland

So how far away are we from being sustainable in our waste generation and disposal practices?

The internationally recognised hierarchy of options for dealing with wastes places waste prevention as the best option, followed by waste minimisation, re-use, recycling, and energy recovery. As a last resort, the remaining wastes which cannot be prevented or recovered should be dealt with by an environmentally suitable method of disposal.

Yet in Ireland we still send around 92 % of our municipal wastes to landfill, and there are no significant economic incentives to prevent, reduce or recover domestic or commercial wastes. This reliance on landfill is contrary to European practice and legislation, it has inhibited the establishment of public or private waste recovery and recycling operations, has slowed up the development of ecologically integrated waste management strategies, and has led to a waste disposal crisis.

Environmentally Unsuitable Landfill Sites

A further feature of the way in which we deal with waste in Ireland is that most of our landfills are located where land was purchased cheaply by the local authority, and where it was accessible and convenient to centres where domestic wastes were generated. Thus most of our dumps are close to major towns, and are sited on bogs, estuarine flood plains or other environmentally unsuitable areas. This may have been acceptable up to the 1960s, when domestic wastes consisted mainly of potato peelings, ash, a few papers and tins, but little else; and when awareness of the environmental effects of landfilling was absent.

Unfortunately, even in the face of increasing environmental awareness, most local authorities have taken no cognisance of recent thinking in the location and management of their landfills. Instead of making serious efforts to reduce the generation of waste, to ensure that as much as possible of the waste is recycled or re-used, and to take steps to find more suitable locations for landfills, many County Councils continue to dispose of growing quantities of wastes on environmentally unsuitable sites.

Local Campaigns Against Landfills

One result of this practice has been the increasing number of occasions when local residents have strongly resisted the siting of new landfills, or have forced local authorities to close unsuitable sites. At Ballymahon, County Longford, and Tralee, County Kerry, locally-based groups took legal proceedings against their County Councils, forcing closure of landfills near these towns. In December 1998, residents of Doora (near Ennis) concluded lengthy proceedings against Clare County Council, requiring the Council to improve their management of the Doora landfill that is located on a waterlogged floodplain near the town, to close the landfill within two years, to rehabilitate the site, and to pay substantial compensation for nuisances suffered over many years. In the same month, the High Court also forced the closure of a dump at Carrowbrowne in County Galway, which was being operated by Galway Corporation in breach of planning conditions. As a consequence of the closure of Carrowbrowne, Galway City's wastes are now being trucked to a most unsuitable landfill site on the edge of the town of Ballinasloe, and legal proceedings against the local authority are currently being contemplated by nearby residents.

Many County Councils are now experiencing considerable difficulties in finding sites for new landfills, and are either expanding operations on existing unsuitable sites or examining possible new sites which may be equally unsuitable for environmental reasons. In recent years, Coillte has sought to increase its cash flow and the value of its landholding by offering potential sites in forests to local authorities. Some of these sites are marginally suitable; others are very unsuitable, being located in scenic areas where the road network will require major upgrading, and the rural quality of the surroundings will be damaged. Landfill sites proposed by Coillte are also frequently in elevated locations with high rainfall, and close to the headwaters of rivers – factors which greatly increase the difficulty of safely controlling leachate. Keeping site acquisition costs low, rather than pursuing the best environmental option, appears to be the principal factor in the local authorities' decision-making.

Under the Waste Management Act 1996, all landfills have to be licensed by the Environmental Protection Agency, and without such a licence a landfill cannot legally continue to accept wastes. Applications for waste licences for existing or new landfills have been made to the EPA by local authorities or private landfill operators, and most of these applications have been strongly objected to by local residents. Local campaigns against existing or new landfills are being conducted in Waterford City, Hardbog (County Tipperary), Sliabh Felim (County Limerick), Drogheda (County Louth), Kentstown (County Meath), Inagh (County Clare), Newbridge (County Galway), Silvermines (County Tipperary) and other places. Residents in all these locations consider that there has been no realistic public consultation or opportunity to participate in the decision-making progress, and that their concerns and fears have been marginalised or ignored. As a consequence, they are determined to prevent the opening of new landfill sites in unsuitable locations, and to ensure that existing unsuitable sites are closed and rehabilitated as soon as possible.

Many of these local groups have recently come together to establish a network (Environment Protection Ireland) aimed at changing the ways in which our communities' wastes are generated and dealt with. Environment Protection Ireland (EPI) has called on the Minister for the Environment to implement the policies described in his policy statement "Waste Management – Changing Our Ways", published over a year ago. EPI has stated that, despite the existence of appropriate policies and adequate financial resources, waste management practices are getting worse, recycling levels are falling, the EU packaging regulations are not being implemented, and effective environmental protection is not being provided.

The Elimination of Landfills

While landfilling may have to remain an acceptable means of dealing with residual amounts of municipal solid wastes in the short term, the only long-term sustainable solution is to completely eliminate the production of materials which cannot be re-used, recycled or naturally biodegraded. This will result not only in a saving of scarce resources, but will re-adjust our

waste

relationship to the earth's material assets from a linear to a cyclical one, enhancing our ability to live comfortably while reducing environmental damage. We can go even further, as suggested by Paul Hawken in "The Ecology of Commerce", and "instead of organising systems that efficiently dispose of or recycle our waste, we need to design systems of production that have little or no waste to begin with". Now that would really be the end of the road for landfills, and it is already within our capability to achieve this.

Hazardous Waste Anne Marie Cunningham Waste Working Group

Hazardous substances are an inherent part of modern consumerist society. They are used in industrial manufacturing, agriculture and commerce and hence are to be found in everyday household goods. The bleach and oven cleaner in your kitchen cupboards, the batteries in your car and remote control and your old cans of paint are all hazardous. Even harmless looking personal computers contain many hazardous substances.

The extent to which humans and the environment are contaminated by hazardous substances is not fully acknowledged. Few statistics about the level of hazardous contamination in Ireland are available although there is now acknowledgement that despite our limited and late industrial development, hazardous substances are as much a part of Irish life as any other 'developed' country.

This acknowledgement is heralding long overdue steps to take responsibility for hazardous substances. As a first step, the Irish Environmental Protection Agency are producing a national plan for dealing with hazardous waste. Already the proposed plan has shown that 30% of the estimated hazardous waste produced in Ireland each year is unreported. A significant 15% is exported whist the remainder is treated or disposed of within Ireland.

Disposing hazardous waste is a dangerous occupation - throughout the world communities fight to stop hazardous waste incinerators and landfills because of the health risks they pose. Yet despite this opposition, society is at present addicted to consuming products which are either hazardous themselves, or are manufactured using hazardous substances. Thus the only real solution to the threat posed by hazardous substances is to move away from hazardous means of production.

Individuals can help to transform production methods by buying hazard-free products. By saying no to PVC, removing chlorine bleach from your shopping list, plugging your radio in rather than using batteries, buying eco-friendly paints and organic food, you can make a difference. If you do have hazardous items in your house, hold on to them until your local

waste

authority can provide a special disposal service.

Read up about clean production (see the Clean Production section) and if you are involved in industry, spread the word. Likewise encourage employers to prevent hazardous waste - after all, this is the only real solution to our hazardous waste crisis. Disposal (even 'safe' disposal) is not a long-term solution and certainly not one that our children's grandchildren will thank us for.

Wetland systems

Feildham Hearty environmental consultant of FH Wetlands Systems

Constructed wetlands are purpose-built wetlands that are specially designed for the treatment of wastewater. A carefully chosen selection of plants in a specially engineered site provides the right biological environment for cleansing and re-oxygenating the water. These wetlands are modelled on natural wetland systems, but are designed to achieve optimum treatment efficiencies. Natural wetlands and their plant communities have evolved to thrive on nutrient rich, silted waters. Such ecosystems are evidently suited to treating nutrient-rich wastewaters.

Constructed wetlands can be used for a wide variety of applications including farm runoff, slurry effluent, silage effluent, domestic and municipal wastewater, urban storm water, landfill leachate and many industrial wastewaters. They have many advantages over conventional wastewater treatment systems including high treatment efficiency, low capital and running costs, minimum maintenance, and low energy requirements. They are tolerant of variable loads, have no chemical requirements and are suitable for polishing effluent from existing overloaded systems. Constructed wetlands have the unusual characteristics of being aesthetically pleasing and of being beneficial for wildlife (they provide the ideal environment for many waterfowl to nest in).

Clean Production **Beverley Thorpe** Clean Production Action, Canada

What Is Clean Production?

Clean Production is not just about producing things in factories in a cleaner way. Instead, it is a holistic way of looking at how our design and consumption of products is causing severe ecological problems.

Clean Production promotes the use of renewable energy and materials as well as sustainable product design. More importantly, it protects biological diversity and encourages an approach to production and consumption that is precautionary, preventive, and democratic.

Clean Production begins with a systems look at material flows in society. In

waste

particular it looks at the product chain; where raw materials come from, how and where they are processed, what wastes are generated along the product chain, and what happens to these products during their use and at the end of their commercial life.

A Clean Production guide is available from the Lowell Centre. The guide offers ways that consumers, taxpayers, retailers, local authorities, labour organisations, producers, and planners - all of us - can take action to move our production and consumption toward a safe and sustainable future. The guide includes a comprehensive international Clean Production contact list. The guide will be available online at www.uml.edu/centers/lcsp or you can order a copy from:

The Lowell Center for Sustainable Production
University of Massachusetts Lowell
One University Ave.
Lowell, MA 01854 USA
phone: 978-934-4312

The author can be reached at:
Clean Production Action
5964 Notre Dame de Grace Avenue
Montreal, Canada H4A 1N1
tel: +1 514 484 4207
fax: +1 514 484 2696
email: bthorpe@web.net

The Natural Step is an agreement between scientists, industrialists and public officials based on four system conditions for sustainability. It is derived from universally accepted principles of thermodynamics and evolutionary biology. Companies such as IKEA and Eletrolux have developed products in co-operation with the Natural Step. These four simple conditions hold immense possibility in reversing our current unsustainable practices.

1. STORED DEPOSITS: Substances from the Earth's crust must not be extracted more rapidly than they are deposited.

2. ALIEN COMPOUNDS: Substances produced by society must not systematically increase in nature.

3. ECOSYSTEMS: Biological productivity and diversity must not be systematically eroded.

4. METABOLISM: Human society must make just and efficient use of resources in meeting human needs.

waste

WASTE BOOKS

Country Plumbing
Hartigan
ISBN: 0911469028, 1986.

Living Water
O. Alexandersson
ISBN: 094655157X, 1990.

Living Energies
Callum Coats
ISBN: 0946551979, 1995.

The Water Wizard
Viktor Schauberger (translated & edited
by Callum Coats).
ISBN: 1858600480, 1997.

Safe to Drink - the Quality of your Water
Julie Stauffer
ISBN: 1898049149, 1996

**Rainwater Harvesting: The collection of
rainfall and runoff in rural areas.**
Pacey & Cullis.
ISBN: 0946688222, 1986.

**Drip Irrigation -
for every landscape and all climates.**
Robert Kourik.
ISBN: 0961584823, 1993.

Fertile Waste
Managing Your Domestic Sewage
Peter Harper
ISBN:1898049025, 1994.

**Sewage Solutions -
Answering the Call of Nature**
N. Grant, M. Moodie and C. Weedon.
ISBN: 1898049130, 1997.

**Humanure Handbook -
A Guide to Composting Human Manure**
Joseph C. Jenkins.
ISBN: 096442584X, 1996.

Worms Eat My Garbage
Mary Applehof
ISBN: 0942256050

Earthworms Unlimited
Amy Brown

ISBN: 0864176317, 1994.
Modern Vermin Control
Michael & Victoria Roberts
ISBN: 0947870105

**The Toilet Papers -
Recycling Waste and Conserving Water**
Sim Van der Ryn
ISBN: 0964471809, 1995.

Backyard Composting
John Roulac
ISBN: 1900322110, 1998.

**The Composting Toilet System Book - a
practical guide to choosing, planning and
maintaining composting toilet systems, a
water-saving, pollution-preventing
wastewater solution**
D.Del Porto & Carol Steinfeld
ISBN: 0966678303, 1999.

WASTE WEBSITES

SalvoWeb
http://www.salvo.co.uk/
Recycler's World
http://www.recycle.net/recycle/
European Recycling and the Environment
http://www.tecweb.com/recycle/eurorec.ht
m

waste

INTRODUCE THE GREEN DOT

FROM THE 1ST JANUARY 2000 REPAK WILL LICENSE USE OF THE GREEN DOT AS A REGISTERED TRADE MARK.

Companies displaying the Green Dot on products they supply are contributing to the cost of recovery and recycling of packaging waste in Ireland.

This contribution is made to Repak, a national packaging recovery and recycling scheme.

THE GREEN DOT IS A PAN EUROPEAN SYMBOL USED BY SEVEN OTHER COUNTRIES TO DATE. LOOK OUT FOR THE GREEN DOT ON PACKAGING IN THE SHOPS

Red Cow Interchange Estate, 1 Ballymount Rd., Clondalkin, Dublin 22

Tel: (01) 467 0190 Fax: (01) 467 0197
E-mail: info@repak.ie Website: www.repak.ie

GENERAL

WASTE WORKING GROUP

Contact: Anne-Marie Cunningham
c/o Voice, 7 Upper Camden St., Dublin 2

Tel: 01-6618123
Fax:01-6618114
E-mail: ammc@irelands-web.ie

Coalition of environmental NGO's including VOICE, Earthwatch and Global Action Plan, to facilitate and co-ordinate NGO contributions to waste management.

CORK COUNTY COUNCIL

Contact: Katherine Walshe
County Hall, Cork

Tel: 021-276891
Fax: 021-342098
Email: kwalshe@cork-county-council.ie
Website: www.corkcoco.com

Waste Management (Local Authority)
The waste management strategy for the Cork Region adopted by Cork Corporaion and Cork County Council for the 25 year period up to 2020 commits the local authorities to act to conserve and protect the environment and natural resources of the region by reducing, re-using and recycling the waste we generate.

BAGÁISTE-COTTON BAGS

Contact: Rick Hanrahan
Clonea, Dungarven, Co Waterford

Tel: 058-41686 / 43637
Fax: 058-41276

Bagáiste is a Transition Year mini-company which sells cotton shopping bags as a viable alternative to plastic bags. We mail order single bags or bulk purchases nationwide. Please ring for details.

RECYCLED PAPER

DAINTREE

Contact: Paul Barnes
62 Pleasants Place, Dublin 8

Tel: 01-4754641
Fax: 01-4754642
E-mail: paper@daintree.ie

Retailers of handmade papers and books; printers of fine quality stationary; book binders. We make paper from waste linen used money as well as our own office and bindery waste. Classes also available.

KLEE PAPER

Contact: Juliane Greene
89 North Circular Road, Dublin 7

Tel: 01-8383544
Fax: 01-8385943
Email: sales@ecoland.com
Website: http://indigo.ie/~ecoland/

Supply of recycled paper in Ireland (32 counties)
Campaign on waste reduction and recycling
Information on paper recycling
Information on waste paper collection in Ireland.

HARVEY-PAPER ANIMAL BEDDING

Contact: Tom Harvey
Seandrum, Inagh, Ennis, Co. Clare
Tel: 087-2679405/065-6836664

Animal paper bedding suitable for horses, cattle - poultry - pigs (also). Mobile Confidential shredding and confidential document disposal, collection mobile shredding is done at your own premises under your supervision.

WETLANDS

THE WETLANDS ADVISORY SERVICE (W.A.S.),

Contact: James Orr
Castle Espie, Comber Down, NI BT23

Tel: 0801-247 874146
Fax: 0801-247 873857
E-mail: james.orr@wwt.org.uk

WAS is an ecological consultancy which offers expertise in the conservation of wetalnds and wetland wildlife drawn from the unique research developed by WWT over the last 50 years. Skills include; wetland design, creating and restoration, reed bed filters and functional wetlands as well as habitat and species management planning. All profits are donated to Wildfowl and Wetland Trust.

WASTEWORKS

Contact: Tim Clarke
P.O.Box, 6 Ventry, Tralee, Co. Kerry
Tel: 066-9159858
Fax: 066-915985
E-mail: tmclarke@iol.ie

Ecological Effluent and Waste Treatment Systems. Reedbeds and other ecological / low energy treatment systems for household, municipal, industrial and agricultural effluents and wastes. From individual houses up to communities of 1000 people, farms etc.

HERR LTD.

Contact: Ollan Herr
Tur na Gaoithe, Philipstown, H.B.X Dundalk, Co. Louth
Tel: 042-9377689
Fax: 042-9377691

Manufacturers of elements for: Reed Bed plastic tanks, dosing systems, valves etc. Clunk click building modules to reduce on site assembly time. All elements pre tested prior to delivery. Installation also. Design service primarily for small domestic and medium scale systems. Full secondary and tertiary treatment optios. Extra stages for reduction of Ammonia and Pathogens can also be added.

HERR LTD.

Contact: Ollan Herr
Tur na Gaoithe, Philipstown, H.B.X Dundalk, Co. Louth
Tel: 042-9377689
Fax: 042-9377691

Domestic waste water treatment, using natural methods. Use of reeds and other water plants. Designs incorporate zero energy for pumping, examining waste water as a useful resource integrate with garden.

ECOLOGICAL SOLUTIONS

Contact: Michele Hallahan
14 Washington St., Dublin 8
Tel: 01-4534344
E-mail: michele-hallahan@yahoo.co.uk

Nature has millions of years experience in treating wastewater. We incorporate ecological design into wastewater treatment for industrial/agicultural /municipal waste. In expensive ecological restoration of rivers, lakes, ponds also.

TBW GMBH

Contact: Hartlieb Euler
Baumweg 10, Frankfurt 60316, Germany
Tel: 069-9435070
Fax: 069-94350711
Email: tbw@pop-frankfurt.com
Website: www.anaerob.com

Anaerobic treatment of waste, studge and waste water for agriculture, industry and municipalities. Planning, design, construction, operation training and development.

METHANOGEN LTD

Contact: Vicky Heslop
Tooracurragh, Ballymacarbry, Co. Waterford
Tel: 052-36304
Fax: 052-36304

We design, manufacture and build Anaerobic Digester Systems that process organic wastes into biogas (energy), liquid fertiliser and compost, specialising in Farm Digesters. Simple technology that provides effective nutrient management, and energy economically.

FEIDHLIM HARTY WETLAND SYSTEMS

Contact: Feidhlim Harty
Jamesbrook, Midleton, Co. Cork
Tel: 021-652429
E-mail: wetland @iol.ie

Feidhlim Harty Wetland Systems was established in 1996 to increase public awareness of constructed wetlands for the treatment of waste water and to provide a design, consultancy and construction service. Since then the business has expanded to include other environmental services.

RECYCLING

BORD NA MONA ENVIRONMENTAL LTD.

Contact: Karen Healy
Main Street, Newbridge, Co. Kildare
Tel: 045-431201
Fax: 045-431647
E-mail: ed.info@bnm.ie
Website: www.bnm.ie

Bord na Mona Environmental Ltd offer a wide range of pollution abatement products and services for the municipal and industrial sectors. A comprehensive range of products and services relating to air pollution monitoring and control, secondary treatment system as well as an environmental consultancy service, make up the core business. All of Bord na Mona Environmetnal Ltd products and services are supported by the extensive ILAB accredited analytical laboratories at its facilities in Newbridge, Co. Kildare.

CONNAUGHT WASTE RECYCLING CO. LTD

Contact: Peter Jordan
Hanley Buildings, Claregalway, Co. Galway

Tel: 091-799297
Fax: 091-798986

Connaught Waste Recycling is a well established Waste Management Company catering for the smallest to the largest companies, meeting your needs by designing, implementing and servicing an in-house recycling programme. Our service cover the full range of recyclable products including: paper, confidential shredding, plastics, timber, lamps, batteries, metal, oil and electronics.

ROGERS ENGINEERING

Contact: John Rogers
Rathowen, Westmeath

Tel: 043-76183
Fax: 043-76251
Email: jkrogers@tinet.ie

We have two main business aims, we supply small scale rural sawmillers with their equipment, this keeps jobs in their locality, our recycling machinery is directly used to improve our environment.

CEREBRAL PALSY IRELAND

Contact: Deirdre McGrath
Unit 31a, Rosemount Park Drive, Rosemount Business Pk, BallyCoolin Rd., Dublin 15S

Freephone: 1800 204304
Tel: 01-8727181
E-mail: cpicom@eircom.ie

Cerebral Palsy Ireland turn donations of clothing into funds for capitol development. Nothing is wasted. 100 textile banks nationwide.

SUNFLOWER RECYCLING,

Contact: Bernie Walsh
44 Lower Gardiner St., Dublin 1

Tel: 01-8787726
Fax: 01-8745824

Sunflower is a community based recycling project who collect recycling from household and business in the inner city of Dublin. We collect bottles, cans and paper. We are at present running a pilot project in computer recycling.

HERR LTD.

Contact: Ollan Herr
Tur na Gaoithe, Philipstown, H.B.X Dundalk, Co. Louth

Tel: 042-9377689
Fax: 042-9377691

Glass house sewage treatment.
Maximised ecological approach to sewage treatment. Water tanks in glass houses with plants, diverse microbiology, sometimes snails and fish. Very beautiful system to work with and possibly live with. A well designed and managed system will provide flowers, lush foliage, remove house toxins and provide passive heat. High treatment standard. Only for people with green fingers and interest in fish. Caution, frequent attention necessary.

CONSERVATION TECHNOLOGY LTD.

Contact: Peter Kelly
Davitt road, Dublin 12

Tel: 01-4559511
Fax: 01-4559616

Recycling service for the recycling of waste flourescent tubes and other waste lamps which includes the collection of waste lamps and the provision of special storage containers.

P.CARNEY LTD.,

Contact: Jim McCabe
Crossakiel, Kells, Co. Meath

Tel: 046-43634
Fax:046-43916
Email: pcarneyltd@tinet.ie

Manufacturers and exporters of aluminium alloy ingots copper granules and aluminium granules. Irelands principle purchaser and reprocessor of scrap and waste aluminium copper cables and aluminium cables particularly factory arisings.

GALWAY METAL CO. LTD,

Contact: Patrick Walsh
Oranmore, Co.Galway

Tel: 091-794358
Fax: 091-790218
Email: galwaymetal@tinet.ie
Website: http//homepage.tinet/~galwaymetal

Over a quarter-century ago Galway Metal Co. Ltd. was established to buy, transport and sell scrap metal to other merchants or processors. Over the years the business expanded and grew steadily, creating full-time employment for 25 people. New processing equipment was installed and the company's principal customers now are steel mills, metal refiners or end users in Ireland and abroad.

SILVER LINING IRL. LTD.

61 Cookestown Industrial Estate,
Tallaght, Dublin 24

Tel: 01-4622822;01-4622833
Website: www.silverlining.co.uk

Silver Lining is dedicated to licenced environmental waste management. We have facilities to dispose of computers, chemicals and all toxic substances in an environmentally friendly manner. We offer a one company waste management service.

KMK METALS RECYCLING LTD.
Bettystown Cross, Bettystown, Co. Meath.

Tel: 041-9827750
Fax: 041-9827914
E-mail: kmk@eircom.net

Recycling waste electrical and electronic
equipment, precious and non-ferrous batteries, PC
monitors etc. EPA licenced recovery facility.

NICRO-METALS LTD.
Contact: Sean Flood
"Villa Maria", Balrath Rd., Kells, Meath

Tel: 046-40357
Fax: 046-41079

Purchase of stainless steel scrap, nickel-containing
scrap and other non-ferrous-metals. Collections.
Sorting, grading and treatment of same, to
international/export standards. Delivery to
home/export markets.

SEE ALSO:

**ECO-VILLAGE ADVERTISEMENT IN COMMUNITY
AND FAMILY SECTION**

BALLYMALOE HOUSE

Wastewater treatment using wetlands, waste
seperation and wormery.

Full listing: Eco-Tourism in Arts and Leisure section

NATURAL TECHNOLOGY SYSTEMS

Reed bed wastewater treatment.

**Full listing: Green Building & Ecological Design
section.**

MAD JOBOOBA STUFF

Teaches recycling and environmental issues
through paper making.

Full listing: Crafts in the Art and Leisure section

JASON HARRIS DESIGN SERVICES

Reedbed construction, compost toilets, general
waste desposal.

**Full listing: Agriculture and Forestry section/
Permaculture.**

page 130 **Introduction** and articles Brian O'Brian

page 132 **Ecological Design**

page 134 **Building and Architecture**

page 135 **Sustainable Materials and Healthy Buildings**

GREEN BUILDING AND ECOLOGICAL DESIGN

Brian O'Brien

Originally from Co Cork, Brian O'Brien graduated with honours from the School of
Architecture at Bolton St (DIT) Dublin in 1991. Brian has taught Sustainable
Architecture at the University of California, Berkeley and now teaches at the School of
Architecture Bolton St. Dublin. He currently contributes to the work of the Energy
Research Group in UCD, acts as consultant to Dublin Corporation and is a founder of
the Integral Solutions Panel of Ireland (ISPI). Brian runs his own practise Solearth
Ecological Architecture in Dublin and concentrates on ecological design, healthy
environments, green buildings and sustainable urban design. He is currently writing
his PHD thesis on living systems architecture under Sim Van der Ryn.

Up to about 70 years ago this section would have been an unnecessary
exercise. Almost all building was, to a large extent, green; composed of
natural materials, built using local skills, assembled to harmonise with the
local climate, and requiring little energy to run.

Over the last five or six decades the effect of humans activities on Earth
has worsened to a catastrophic level. Apart from car use the single biggest
impact each of us has on the environment in Ireland is probably attributable
to our building(s) and the way we run them. Most buildings behave like the
gas guzzling cars of the '70s; consuming energy voraciously to heat, cool,
light, secure and maintain themselves and creating waste profusely. In
Ireland and the UK building(s) account for 40 - 50% of the energy, water and
resources consumed and for a similar amount of the pollution created.

Looked at on their own most buildings are huge, leaky, inefficient and, to
anyone who sees with more than their eyes, ugly, even when new. Looked
at together with other buildings the effect is compounded; our cities are
growing cancerously - appallingly Dublin now sprawls at the same density
as Los Angeles. Looking at them as habitats for human life they are actually
dangerous; the majority of their materials being chemical-based synthetic
compounds. Since we now spend almost 90% of our time indoors exposed
to these synthetic materials our own health is being affected alarmingly.

Added to this we have begun to use buildings unsustainably too. They have
become commodities more valuable as an investment than a home. The
skills of shelter-making, long considered as vital as the ability to cook or
cultivate food, are disappearing, increasing our dependence and alienating
us from our place. The very fact of building built a sense of community in
the past, now the opposite is true.

Planet Earth acts as a living system (Gaia), continuously adjusting to
changes in solar energy levels to maintain the conditions for life. Its health
and our own well-being are dependent on each other. What is healthy for
us is to live in buildings and cities that allow the natural environment

influence us, what is healthy for the planet is to have these buildings (including the occupation and activities within them) operate as an extension of its own natural processes.

The question then is how can we create buildings and towns that are low impact, healing, durable and beautiful and that foster connection with our environment? Firstly building greenly involves following two approaches to construction. The outward facing approach tries to avoid any adverse impact on the environment, present and future, while the inward looking approach attempts to avoid adverse affects on the health of the occupants. In fact a green building can go further, to actually regenerate the environment and be a source of healing for the occupants.

Secondly a green building must try to mimic an ecosystem or habitat. It must be built to power itself as directly as possible from renewable energy. It must cycle materials as ecosystems do; using natural materials, changed as little as possible, and allowing them be reused as raw materials or cycled back to nature afterward. Also the building must integrate both the hard form of the building itself (walls, roofs, etc.) and its living elements (plants, flowing water, green roofs) must be integrated together.

Lastly a green building must facilitate us being stewards of the planet and being aware of its health. To do this we must create buildings that help us maintain our connection to the planet by preserving our openness to the influences of the environment. Human beings emerged in the comfortable part of the planet between 20°N - 20° of the equator. Our bodies and spirits evolved as a response to the physical conditions present there. These conditions – temperature, humidity range, electrical environment (ions, etc.), range of smells, sounds, colours and textures – are the ones we now find ourselves most comfortable and healthy in. Good buildings now must be constructed to match these conditions and to preserve our relationship with the environment.

Firstly thinking greenly about building requires that we avoid building at all if possible; no development is the greenest development. Ways to avoid building include managing an existing building more creatively to use the same spaces more intensively, time shifting activities around and sharing spaces with other buildings to exploit underused facilities nearby. Thinking greenly at the design stage of a project uses 'intelligence to displace energy', i.e. by spending much more of our time questioning where the building should be, what it must do, how it will evolve etc, we can avoid investment of excessive material and energy in the building itself.

Ireland in some ways is the most easy building context in the world for green building; our geology and climate is largely benign; earthquakes are unknown and our solar radiation levels are actually more favourable than in, say, Belgium. The presence of the gulf stream prevents prolonged periods of snow or frost. In other ways though building here is a difficult proposition; continuously high levels of dampness mean that condensation is a constant problem and ambient temperature ranges of 4°-17° mean that keeping a building comfortable usually will require some heating.

Building greenly must be based on combining traditional techniques and skills (which have always responded to local material and weather conditions) with advances in designing, construction and building management techniques, blending tradition with technology to create a good ecological 'fit'.

Finally then it is vital to remember that building greenly is undermined if the building is not operated in a green way after construction. In most cases buildings are so greedy for resources that the energy and material in their construction is actually overtaken by the day-to-day resources required to run them within about five to eight years.

In the future we will see building being arranged as both producers and consumers linked together to share energy, heat, water and food. This web-like network is similar to the food webs found in nature and provides the blueprint for the sustainable building and sustainable towns of the near future.

Though it is romantic to think of green building as being a return to the past that is not the case. Ecological design and sustainable construction are, in and of themselves, new approaches to shelter-making and land use. To a greater or lesser extent all large-scale cultures now build and use buildings in a non-sustainable way. Green building represents a step forward in our evolution as a society and is one that need not imply significant sacrifice. It is also one that, in hindsight, will seem as (r)evolutionary as it was inevitable.

> When I am working on a problem, I never think about beauty. I think only how to solve the problem. But when I am finished, if the solution is not beautiful, I know it is wrong. R. Buckminster Fuller

Ecological Design

Eco settlements, water harvesting and reduction, habitat and food, permaculture and land use.

Ecological design is the discipline that integrates human activities into Nature and her processes, to create a mutually beneficial relationship - by design. Based on the science of ecology, the study of the interrelationship between a being and its environment, it is more rigorous than the 'humans above all else' attitude of 'sustainable' development and is the overriding framework onto which the other sections of this chapter fit. Ecological design explores the relationship between natural processes: energy, material, water, food, habitat and the project. We will concentrate here on looking at the issues of water, food, habitat and larger scale planning issues (eco-villages and eco-cities) covered by ecological design.

Water, habitat and wastewater

Reducing a building's appetite for water can be done through installing low flow appliances and minimising the use of potable water (only about 8 % of the water used in our homes is used for drinking but all of it is treated to drinking water standard). Taking responsibility for treating our own wastewater is not difficult. Water from sinks, baths and washing machines (grey water) can be easily treated in reed beds and used for flushing toilets or irrigating gardens, as can rainwater. Including reed beds as part of a project's landscape design is often done in Germany and the Netherlands. Water that is dirtier, say from toilets or industrial processes, can be treated in 'living machines'; a more intensive natural treatment system, suitable for urban and indoor applications. Compost toilets are an excellent way of avoiding water use in the WC at all and produce fertiliser for the garden.

Eco village and eco-city

At the larger scale, planning and city design must amalgamate all of these approaches into the design of villages and cities. There are already a number of eco-villages, intentional communities and co-housing projects under development in Ireland and the prospects are good. Extending these ideas to the scale of a large town or city is more challenging but there are many examples from around the world. An eco-city would be elegantly dense, based on pedestrian, bicycle and public transport, provide much of its own energy, food and water as well as caring for its waste.

Habitat and Food

Habitat is vital to biodiversity and maintaining it must play a part in all integrated design of shelters and settlements. Reed beds and wetlands as well as mixed-use farmland, wilderness and even green urban areas can provide much needed habitat for many species. The inclusion of food as an integral requirement of any green project especially in urban settings is vital. By designing sun-spaces, roofs and balconies carefully, growing crops can become almost effortless and will help us supply some of our own food needs, create habitat, pleasant smells and clean the air around us. Composting and biological treatment of all wastes (as the energy source they really are) are integral to this also.

Solar power, 'waste to energy' and the consideration of processes over a long period are the approaches upon which ecological design is based.

Buildings and Architecture (Build. Techniques & Energy)

Construction Techniques and Energy Efficiency

Building greenly in Ireland is a unique adventure. The things that drive green builders mad elsewhere, hurricanes and termites, do not exist here, yet simple things, humidity and moderate temperatures make building greenly here complicated. Many green construction techniques are applicable here. Most are updated versions of traditional techniques which start by mixing clay and straw together in some kind of semi-structural frame.

Cob, wattle and daub, and techniques based on the German 'light clay' and 'straw clay' are enjoying renewed popularity all over the world. Rammed earth and PISE (spraying the mix onto a half mould) is also popular abroad and is possible here. Of course building with wood, whether milled or 'green', is potentially the most effective green building technique if sourced from a sustainably managed plantation. Straw bale building, using the bales as large building blocks, is now being done in Ireland. While conditions here make it a little less ideal than abroad it is still attractive given that it is renewable, highly insulative, natural and encourages group self-building.

Portland Cement is responsible for almost 10% of the carbon problem in the atmosphere so avoiding it by using lime or other binders is advisable. Green building is of course also possible in large urban settings and the environmental benefits of doing it on urban scale are great.

Energy and Resources

In Ireland passive solar design is the basic tried and true approach to modern green building. Careful sizing and orientation of windows and walls to provide high levels of insulation (probably the single most important thing to get right) can save a lot of energy. Solar panels that create heat as hot water or air are already in widespread use in this country. PV solar panels that create electricity (hundreds of square meters of which have been installed in the UK) are also very feasible technically but because of pricing structures here take a long time to pay back. Wind, small-scale hydro, and biomass systems can also be used.

If renewable energy sources are not being used it is vital to design a system that maximises the efficiency of whatever fuel is being used. Gas is far more sustainable than electricity if the power station and its performance is taken into account. Also of course, and especially in larger scale or commercial buildings, care must be taken to avoid overheating and counter-productive solar gain by shading the building facade using shades, shutters or foliage, especially in summer.

All walls should be designed to act as a 'third skin', preserving our connection to the environment. Breathing walls, whose use is on the increase in Ireland and the UK, is really a 'sweating' construction allowing the passage of moisture but not air. This is compatible with an energy efficient strategy and is very beneficial to our health.

Remember that saving energy saves money, a benefit that will increase as electricity charges rise and carbon fines are introduced to help us reduce our greenhouse gases. Also of course, since most energy in use now produces pollution, switching to renewable sources doubly benefits the environment.

Sustainable Materials and Healthy Buildings

Conventional building materials are very problematic, being predominantly made from synthetic compounds (up to 75% of a typical building's make-up). These mean our homes and workplaces are unhealthy and increasingly lethal to the environment. Some (including the dioxins associated with PVC, asbestos, etc.) are defined as known carcinogens.

These materials are almost all oil based and as such require massive amounts of energy (and create massive amounts of pollution) in construction. The most important choice from an environmental point of view is the question of: how much energy (embodied energy) goes in to the mining, processing, transporting and use of the material? Next we have to consider the durability of the building and what will happen to the material after its reaches the end of its life. While designing to be as durable as possible is the best approach, assuming some flexibility is also advisable. The choices are complicated: steel for instance has a higher embodied energy than concrete but at the end of 80 years it is safe to assume it will be reused (because it is so valuable) without the need to reprocess it. Concrete on the other hand will almost certainly be ground up and 'down cycled' to become gravel so that the energy invested in it is lost. The question of transport and how far the material has to be transported is also important.

In terms of health the aim is to create spaces where we are exposed to only natural materials as we eat, live and sleep. The materials used in a building affect the quality of the air in it. Artificial finishes to walls, floors and furniture give rise to asthma, allergies and debilities such as Sick Building Syndrome and Chemical Sensitivity, not surprising since we now spend almost 90% of our time indoors. The formaldehyde that holds most plywood and laminated boards together, and many of the ingredients in conventional paints are volatile and seep out of walls, furniture and floors over a long period of time. Using organic or water based finishes, avoiding preservatives and products that use binders and synthetic glues helps. Ensuring generous ventilation even where 'tight' over 'breathing' construction is favoured is also essential. Another case for concern is the effect of electromagnetic fields. Sensitive people (the old, young, and ill, those that spend a large part of their time in the same position) are susceptible to these and a good green building should design these effects out.

A healthy interior environment will combine a 'radiant' heat regime with high levels of negative ions and a healthy palate of colours, textures and aromas.

GREEN BUILDING AND ECOLOGICAL DESIGN BOOKS

The Whole House Book - ecological building design and materials
Pat Borer and Cindy Harris
ISBN: 1898049211, 1998.

Build it with Bales - a step-by-step guide to straw-bale construction
MacDonald & Myhrman,
ISBN: 0964282119, 1997.

The Straw Bale House Steen
Steen & Bainbridge
ISBN: 0930031717, 1994.

Biomimicry
Janine Benyus
ISBN: 0688160999, 1998.

Places of the Soul
Christopher Day
ISBN: 1855383055, 1993.

The New Natural House Book
David Pearson
ISBN: 1850299854, 1998.

The Slate Roof Bible
Joseph Jenkins
ISBN: 0964425807, 1997.

Shelter
Edited by Lloyd Khan,
ISBN: 067976948X, 1996.

Independent Builder - Designing and Building a House your Way
Sam Clark
ISBN: 0930031857, 1996.

Buildings of Earth and Straw - Structural Design for Rammed Earth and Straw Bale Architecture
Bruce King
ISBN: 0964471817, 1997.

Earth to Spirit - In Search of Natural Architecture
David Pearson
ISBN:1856750469, 1994.

Craft Techniques in Traditional Buildings
Adela Wright

ISBN: 0713464194, 1991.

Green Design - Sustainable Building for Ireland
Ann McNicholl & J. Owen Lewis (eds)
ISBN: 0707623928, 1997.

Green Building Handbook
Wooley, Kimmins, Harrison & Harrison,
ISBN: 0419226907, 1997.

Small-Scale Lime-Burning - a practical introduction
M. Wingate *et al*
ISBN: 094668801X, 1985.

A Pattern Language
Christopher Alexander
ISBN: 0195019199, 1978.

Building Green
J. Johnston & J. Newton
ISBN: 1871045177, 1992.

Building with Earth
John Norton
ISBN: 1853393371, 1997.

Building with Lime: A Practical Introduction
Holmes & Wingate
ISBN: 1853393843, 1997.

Building Stone Walls
J. Vivian
ISBN: 0882660748, 1996.

The Earth - Sheltered House - an architect's sketchbook
Malcolm Wells
ISBN: 1890132195, 1998.

The Rammed Earth House
David Easton
ISBN: 0930031792, 1996.

The Passive Solar House: Using Solar Design to Heat and Cool Your Home
James Kachadorian
ISBN: 0930031970, 1997.

Irish Stone Walls; history- building-construction
Patrick McAfee

ISBN: 0862784786, 1997.

Fences, Gates and Bridges
G.Martin
ISBN: 0911469087

Barns, Sheds and Outbuildings
B. Halstead
ISBN: 0911469125

Ireland's Earthen Houses
Frank MacDonald & Peigin Doyle
ISBN: 189904728X

Simply Build Green
John Talbot
ISBN: 1899171908, 1995.

Eco-Design
Stuart Cowan and Sim Van der Ryn,
ISBN: 1559633883, 1995.

Design Outlaws on the Ecological Frontier
Chris Zelov ed.,
ISBN: 096503061X, 1997.

Restoring the Earth: Visionary Solutions from the Bioneers
Kenny Ausabel
ISBN: 0915811766, 1997.

Eco-Renovation - the Ecological Home Improvement Guide
Edward Harland
ISBN: 1870098528, 1993.

GREEN BUILDING AND ECOLOGICAL WEB SITES

Ecodesign Magazine
http://www.salvo.co.uk/mags/EcoDesign.htm
Sustainable Architecture, Building and Culture: http://www.sustainableabc.com/
Ecological Design Institute
http://www.ecodesign.org/edi/
Natural Building Resources
http://www.zianet.com/blackrange/br_pages/home.html
CalEarth: http://www.calearth.org/

ARCHITECTS AND DESIGNERS

GREEN BUILDING DIGEST

Contact: Tom Wooley
School of Architecture, Queens University,
Belfast BT9 5BY
Tel: 0801-232 335466
Fax: 0801-232 335466
Email: wooley.tom@talk21.com
Website: www.qub.ac.uk/tbe/arc/research/gbd/

The Green Building Digest is a quarterly publication available on subscription. It is the leading source of information in the UK and Ireland on green building. We can also give advice on a range of topics, building, paints, strawbale building etc.

IRISH ECOLOGICAL DESIGN ASSOCIATION (IEDA)

Contact: Sally Starbuck
11 Upper Mount Street, Dublin 2
Tel: 01-6610957
Fax: 01-6785124
E-mail: sgarry@iol.ie

Promotion of sustainable and ecological design in all aspects of physical environment.
Irish Ecological Design Association links designers of all disciplines, in a network providing information, education, exchange of ideas and stimulation to encourage and sustain the practice of eco-design as a branch of EDA (UK).

ECOLOGICAL DESIGN ASSOCIATION (N.I. Branch)

Contact: Tom Woolley
80 Church Road, Crossgar, Co. Down BT30 9HR
Tel: 0801-232 335466
Fax: 0801-232 335466
E-mail: t.woolley@qub.ac.uk

The EDA(NI) is an association of designers from various disciplines, architecture, landscape, design, ecology interior design etc. We are affiliated to the UK EDA and organise meetings, seminars and exhibitions as well as putting people in touch with ecological designers.

IRISH LANDSCAPE INSTITUTE

Contact: Karen Foley
6 Merrion Square, Dublin 2
Tel: 01-6627409
Fax: 01-676 9502

Landscape Architecture.
The Irish Landscape Institute is the professional body for landscape architects in Ireland. Members are in private practice and in public service and are involved with the design and management of parks, gardens, residential and industrial landscapes, EIA's urban design, leisure and planning studies.

NJBA ARCHITECTS & URBAN DESIGNERS

Contact: Noel J. Brady
4 Molesworth Place, Dublin 2
Tel: 01-6788068
Fax: 01-6788066
E-mail: njbarchictects@tinet.ie
Website: http://homepage.tinet.ie/njbrady1/

Architecture, landscape, urbanism focused on the search for a unified sustainable environment from houses to cities.

JOHN O'KEEFE & ASSOCIATES

Contact: John O'Keeffe & Roisin Quinty
The Paddock, 17 Ailesbury Grove,
Dundrum, Dublin 16
Tel: 01-2960876
Fax: 01-2982941

Our practice was established to allow clients a real option in securing concept based architecture of the highest quality design. We encourage design and build in an environmentally conscious fashion and have a long track record in the development of solar and energy efficient buildings.

RACHEL BEVAN ARCHITECTS

Contact: Rachel Bevan & Tom Woolley
80 Church Road, Crossgar, Co. Down BT309HR
Tel: 0044-2844 830988 / 0801 396-830988
Fax: 0044-2844 830988
Email: woolley.tom@talk21.com

We are an architectural practice established in 1992 carrying out full architectural and design services with an emphasis on environmentally friendly design, renovation of old buildings and user / client participation.

GAIA ECOTECTURE

Contact: Paul Leech & Sally Starbuck
11 Upper Mount Street, Dublin 2
Tel: 01-6610957
Fax: 01-6785124
E-mail: sgarry@iol.ie

Established 1979, this practice specialises in ecological, sustainable design and ecotechniques. Part of the Gaia International Network of Architects and Environmental Professionals. This practice has been involved in realising innovative, ecological architecture across different sectors, winning many awards, published internationally.

MIKE KEEGAN DESIGN

Contact: Mike Keegan
Gortavrulla, Caher, Co.Clare
Tel: 061-924186
Fax: 061-924186

Ecological design, building and architecture. 'Buildings as if people mattered'. I aim to help people create dwellings with 'soul'... buildings which have a sense of well-being and harmony... 'Art of Living'.
PROCESS: by being intimately connected to the design process, people naturally will create dwellings with individual character... DIVERSITY reflecting life.
GROUP APPROACH: from concept through to models, drawings and final plans. This is an enriching experience where roles of teacher and student often switch about. Once building commences I will be available for site teaching and consultation.

ICON ARCHITECTURE AND URBAN DESIGN

Contact: Delphine Geoghegan
Ballymurrin House, Kilbride, Co.Wicklow
Tel: 0404-48206
Fax: 0404-48206
E-mail: icon@esatclear.ie

Architecture - climatic design.
To provide a built response to the site that recognises climate, orientation, landscape and surrounding buildings, so that energy efficiency is enhanced and the building 'belongs' in a way that is satisfactory and sustainable.

HAPPEN

Contact: Jacqueline O'Keeffe
35 Findlater Street, Dublin 7
Tel: 01-8387167

Fax: 01-8387167
E-mail: xela@indigo.ie

Ecological design (interior & furniture).
A friendly, professional service to architects, corporate and private clients who wish to incorporate contemporary environment, careful interiors and furniture. We provide rapid quotes and professional advice including 3D space planning, precise specifications, prompt delivery and installation.

CAMP

Contact: Carolanne Moroney
137 Church Road, Dublin 3
Tel: 01-8553177 / 087-6893879
E-mail: camoroney@yahoo.com

Young, energetic architect committed to ecologically sound work, permaculture, energy efficiency, natural alternative materials, self-build community architecture, low-tech solutions emphasis on working with rather than for people.

PAUL O'CONNOR ARCHITECTS

Contact: Paul O'Connor MRIAI
3 St. Josephs Court, Prussia Street, Dublin 7
Tel: 01-8681809 / 087-8149663
Fax: 01-4530280
E-mail: oconnor@iol.ie
Website: www.iol.ie/~oconnor

We aim for the highest levels of satisfaction for our clients, the communities within which we work and those whom our clients serve, through holistic and sustainable eco-design and construction.

THE MAGIC BADGER

Contact: Lian Callaghan
Knockfadda, Roundwood, Co. Wicklow
Tel 01-2817007
Painting interiors with beautiful natural pigments, interiors, especially floors - energetic symbols and feng shui colour system. Also: willow sculptures and structures for indoors and outdoors. Tuition available.

SOLEARTH ECOLOGICAL ARCHITECTURE

Contact: Brian O'Brien
A16 Isoldes Tower, Lower Exchange Street, Dublin 8
Tel: 01-6771766
E-mail: solearth@iol.ie

Architectural design and consultancy. SOLEARTH is run by Brian T O'Brien (BArch SciDIT 1991, March - Berkeley, in process, Bau-biologist). We provide architectural design and consultancy in the areas of ecological design, sustainable urban design, green and low impact buildings, healthy and natural environments, Bau-biologie and energy efficiency.

ANTHONY COHU, B.ARCH. R.I.B.A.

Contact: Anthony Cohu
Borlin, Bantry, Co.Cork
Tel: 027-66042
Fax: 027-66042

Architecture, planning, landscape design, woodland management. Ecological principles guide our project work from landscape appraisal and management, to building materials and services selection. Extensive experience in passive solar, timber-frame, self-build and vernacular housing solutions.

ORGANIC PAINT
a Healthy Alternative

Traditional Organic Paints - Limewash and Distemper - for interior and exterior walls in 16 beautiful classical colours freshly hand-mixed to order.

Introducing Autumn '99: A Shaker-type Milk Paint, a Linseed Oil Paint for woodwork and a natural, nourishing Wood Oil. Agent for Stones natural Beeswax Polish.

Please phone our workshop for a Colour Card, Mail order information and/or your nearest stockist.

Organic paints made in Ireland by

PETRA BERNTSSON paintmaker and designer

8 Partnership Court, Park Street, Dundalk, Co. Louth.
Tel: 042-93 51050

ADRIAN JOYCE ARCHITECTS

Contact: Adrian Joyce & Rachael Ludlow
The Forge, Main Street, Dundrum, Dublin 14
Tel: 01-2988500
Fax: 01-2988622
E-mail: amjoyce@iol.ie

Architecture, new buildings, restoration, conservation. Our principal objective is to include environmental considerations into all our work leading to lifelong benefits for our clients, local communities and the planet. Energy efficient design is a speciality.

ECO-COMMUNITY ARCHITECT

Contact: Emer O'Siochru BArch MRIAI
39 Windsor Road, Rathmines, Dublin 6
Tel: 01-4972564
E-mail: siochru@iol.ie

Building / design, community, education. We provide an integrated service to help build sustainable communities including planning and development, valuation, ecological settlement and building design. Human and community transformative education.

FEHILY TIMONEY & CO.

Contact: Marcia D'Alton
Centre Park House, Centre Park Road, Cork
Tel: 021-964133
Fax: 021-964464
Email: postmaster@ftco.ie

Environmental and civil engineering consultancy. To combine engineering and scientific skills in a unified approach to achieve the right environmental balance in the design and construction of the engineered environment.

CHRISTOPHER SOUTHGATE AND ASSOCIATES

Contact: Peter Stacey
139 Sunday's Well Road, Cork, Co. Cork
Tel: 021-211631
Fax: 021-211109
E-mail: pstacey@csassoc.com

Sustainable building design. Conservation of historic building. Facilitating land owners to manifest sustainable housing projects, by offering design, construction and financial advice.

RICHARD WEBB & ASSOCIATES

Chartered Landscape Architect and Consultant in Sustainable Development.
Contact: Dr Richard Webb
"Springfields", 3 Hollybrook, Ballywaltrim, Bray, Co. Wicklow
Tel: 01-2866991
Fax: 01-2866990
E-mail: rwebb@indigo.ie

Sustainable development, agriculture and forestry, Agenda 21, environment. Helping you to develop a sustainable future for your organisation is a key mission of Richard Webb & Assoc. We focus on key areas which are essential to developing a viable and abundant future: business and environmental training, community development, local agenda 21; children's play consultant, permaculture designer and teacher, feng shui advisor, healing gardens, REPS, wetland waste water treatment.

ENERGY RESEARCH GROUP, UCD

Contact: Prof J. Owen Lewis & John Goulding
School of Architecture, UCD, Richview,
Clonskeagh, Dublin 14

Tel: 01-2692750
Fax: 01-2838908
E-mail: lewis@erg.ucd.ie goulding@erg.ucd.ie

Energy-efficient building design. Research,
consultancy and information dissemination with a
strong European dimension since 1975. In recent
years the group's activities have included design
consultancy for public and private clients in
Ireland and abroad.

BUILDING

HEALTHY BUILDINGS CONSULTANCY

Contact: Wilhelm Bodewigs
Doon Lough, Fivemilebourne, Co.Leitrim

Tel: 087-2785790
Fax: 071-44452
Email: ecohouse@iol.ie
Promoting building solutions and material
concepts of consistent natural character with
special attention to low energy design in
manufacture use and transportation. Product
advice for allergy sufferers. Associated with Klee
Paper, Dublin. **See advert p.136. ORGANIC PAINT.**

SUSTAINABLE HOUSING

Contact: Andy Frew
88 Clifton Street, Belfast, Co. Antrim BT13 1AB

Tel: 0801-232 438662
Fax: 0801-232 238057
E-mail: andy.frew@net.ntl.com

Energy conservation & renewables advice for
housing. Sustainable housing promotes energy
conservation and renewables used in housing
focusing on reducing carbon dioxide emission.

NARROW WATER LIME SERVICE

Contact: Dan McPolin
Newry Road, Warrenpoint, Co. Down

Tel: 0801-69 3753073
Fax: 0801-69 3753073

A Craft Reborn - for anyone involved in the
conservation or repairing of traditional buildings an
understanding of the properties and the use of
lime mortars is becoming increasingly important.

GARRY GLEESON ASSOCIATES

Eco Builder and Conservationists
Contact: Gerry Gleeson
Carrigmore, Clogheen, Tipperary

Tel: 052-65235
Fax: 052-65488
E-mail: ggass@tinet.ie

Consultants in environmental control of dampness,
dry rot and wood / joinery defects. Specialists in
on-site treatment and restoration of windows and
structural wood.

THERMONEX

Contact: Martin Mulligan
75 Richview, Castlecomer Road, Kilkenny,
Co. Kilkenny

Tel: 056-71747
Fax: 056-23319
E-mail: thermonex@tinet.ie
Website: www.erin.ie/thermonex

Architecture & engineering.
The application, design and construction of
buildings in the residential, commercial, leisure
and industrial sectors using X-concrete, a Swedish
precast lightweight insulating building system.

MATERIALS AND TECHNOLOGY

BIOCHROME LTD.

Contact: Piet Verhagen
Tulla, Co. Clare

Tel: 065-6835559
Fax: 065-6835559
E-mail: pverhagen@tinet.ie

Natural Paints.
Biochrome imports & distributes natural paints,
wood preservatives and household cleaners, as well
as advising on their use. It also provides
architectural design and advice on green building.

PETRA BERNTSSON PAINTMAKER & DESIGNER

Contact: Petra Berntsson
8 Partnership Court, Park Street,
Dundalk, Co. Louth

Tel: 042-9351050

Organic Paintmaking, natural design.
Organic paint - a healthy alternative. Traditional
organic paints - Limewash and Distemper - for
interior and exterior walls in 16 beautiful classical
colours freshly hand mixed to order. Introducing
Autumn '99: a Shaker-type Milk Paint, a Linseed
Oil Paint for woodwork and a natural, nourishing
Wood Oil. Agent for STONES Natural Beeswax
Polish. Please phone our workshop for a colour
card, information and your nearest stockist.

FOREST FRIENDLY FLOORS LTD.

Contact: Vincent Daly & Ruth Schleicher
12 Sullivan Street, Dublin 7

Tel: 01-8681757 / 087-288 9701

Architectural renovations and conversions pitch
pine and other reconstituted timber. Wooden decks
salvage. Wood and flooring.
Salvage pitch pine and other reconstituted timber,
architectural renovations and conversions, old style

refurbishment, top quality salvage wood flooring, native cedar wood and larch garden decks. Eco friendly.

SPILLANE INSULATIONS LTD.

Contact: John Spillane
Cunnahert, Nenagh, Co.Tipperary

Tel: 067-31057
Fax: 067-31053

House Insulation.
We supply and install insulation for attics and timber frame houses. The material is totally recycled newsprint.

NATURAL TECHNOLOGY SYSTEMS

Contact: Heather Thomas
Derrynaneal, Feakle, Co. Clare

Tel: 061-0924287 / 061-924287
Fax: 01-6335854
E-mail: hkthomas@tinet.ie mlomas@tinet.ie
Website: www.surf.to/naturaltechnology

Reed bed wastewater treatment / eco timber builders. Reed bed treatment systems. High green specification timber houses incorporating: breathing construction, active and passive solar design, warmgell insulation, organic paints. Natural healthy homes using traditional craftsmanship and latest technology.

FULL SPECTRUM LIGHTING LTD.

Contact: Pam Llyod
Lincoln Road, Cressex business park, High Wycombe, Buckinghamshire HP12 3FX, UK
Tel: 0044-1494-526051
Fax: 0044-1494-527005
Website: www.sad.uk.com

Full spectrum lighting brings the benefits of natural outdoor light indoors, specialising in daylight lighting, tubes and bulbs to fit existing fittings. Light Therapy equipment available to help SAD sufferers. **See advert p.136.**

RESTORATION

ULSTER ARCHITECTURAL HERITAGE SOCIETY

Contact: Rita Harkin
66 Donegall Pass, Belfast, Co. Antrim

Tel: 0801-232 550213
Fax: 0801-232 550214
E-mail: uans@btinternet.com

The UAHS exists to promote the appreciation and enjoyment of architecture from the prehistoric to the present in the nine counties of Ulster, and to encourage its preservation and conservation.

GEORGIAN HOUSE AND GARDEN

Contact: Dorothy Meaney
Tontine Buildings, No.2 Pery Square, Limerick, Co. Limerick

Tel: 061-14130

Fully restored Georgian town house and enclosed garden. No. 2 Perry Square is one of a terrace of 6 Georgian architecture houses, built by the Perry Square Tontine Company in 1838. The original architecture detail and decor have been precisely re-instated. The town house garden is based on the original layout as per 1840 OS map. The house is open to the public and is also a museum on the history of Georgian Limerick. Advice is available in restoration techniques.

LIMERICK CIVIC TRUST

Contact: Denis M Leonard
Bishop's Palace, Kings Island, Limerick, Co. Limerick

Tel: 061-313399
Fax: 061-315513

Limerick Civic Trust undertakes projects which restore / enhance Limerick's architectural environment and heritage. The trust is a voluntary organisation and since its foundation in 1982 it has completed 80 projects.

ECO COTTAGE (TOURISM DEVELOPMENT) PROJECT

Contact: Terry Cunningham, Rural Enterprise Adviser Teagasc, Carrigeen, Clonmel, Co. Tipperary

Tel: 052-21300
Fax: 052-21199
E-mail: c.kenny@tipperarysr.teagasc.ie
Website: www.ecobooley.com

Research eco-friendly technologies that can be used to restore remote rural houses for the eco-tourism market including the restoration of one cottage in South Tipperary. For information, write, fax or check website, to rent see Eamonn Looby.

ARCHAEOLOGICAL SURVEYOR AND HERITAGE MANAGEMENT CONSULTANT

Contact: Andrew Croft
Tooreen, Glengarriff, Co. Cork

Tel: 027-63576

Archaeological survey and heritage management and advice for all forms of development, planning and land use change. Discounts for community-led and sustainable development projects.

FENG SHUI

CARMEL O'CONNOR
2 Willmount Cottages, Glenalva Rd., Killiney, Co. Dublin

Tel: 01-2858611/087-2416549
Fax: 01-6600868
Email: carmel_o_connor@yahoo.com

Carmel, a design consultant for over 25 years now incorporates the practical principles of Feng Shui into her work, having trained in the U.K. with the Feng Shui Network International and the Feng Shui Academy. She has just started to lecture in Ireland.

CATHERINE LARKIN.
61, Wilfield Road, Sandymount, Dublin 4.

Tel: 01-2600826
Fax: 01-2600826

Feng Shui, an ancient Chinese practice, looks at how our home and work environment affects us and recommends changes so that the energy around us works for us, rather than against us.

FENG SHUI DESIGN

Contact: Vincent Gill
St.John's Court, Devenish, Athlone, Co.Westmeath

Tel: 087-228-4159
E-mail: info@holistic.ie
Website: http://www.holistic.ie/fengshui
Feng shui design for harmonious living.
I will assist groups and individuals to learn the art of placement with respect to cultural heritage, so that they may enjoy a more prosperous and harmonious life.

INTERIOR ALIGNMENT & FENG SHUI PRACTITIONER

Contact: Eilish Foley
Ballynoran House, Charlville, Cork

Tel: 063-81228

Feng shui is the pursuit and creation of a more harmonious place to live and work. CHI (energy) and Yin and Yang opposites are balanced. The philosophy is that we are affected by every aspect of our surroundings.

ELIZABETH STUDENSKI
Pond Lodge, Doon, Boyle, Co. Roscommon

Tel: 079-66072
Fax: 079-66072

House plans checked for ideal orientation of house,rooms, windows, doors and contents. Existing house Feng Shuied for more harmonious living, colour schemes and garden. Sites and buildings dowsed for geopathic stress.

JAYA MORAN
97 Glenageary Ave., Dun Laoghaire, Co. Dublin

Tel: 01-2854807
Fax: 01-2806185

Millennium feng shui frogs, for house, garden and business. Limited edition. £70-£100. Crafted and hand-painted by Jaya Moran, artist and achemist. The frog stands for prosperity. Love and success. Ideal christmas and millenium gift.

SEE ALSO

ENERGY ACTION LTD.
Home insulation of elderly and needy people.
Full listing: Energy and Transport section.

TRISCLE HEATING
Provide energy efficient Bullerjan Stove.
Full listing: Energy and Transport section.

BIG GREEN ART
Eco-house / space design and building.
Full listing: Arts and Leisure section.

Teach Ban, The Home of Healthy Living
Feng Shui courses available to design your home and maximise your energy.
Full listing: Food and Drink section.

MONEY + WORK

page 147 **Introduction to money** by Richard Douthwaite

page 150 **LETS** Julia Kemp

page 151 **Co-operatives** Pauric Cannon

page 152 **Tele-working** Riona Carroll

page 153 **Credit Unions** Des Gunning

page 154 **Ethical Investment** Tony Weeks

page 157 **Reinventing Work** Mathew Fox

MONEY Richard Douthwaite

Richard Douthwaite lives in Westport, Co Mayo and is a former economic advisor to the governments of Jamaca and Montserrat. He is the author of *The Growth Illusion: How Economic Growth Enriched the Few, Impoverished the Many and Endangered the Planet and Short Circuit: Strengthening Local Economies for Security in an Uncertain World*. Richard was one of the founders of FEASTA: The Foundation for the Economics of Sustainability that is based in Dublin and the economic advisor to the Global Commons Institute.

Gold had a big advantage in the days when it was used as money: anyone could obtain it. All they had to do was to find a bed of gravel containing nuggets beside a stream or a vein of gold-bearing quartz in a cliff-face and set to work to convert their time and energy, plus a certain amount of bought-in supplies, into something that was exchangeable for goods and services all over the world.

Gold rushes were all about the conversion of human energy into money. They were a democratic form of money creation in the sense that prospecting for gold was open to anyone whenever society had sufficient resources to allow them to spend their time that way. Obviously if supplies of food, clothing and shelter were precarious, people would never devote their energies to finding something that they could neither eat nor live in and which would not keep them warm. In other words, gold supplies swelled whenever a culture was producing a surplus and once there was more gold about, the use of the precious metal as money made more trading possible and thus catalysed the conversion of whatever surpluses arose in future years into buildings, clothes and other things that people wanted.

Until the mid-1960s, the inhabitants of Yap, a group of islands in the Pacific Ocean, converted their surplus into money by carving stones into special shapes. According to Glyn Davies' mammoth study *A History of Money*:

The stones known as 'fei' were quarried from Palau, some 260 miles away, or even the more distant Guam, and were shaped into discs varying from saucer sized to veritable millstones. The larger specimens had holes in the centre through which poles could be pushed to help transport them. Despite centuries of at first sporadic and later more permanent trade contracts with the Portuguese, Spanish, German, British, Japanese and Americans, the stone currency retained and even increased its value, particularly as a store of wealth.

The largest of the stone discs now in Yap include two that are fully 20ft in diameter, which remained until the mid-1950s at the bottom of Tomil harbour where they had accidentally sunk. They had been quarried under the direction of a certain Captain O'Keefe, an American-Irish sea captain who, shortly after becoming shipwrecked in Yap in December 1871, set himself up as the largest trader in that part of the Pacific and 'ruled' as 'His Majesty O'Keefe' until his death in the great typhoon of 1901.

Davies adds that shell necklaces, individual pearl shells, mats and ginger supplemented the stone currency but quotes from a book published in 1952 when fei were still in use, to the effect that the stones were 'the be-all and end-all of the Yap islander. They are not only money, they are badges of rank and prestige, and they also have religious and ceremonial significance.'

It is often said that gold made a good currency because of its 'intrinsic value' but this is nonsense. Gold is no more or less intrinsically valuable than the Yap stones or any of the many other things that people have used as a base for their money systems. These have included livestock - the word "pecuniary" comes from "pecunia," the Latin for "cow" and "fee" is a corruption of the German word "Vieh," meaning cattle - salt, silk, dried fish, feathers, stones, cowrie shells, beads, cigarettes, cognac and whisky. In 1715, the government of North Carolina declared seventeen commodities, including maize and wheat, to be legal tender.

In ancient Egypt, grain was the monetary unit. The farmers would deposit their crops in government-run warehouses against receipts showing the amount, quality and date. These stores suited the farmers because they protected the grain against theft, fire and flood and also saved them the cost of providing their own storage facilities or selling their crop immediately after harvest when prices were low. The stores also enabled them to pay their rent and to buy goods simply by writing what was effectively a cheque transferring grain from their account in the store to that of someone else. People using another grain store in another part of the country could be paid with these cheques. The various stores would balance out their claims against each other just as banks do today and the grain itself would only be moved if there was a net flow of cheques from one town to another and the grain was actually needed there for consumption

The earliest account of the use of wampum - the shells of a clam, Venus Mercenaria - as money in North America dates from 1535. Both native Americans and the European settlers used the shells which were made legal tender for payments of up to a shilling in Massachusetts in 1637 at a rate of six white ones or three of the rarer blacks a penny. The last factory drilling the half-inch long shells lengthways and putting them on strings for use as money closed as late as 1860.

The essential feature of all these commodity currencies is that they were open to anyone with time and access to land or seashore to produce. This didn't mean that they could be produced without cost and that the money supply was therefore unlimited, however. If that had been the case, the monetary unit would have had no value. The currencies worked because people would only spend their time making something which served as money if that was the best way of satisfying their needs. In other words, whenever they could get food, clothing or house-building materials more easily and conveniently by going out and growing them or collecting them themselves instead of panning for gold or collecting wampum shells, they would obviously do so. As a result, money was only produced and spent into circulation when its exchange rate with real goods was favourable, a feature which generally guaranteed that it would maintain its value.

Because they enable people to create spending units for themselves, Local Exchange and Trading Systems - LETS - are a modern equivalent of wampum and the other types of popularly-produced commodity currencies. They are generally set up by a group of people living in the same area who have time on their hands and who have too little national currency to meet their requirements. The first system was set up by a Scots-born Canadian, Michael Linton, in the early 1980s in the Comox Valley in British Columbia as a response to the unemployment caused when an air base closed down.

Between 1-2,000 places throughout the world have LETS systems and many variants on Linton's original model have been developed. The common feature of every LETS, however, is that members trade with each other using a monetary unit of their own devising and that records are kept of all transactions, usually on a computer, so that it is possible to spot members who are taking more value out of the system than they are putting in.

There are important differences between LETS and currencies of the wampum type, however. For example, wampum shells were used to allow their holders to trade beyond their communities while LETS systems are set up to enable people to trade within them. In addition, LETS systems have no need to establish the value of their unit by requiring people to do a certain amount of work to produce them. They normally use the value of their national currency unit as their measuring stick, although some systems have experimented with units based on time. This saves all the effort some of the old-style systems wasted on producing goods which were totally unnecessary apart from their monetary use.

The restorative economy comes down to this: We need to imagine a prosperous...culture that is so intelligently designed and constructed that it mimics nature at every step, a symbiosis of company and customer and ecology. Paul Hawkin

L.E.T.S. **Julia Kemp** journalist and member of the Bantry L.E.T.S.

L.E.T.S. stands for Local Exchange Trading System. It is a group of people who agree to trade with each other, but with no exchange of money. Instead, they create their own unit of exchange - local currency - for which they choose a name. In Ireland we have Reeks, Sods, Acorns, Skills and Cuids among others.

The members of the association offer goods and services priced in these units in their ddirectory, which is circulated to all members and updated regularly. Transactions are recorded by means of cheques written in the local currency, and the administration sends out regular statements, just like a bank (there is an annual subscription payable in money to cover postage and printing costs, but administration labour costs are usually paid in LETS.).

A special feature of LETSystems is that the balances of all members are made known in the Trading Summary. Thus everyone can see who has a plus balance and who has a minus balance. Debts are known as commitments, but no interest is charged. It's important to remember that some members have to be in commitment otherwise no-one could be in credit.

Unlike the money system, being in credit is not rewarded by the payment of interest. It is therefore in the interest of members not to hold on to too many LETS, but to spend them quickly and allow others to be in credit!

LETSystems have great social potential. People get to meet each other during the course of trading, and of course help each other by doing simple tasks such as baking, walking the dog or making curtains. Other more specialised jobs may be available as well, for example plumbing, decorating, carpentry, and various aspects of health care, such as massage. As far as community values are concerned, there is a spirit of helping each other as different needs arise, without having to worry about money.

LETS was first conceived in 1983 by Michael Linton, a Canadian, who designed the system as a response to high unemployment in his home town. Since then it has spread all over the world, and there are over twenty groups in Ireland. You can find out more about the different groups by visiting the website of LETSlink Ireland at;
http://www.iol.ie/~ptempan/letslink

Everywhere I go it seems people are killing themselves with work, busyness, rushing, caring and rescuing. Work addiction is a modern epidemic and it is sweeping our land. Diane Fassel

Co-operatives Pauric Cannon secretary of the Dublin Food Co-op.

A major shift is needed to move towards people-centred business structures that nurture a sense of community. The co-operative method of economic organisation may be one way to achieve this.

What is a co-operative?
A co-operative is a group of people who come together to pool their resources, skills and knowledge to provide goods and services to meet their member's needs.

Legal structure.
In Ireland, the Registrar of Friendly Societies incorporates co-operatives under the Industrial & Provident Societies Acts 1893 to 1978.

Do co-ops enjoy limited liability status?
Yes.

Who can join a co-op?
Anyone can join a co-op who is prepared to accept the responsibilities of ownership.

How many can join a co-op?
The minimum number is four: there's no upper limit.

Are co-ops democratic?
Co-ops are based on democratic and ethical trading principles.

How many different types of co-op are there?

There are four main types:

* Worker co-op: owned and managed by its workers.
* Consumer co-op: owned and controlled by consumer-shareholder members.
* Housing co-op: owned by and for the benefit of a community.
* Secondary co-op: owned and controlled by the users of its services (these are often small businesses or co-ops).

Useful addresses

Information on consumer-owned Food Co-ops
Dublin Food Co-op Society Ltd.,
12a North King St., Dublin 7
Tel: 873-0451 Fax: 873-0451
email: dfc@clubi.ie
Website: http://www.clubi.ie/dfc

Information on funding and model rules for worker co-ops
Co-operative Development Unit

Fas Training Centre
Baldoyle Industrial Estate
Dublin 13
Tel: 8391144

Information on grants for worker co-ops
The Irish League of Credit Unions
33 Lower Mount St
Dublin 2
Tel: 614 6700   Fax: 614 6701

Where to register your co-op
The Registrar of Friendly Societies
14 Parnell Square
Dublin 1
Tel: 8045499

Advice on Model Rules for co-ops
The Co-operative Development Society
41 Lower Dominick St
Dominick Court
Dublin 1
Tel: 873 3199   Fax: 873 3612

Tele-working

Riona Carroll the Executive Officer of Telework Ireland

There are many definitions of teleworking, and therefore much confusion as to what teleworking really is. The 1999 Report of the National Advisory Council on Teleworking (NACT) defines teleworking as "a way of working using information and communication technologies in which work is carried out independent of location". In other words, teleworking can currently and most simply be perceived as using a computer, modem and telephone line to send work from place A to place B, rather than the worker going to place B to do the work.

Using today's enabling technologies, teleworkers can work on the move, from a satellite office, a telecentre or home.

Teleworking offers many significant advantages to the teleworker, including:

- Freedom to chose where to live
- Flexibility in work and lifestyle
- The opportunity to merge work and personal commitments to suit personal circumstances
- Development of economic opportunities for people with disabilities and mobility problems

Teleworking has also huge potential for positive environmental and economic impact in terms of reduction of gridlock, overcrowding and urban congestion.

In addition, teleworking offers benefits to the employer in terms of increased productivity, staff loyalty and reductions in fixed overheads.

It is important to be aware that teleworking is not a job per se, but is a way of doing a job or delivering a skill. Examples of skills currently being teleworked by Telework Ireland members include data processing, translations, event management, sales management, web site design, software development and localisation.

In addition, it is important - if starting to telework or considering the introduction of teleworking into an organisation - to remember that this is a process which requires advance thought and preparation, and where difficulties which may arise or be aggravated through the distance factors inherent in teleworking, be anticipated and managed so as to maximise the potential benefit of teleworking to all concerned.

> **Capitalism is about using money to make money for people who already have more of it than they need. Its institutions, by their very nature, breed inequality, exclusion, environmental destruction, social irresponsibility and economic instability while homogenising cultures, weakening the institutions of democracy, and eroding the moral and social fabric of society.** David Korten

Credit Unions

Des Gunning author of *The Fate of the Third Sector in Ireland*, 1993 and contributer to Common Ground Magazine.

The term 'the people's bank' is often applied to the credit union organisation. This very impressive organised network of independent mutual societies has its origins in a Co-operative Development Society which was formed in Dublin in the mid 1950's.

The early years of credit unions were marked by a dramatic 'movement' from the state of there being no credit unions to the state of there being several hundred such institutions. The movement created the network of some 400 credit unions which are to be found throughout the State.

Insofar as one apply the 'movement' idea to credit unions nowadays it is perhaps most appropriate to do so in terms of the different tendencies that ebb and flow within the organisation that has been established to maintain the network as a whole. The most significant of these are two 'movements' that could with equal validity be viewed either as antithetical or complementary.

Worldwide, credit union organisations reflect different approaches with the Irish Credit Union organisation having most in common with the credit union organisations in English speaking countries, most especially the United States.

By and large, the older credit union organisations of mainland Europe tend to more deliberately complement their customer focus with strategies designed to help build and maintain their local economies while the credit unions of the English speaking world tend to shy away from acting locally as mandated institutions in their own right.

These two views, namely the credit union as a 'mere servant' of its members individual credit needs and the credit union as a significant player in the local economy in its own right are perhaps the two most significant perspectives which inform decision-making at local Credit Union level.

In Ireland, as many as a half-dozen or so credit unions have become significant generators of economic sustainability in their 'Common Bonds' (not just through the efforts of individual members but as institutional actors in their own right).

More credit unions are likely to explore this approach, enabled in particular by Section 44 (The 'local investment clause') of the 1997 Credit Union Act.

A key question is not just what credit unions can enable their individual members to do but also what can credit unions in themselves achieve as economic players in their own right while continuing to deliver quality services to their members?

Ethical Investment Tony Weeks

Since the mid-eighties, there has been a growing realisation that our spending and saving decisions can have an influence on corporate business and that a committed campaign, based on the way we spend and save, can change things. For many, their first experience of this aspect of 'people power' arose from the campaign against the apartheid regime in South Africa. In England, Barclay's Bank - perceived by many people as supporting the apartheid regime - lost personal (and some corporate) customers. South African produce was boycotted. Questions were raised about the morality of receiving an income from the profits of companies investing in South Africa. These activities were important parts of a wider movement against apartheid.

Since those early days, both the ethical issues and the debate have widened. The ethical policies of companies are increasingly being monitored and the results made public. The Manchester-based Ethical Consumer Research Association publishes the results of its research into corporate conduct on a wide range of ethical questions - involvement in the arms trade, respect for human and animal rights, pollution and waste disposal, irresponsible marketing, to name a few. The Ethical Investment Research Service in London offers a similar service to investors in the corporate sector, both personal and institutional. Many personal financial advisors in Britain can now consider their clients' ethical wishes in offering advice.

As the movement develops, more positive aspects are beginning to appear. We are now encouraged to see our saving and spending directed to supporting activities such as organic agriculture, the relief of homelessness and sustainable community development rather than avoiding support of the unethical. In the UK, the Ecology Building Society, Triodos Bank and Shared Interest direct savings towards ecologically sound and people and planet friendly projects. The Co-operative Bank has an excellent statement of its ethical position. The Fair Trade movement ensures that what we buy is produced in ways which recognise the human needs of the producers as well consumers. There are pressure groups which raise questions about the ethical policies of pension funds, and about the investments of the churches as corporate bodies.

The task of bringing an ethical stance into our getting and spending has hardly begun. Ireland, both North and South of the Border, has some way to go. This note is to encourage collaborative action to further these ideas.

Issues to Consider for Investors

Before making any investments find answers to the following questions:

- Does the company, manufacturer or supplier have an environmental policy or environmental management system, e.g. ISO 14001 or EMAS, in operation?

- Is environmental legislation being complied with?

- Is any future liability being built up as a result of ongoing environmental damage which could effect the value of your investment?

- Does the company report on its environmental performance separately or in its annual report?

- Does the company practice ethical trading?

It's easy to make a difference.
Extracts from the forthcoming ENFO SUSTAINABLE LIVING GUIDE for shoppers and investors.

ENFO

EOLAS AR AN gCOMHSHAOL
INFORMATION ON THE ENVIRONMENT

17, St Andrew St., Dublin 2, Ireland
Tel 1890 200 191 or 01 888 3001
Fax: 01 888 3946
e-mail: info@enfo.ie
Website: www.enfo.ie

Symbols for Business/Services
ISO 14001

Approx. 100 organisations have been certified to ISO 14001, the international standard for environmental management systems. Some businesses regard this standard as the first step towards the more onerous EMAS certification which is detailed below.

EMAS (the EU Eco-management and Audit Scheme)

The EU's voluntary scheme for industry requires companies, which wish to be awarded the logo, to:
• have an environmental management system
• be certified as being legal compliant
• be committed to ongoing environmental improvement, and
• publish a report on progress made in achieving targets, all of which must be independently verified. The National Accreditation Board, which administers the scheme in Ireland, has awarded the logo to eight companies (approx. 2,000 in Europe).

The **EMAS** Regulation is being revised at EU level to extend the scope to cover all industrial sectors and services and will involve a change of logo.

ETHICAL TRADING. Companies are under increasing pressure to provide evidence to their stakeholders, including customers, that their products are made in accordance with ethical values and principles. Issues include child labour, health and safety, freedom of association, paying living wages and working hours. The Council on Economic Priorities (CEP) was founded in 1969 to provide accurate and impartial analysis of corporate social performance and to promote excellence in corporate citizenship. The international standard for social accountability SA 8000 was developed by the Accreditation Agency of CEP.

The **ETHICAL TRADING INITIATIVE - IRELAND** is a partnership of companies, non-governmental organisation, and trade unions, with the following aims:
• to encourage companies to implement codes of conduct embodying internationally agreed labour standards and human rights in the workplace, and
• to develop and encourage the use of best practice monitoring and independent verification methods.

Voluntary **CODES OF CONDUCT** (preferably independently monitored) for companies and their suppliers are a way of ensuring that minimum standards are respected across the whole range of goods bought from Third World producers. Ask the management of your local supermarket, store or other supplier, if they have an independently monitored **CODE OF CONDUCT** for the suppliers of all their goods from Third World producers.

EOLAS AR AN gCOMHSHAOL
INFORMATION ON THE ENVIRONMENT

17, St Andrew St., Dublin 2, Ireland
Tel 1890 200 191 or 01 888 3001
Fax: 01 888 3946
e-mail: info@enfo.ie
Website: www.enfo.ie

It's easy to make a difference.
Extracts from the forthcoming ENFO SUSTAINABLE LIVING GUIDE for shoppers and investors.

WORK / LIVELIHOOD Mathew Fox

Mathew Fox is a a post-modern theologian who has been an ordained priest since 1967. Fox is founder and president of the University of Creation Spirituality in Oakland, California, and author of 21 books. He is a lecturer whose travels throughout North America, Europe and Australia have brought his message of ecological and social justice, to eager and ever-growing audiences

Reinventing Work

Today there are close to one billion human beings out of work. In the United States alone there are more unemployed people now than at any time since the Great Depression. At the same time in the industrial world, there are a great number of persons who are overworked – who are, in Meister Eckhart's phrase, "worked" instead of working – giving rise to a new addiction: workaholism. Of those who are employed, some are in jobs that are inimical to the health of our species and the planet, for example, tearing down rainforests or killing endangered animals or selling drugs or making armaments.

Some politicians, looking for a quick fix, shout that we need "jobs, jobs, jobs." But such simplistic slogans simply do not cut deeply enough. They avoid the questions that must be asked of work at this critical juncture in human and planetary history when, as Lester Brown concludes in his State of the World Report, the planet has only 20 years remaining unless human beings change their ways.

And changing our ways includes changing the way we look at work, define it, compensate for it, create it, and the way we let go of work and learn to confuse it and fuse it with play and ritual. We should not allow ourselves to be deceived that today's crisis in jobs is just about more "jobs, jobs, jobs" - it is not. It is about our relationship to work and the challenge put to our species today to re-invent work. The issue is at bottom an issue in spirituality, which is always about "all our relations" as the Lakota people pray.

Work is clearly a deep partner in our relationships: the middle class prepares itself for work by getting an education, working, recovering from work, and trying to raise children who can successfully enter the work world. Clearly work is at the centre of adult living. This is one reason that unemployed persons can so readily succumb to self-hatred and despair: not having a vehicle to express one's blessing in the basic meaning of work renders one mute and blocked up inside. The artist within, the Imago Dei, never gets a chance to express itself.

The fact that Communism has collapsed only exacerbates the issue at stake when we talk about work. This is not only because C ommunism had a definite (and often appealing) philosophy about work which raised such important issues as "alienation of the worker," "exploitation of the worker," and "work for everyone," but also because Communism's demise leaves capitalism standing naked for everyone to observe. What are its values vis-a-vis the worker? The unemployed? The uninsured? The addicted worker? The gap between workers' salaries and top management's salaries? The relationship of top management and owners of industry (including the media industry and the defence industry) to government decision-making, legislative law-making, and candidate-anointing in the civic process? What is Capitalism's attitude toward minority hiring and training? Toward work in ghettos where there are no jobs? To the educational agendas in schools that in turn create the market place of workers? In retraining persons who are being expelled from the war industry to other industries? What about the relationship between crime, violence, a burgeoning youthful prison population, and no work? The money that money makes versus the money that workers make? In other words, Capitalism itself is now in the limelight once again, as it was in the Great Depression. The lessons of the get-rich-quick artistry of Ivan Boessky, Michael Milkin, and Thomas Keating must not be lost when we reflect critically on work in our world today.

Another dimension in our consideration of work today must be the environment. All work depends on healthy soil, water, air, bodies, minds, spirits. In short, work is subject to the laws of interdependence that operate throughout Nature. Humans are Nature, humans are in Nature, Nature is in humans, and work is Nature. When humans work it is nature at work. Indeed, Hildegaard of Bingen said in the twelfth century that "when humans do good work they make the cosmic wheel go around." In other words, work has a cosmic dimension to it. But evil work- that which interferes with the intentions and plans of Nature- also has a cosmic dimension to it; the powers and principalities come unleashed as a result of misbegotten and evil work. All injustice is that sort of work; this is why the Scriptures say that "when the widow and orphan are dishonoured all the pillars of the Earth are shattered." A cosmic rupture occurs when humans do bad work.

The environmental crisis tells us much about our crisis in work today. Lester Brown and the Worldwatch Institute point out that industrial countries have declined in their work output the world over as a result of diminishing natural resources over the past few decades. For example in the United States alone, our GNP has effectively declined since 1979 when it reached its peak. So too has the health of our soil, water, forests, and therefore food and bodies. In other countries the reality is even more stark. In the Philippines, for example, and Ethiopia and Peru.

There can be no question that good work presumes good health- not only human health but the health of the environment that gifts the worker with everything from food to clothes, from moments of beauty and grace to hope in bringing new children into the world.

The environmental crisis, then, furnishes us with an opportunity and a responsibility to ask deeper questions of work: to ask how a spirituality of work might assist us in redefining how, why, and for whom, we do our work. It also clearly opens the door for creating new kinds of work that will invent and install sustainable energy and sustainable agriculture and sustainable minds (i.e., education) and spirits (i.e., worship). A time like ours is a time for whole new forms of work to emerge. The decline of the 'defence' industry, understood as war making, can make way for the emergence of a defence industry understood as defending the hopes and spirits of our children, as defending the Earth: tree planting; soil preservation; water purifying; air cleaning; recovery of streams in cities and recycling of wastes as well as the creating of new rituals. All these constitute potentially new " industries", albeit small and people-owned.

The spiritual results of a lack of work are devastating. When people lack work they lack pride; they lack an opportunity to return their unique gifts to the community; they also lack the means to provide the taxes that make services possible in the greater community. Welfare ought never to be a replacement for work. When the despair that unemployment creates sets into a community or neighbourhood, the results can be seen everywhere: the increased crime, drugs, a bloating of the prison population, racism, resentment. As Thomas Aquinas observed, "despair is the most dangerous of all sins," for when despair takes over "all kinds of wickedness follow."

All these considerations point to how the issues raised by the crisis in work around the world today are spiritual issues. They demand a radical critique of the way we have been defining work during the modern era, an era that is rapidly disappearing.

Work versus Job

First, we must speak of the difference between a job and work. A job may be helping at a fast-food place for the minimum wage in order to pay one's bills or make some spending money as a youth; but work is something else. Work comes from inside out; it is the expression of one's soul, one's inner being. Work is unique to the individual. Work is creative. It is an expression of the Spirit acting in the world through us. Work is that which puts us in touch with others- not at a level of personal interaction so much, as at the level of service in the community.

Work is not just about getting paid. Much work in our culture is not paid for at all, for example, raising children, cooking meals at home, organising youth activities, singing in the choir, listening to a neighbour or a friend who has undergone trauma, tending a garden. And yet, in a fuller critique of work, these questions need to be asked: how is it possible that these examples of good work might be rewarded in some way so that they get counted in our understanding of "gross national product"?

In pointing out the distinction between "job" and "work" we don't want to create an irresolvable dualism. Given a deep spirituality even a job may be turned into work. That is a worthy task that a person needs inner work to develop.

Taken from an article that first appeared in Creation Spirituality Magazine, Volume VIII, Number 3, May/June 1992, under the title "Reflections on a Spirituality of Work."

MONEY & WORK BOOKS

The Reinvention of Work
Matthew Fox
ISBN: 0060630620, 1990.

Corporate Renaissance
Rolf Osterberg
ISBN: 1882591127, 1993.

**Do What you Love,
the Money Will Follow**
Marsha Sinetar
ISBN: 0440501601, 1989.

**The End of Work: The Decline of the
Global Labor Force and the Dawn of
the Post-Market Era**
Jeremy Rifkin
ISBN: 0874778247, 1996.

**Beyond Growth : The Economics of
Sustainable Development**
Herman E. Daly
ISBN: 0807047090, 1997.

**The New Economics of Sustainable
Development**
James Robertson
ISBN: 0749430931, 1999.

Transforming Economic Life
James Robertson
ISBN: 1870098722, 1998.

The Case Against the Global Economy
Jerry Mander and Edward
Goldsmith ed.s
ISBN: 0871568659, 1997.

Future Worlds
Norman Myers
ISBN: 1853651230, 1995.

Wealth Beyond Measure
Paul Elkins
ISBN: 1856750507, 1992.

Towards a Sustainable Economy
Ted Trainer
ISBN: 1897766149, 1995.

**Short Circuit -
strengthening local economies for
security in an unstable world**
Richard Douthwaite
ISBN: 1870098641, 1998.

The Growth Illusion
Richard Douthwaite
ISBN: 0946640882

After the Crash
Guy Dauncey
ISBN: 1854250876

Small is Beautiful
E.F. Schumacher
ISBN: 0099225611, 1993.

Factor Four
Amory Lovins
ISBN: 1853834068, 1998.

MONEY & WORK WEB SITES

Feasta
http:www.sustainable.buz.org/feasta
_pages/

Ithaca HOURs
http://www.lightlink.com/hours/ithac
ahours/

The LETSystem Design Manual
http://www.gmlets.u-
net.com/design/home.html

Corporate Watch
http://www.corpwatch.org

Matthew Fox, Creation Spirituality
http://www.creationspirituality.com

SUSTAINABLE ECONOMICS

FEASTA

Contact: Davie Philip at Source
166 Lower Rathmines Rd., Dublin 6
Tel: 01-4911711
Fax: 01-4911710
E-mail: feasta@ anu.ie
Website: www.sustainable.buz.org/feasta_pages/

Feasta exists to challenge the assumption that we can continue with everlasting expansion and growth in a finite world. The foundation seeks to identify what a sustainable economy looks like and how it might operate.

JOSEPH GLYNN

1 Townview, Flower Hill, Navan, Co. Meath
Tel: 046-74278

Land taxation advocate - market research consultant. Writer/researcher on the new economics, green issues, the emerging sustainable markets and ethical land tenure.

ATTAC-IRELAND

Contact: Claudine Gaidoni
47 Ailsbury Grove, Dundrum, Dublin 16
Tel: 01-2984879
Fax: 01-2984815
Email: attac@tinet.ie

We advocate the introduction of a Tobin Tax on currency transactions. Such a tax could minimise currently fluctuating and general revenue to fund development projects, primarily in the Third World.

SCHUMACHER IRELAND INITIATIVE

Contact: Tony Weekes
16 Pakenham St., Belfast, Co. Antrim
Tel: 0044-2890-249112 / 0801-232 244772
E-mail: tony.weekes@cwcom.net

Schumacher Ireland will promote and develop the ideas of Dr EF Schumacher, whose best known work is *Small is Beautiful*.
Our 'flagship' project is to hold Schumacher lectures in 2000.

LETS GROUPS

Cork LETS

Contact: Michael O'Callaghan
3 Beaumont Place, Cork
Tel: 021-295369
Fax: 021-295370
E-mail: woz@indigo.ie

Cork LETS is approaching a membership of 200, ages 7-70. Regulare meetings and very lively social calender. Much sharing of ideas and contacts. No obligation to trade. Tuesday nights -

9.30 Grosvenor Pub (Back room), McCurtain St., Cork City. Strong environmental and ecological slant.

SLIGO LETS

Contact: Gerry McEvoy
Business Centre, Market Yard, Sligo, Co. Sligo
Tel: 071-46069
Fax: 071-41978

Local Enterprise Trading System.
LETS uses a local currency that members use to trade goods and services with each other. We are also involved in an organic community urban farm.

BEARA LOCAL ECONOMY SYSTEM BEARA LETS

Contact: Anne O'Leary
Inches, Eyeries Cross, Castletownbere, Co. Cork
Tel: 027-70163

In Beara we barter Hags named after the Hag of Beara. Friday is LETS stall day in Castletownbere – an opportunity to free up more of your punts and pence.

MEITHEAL BHREANNAIN

Contact: Ruth O Quigley
76 Boherbue, Tralee, Co. Kerry
Tel: 066-7123459
Fax: 066-7123459
E-mail: ptempan@iol.ie

Meitheal Bhreannain is a network of people

exchanging goods and services through the medium of local currency as far as it is practicable.

SHANKHILL SWAPSKILLS

Contact: Benny or Kathy Nugent
13 Cois Sleibhe, Southern Cross, Bray,
Co. Wicklow
Tel: 01-2821432 / 01-2829798

Our directory carries over 100 members, including local businesses. Members trade goods or services using "checkbooks" in our local currency (1 skill equivalent to £1) Membership fee £10 (£5 unwaged)

NORTHSIDE EXCHANGE & TRADING SYSTEM

Contact: Bernie Kirrane and Seamus Reid
c/o FOCUS, 15 Sedan Ave., Omagh, Co. Tyrone
Tel: 0801-662 246252 / 0801-662 250365
Fax: 0801-662 242990
Email: bkirrane@talk21.com
Website: www.netsystems.net/omagh2directory/

The Northside Exchange & Trading System offers goods and services without cash to members in and around the Mullaghmore/Castleview area in Omagh. Local currency = spires
Local contacts = Bernie Kirrane (co-ordinator)

MEITHEAL NA MART

Contact: Mieke and Stephan Wik and Dr. Lucille O Shea Ryan
c/o ANU Internet Services, James Street, Wesport, Co. Mayo
Tel: 098-28423 / 098-27730
Fax: 098-28593
E-mail: mieke@anu.ie or lryan@imsgrp.com

Started in Febuary 1993 and founded by Richard Douthwaite and others. At its peak in 1997 it comprised of over 200 traders. A directory of traders is available at the above address. The currency is called 'REEK'. Currently Meitheal na Mart is being reorganised with over 100 traders.

BANTRY LETS

Contact: Fred La Haye or Andrew Kenward
Maugha, Kealkill, Bantry, West Cork
Tel: 027-52136 / 027-51333

Bantry Area Trading System. Unit of currency: BATS.

CREDIT UNIONS

BALLYPHEHANE CREDIT UNION

Contact: George Cantwell
Lower Friars Walk, Cork
Tel: 021-965134
Fax: 021-313350
E-mail: ballyphehanecu.ie

Website: www.ballyphehanecu.ie
With a membership in excess of 15,000 Ballyphehane Credit Union is totally member-focused and pride ourselves on the quality of service provided to members.
Open 6 days a week.

ST CANICE'S KILKENNY CREDIT UNION LTD.

Contact: Clare Lawton
78 High, St. Kilkenny
Tel: 056-22042
Fax: 056-64811

Ireland's largest community based credit union serving the needs of 28,000 members in the Kilkenny area.

CASHEL CREDIT UNION LTD.

Canopy St., Cashel, Tipperary
Tel: 062-61699
E-mail: cashelcreditunion@eircom.net

Member-owned, not-for-profit co-operative enabling persons to attain their financial objectives fairly and with dignity. Services include savings, loans, insurances, foreign exchange, drafts, bill payment, advice.

CASTLEBAR CREDIT UNION.

Castlebar, Co.Mayo
Contact: P. Walsh
Tel: 094 - 22969

ETHICAL INVESTMENT

THE ETHICAL INVESTMENT CO-OPERATIVE

Contact: Guy Hooker
119 Bruntsfield Place, Edinburgh,
Scotland EH10 4EQ
Tel: 0044-131-466 4665
Fax: 0044-131-466 4667
E-mail: ethicalmaoney@gn.apc.org
Website: www.gn.apc.org/eic

The Ethical Investment Co-Operative is a firm of independent financial advisers dedicated solely to socially responsible investment. It transacts ethical investment business across the EU, and its directors have collectively over 30 years experience in Ethical Investment.

AEGIS

Action for Ethics in Getting, Investing and Spending.
Contact: Tony Weekes
16 Pakenham St., Belfast BT7 1AB
Tel: 0801 232444772 / 0044 02890244772
E-mail: tony.weekes @cwcom.net

To encourage an ethical stance in getting, spending and saving.

CO-OPERATIVES

ECO CO-OP

Contact: Alistair Mullan
Flat 3 ,144 Antrim Road, Belfast,
Co.Antrim BT15 2AH

Tel: 0801-232 740120
E-mail: ecocoop@hotmail.com

Eco Co-op is a new initiative to support and promote grassroots sustainable worker co-ops in Ireland. A fair and co-operative society is what we are aiming towards which is both environmentally and socially sustainable. In our pursuit of this we hope to establish a secondary co-op which will be a network of co-ops aimed at supporting each other through the sharing of skills, resources and finances. Through talks and workshops we aim to (i) promote principles and values of co-operation, and, (ii) help encourage people setting up their own worker and housing co-ops.

ECOLOGICAL TRADES COMMUNITY

Contact: Joe Gowran and Mark Wilson
Drumcliff, South Sligo

Tel: 061-927456
Fax: 071-45504
E-mail: joegowran@ireland.com

Shows emphasizing practical demonstration and solidarity.
Organising the gathering of ecological traders service providers with a view to public education,

cross fertilization of ideas and capacity building in the "environmental sector" of the economy to strengthen the isolated, marginal and obscure trades and crafts by increasing confidence through socialisation and the "strategic skills" notion.

ECOSEEDS

Contact: Jackie Morgan
1 Barview Cottages, Strangford,
Co.Down BT30 7NN

Tel: 0801-396 881227

Workers Co-op growing native wildflowers in organic peat-free media. EcoSeeds is a non-profit making co-op dedicated to promoting biodiversity, and sustainable and/or ethical co-ops.

CO-OPERATIVE DEVELOPMENT SOCIETY

Contact: Dermot McKenna S.J.
Dominick Court, 41 Dominick St. Lower., Dublin 1

Tel: 01-8733199 and 01-8386788
Fax: 01-8733612
email: coopsoc@tinet.ie

The Co-operative Development Society has over forty years experience in promoting the co-operative system. In Ireland in particular, it helps co-ops to register with the Registrar of Friendly Societies.

L'ARCHE KILKENNY

Contact: Mairead Boland-Brabazon
Fairgreen Lane, Callan, Co.Kilkenny

Tel: 056-25628
Fax: 056-25946
E-mail: larche@iol.ie
Website: http://www.weberin.com/larche

L'Arche Communities are places where people with a mental handicap and those society calls normal, live and work together. Their small-scale produce includes weaving, candle-making, card-making and organic vegetables.

TELEWORKING

TELEWORK IRELAND

Contact: Riona Carroll
Website: www.telework.ie

Telework Ireland is the professional association of teleworkers in Ireland. TWI provides an advisory and information service to teleworkers, employers and management. It can recommend a panel of members trading specifically on the implementation of telework projects and is currently developing an internet delivered training course with the support of the EU Adapt Programme.

SEE ALSO '

BEALTAINE LTD. Full listing: Energy and Transport

page 166 **Introduction** and articles Ben Whelan

page 167 **Ecotourism**

page 167 **Art and Sustainability**

page 168 **Festivals**

ARTS AND LEISURE Ben Whelan

Ben Whelan studied Theology in Trinity College Dublin. He completed his MA at The University of Creation Spirituality in Oakland studying Sustainability, Economics, Cosmology, and Indigenous Wisdom under Stuart Cowan and Matthew Fox. He is assistant editor for the Sustainable Ireland Source Book. Contact: see Janus listing.

In general we enjoy more leisure time today than we did in the past. The future holds even more promise for extending the time we can spend creatively. With excellent resource-saving technology and ideas such as alternative energy and permaculture becoming available, we can look to a future where intelligent design can free up much of the time previously spent on making a living. This means that in the long run there is practically no good reason why we should spend most of our time making money. We would expect, then, that people would feel more creatively fulfilled. Unfortunately, as with most things, leisure has become just another commodity.

Through mismanagement of the Earth's resources we have lost sight of the abundance we could be enjoying. Tribal peoples generally "work" (meaning the gathering of food) for four hours a day and spend the rest of their time partaking in creative activities that also serve a useful purpose. Activities such as crafting, and building have obvious benefits for community life but so does dancing, singing, and story telling as these activities help keep the cultural fabric and identity of the people alive.

By removing ourselves from the creative we objectify art placing it the hands of those few who call themselves artists. We buy reproduction prints and support heavily sponsored performances and productions while spending practically no time with our own creative urges. We spend our time in front of the television watching others be creative as if it were someone else's job. This attitude is so prevalent in the Western world that there is a tendency to think of leisure time as do-nothing time. In fact it is just the opposite.

The word recreation or re-creation would seem to hark back to a time when leisure activities were largely creative. A time when mental ability and craftsmanship were given equal respect and, to an extent, were seen to be the same thing. Re-creation should be a call to all of us to use our leisure time more creatively. If we did we would be less inclined to make the arbitrary distinction between what constitutes work and what constitutes leisure.

> **When everything we create is far in spirit from the festive, in the midst of our turbulent days let us think of what festivals were.** Rilke

> **A male lion living for seven years [in Kenya] is estimated to be worth $515,000 to tourism, versus $1,000 for its skin.** Kenny Ausubel

Ecotourism

We now realise that tourism in its present, most common, form actively destroys local ecosystems. By transforming landscapes into tower blocks, swimming pools and highways we end up ruining the very features that we originally came to admire. For the tourist industry to come full circle and actually help in sustaining ecosystems it must begin to follow the principles of ecotourism.

Ecotourism is an initiative designed to help the tourist industry become more sustainable while in turn helping local populations economically. This gives people the motivation to preserve, for instance, a forest which would formerly be sold for timber. From here we can see the possibility of preserving not just the landscape but the culture, rituals and way of life of many vulnerable people. Any ecotourist venture must aim to preserve and maintain the local area from which it seeks to profit. The notion of profit can then take on a new definition, beginning to refer to the health and quality of cultural life and the local environment.

Ecotourism is something the Western world can give back after the wholesale destruction of culture and environment performed in the name of a market driven economy. It is a step on the path to giving people back the ability to see the wealth inherent in their own locality and culture. It also has the added benefit of curtailing the tidal wave of people vacating rural areas to form shanty towns at the edges of huge cities.

Ecotourism is not limited to exotic species and rainforests although it is in these areas that the most work needs to be done. In Ireland, although having been fortunate not to have had a very destructive industrial revolution, we now have many vulnerable ecosystems. Continuing the trend of building golf courses and large multifunction hotels will only result in more damage.

Of course the whole of the tourist industry has to be seen in relation to the transport industry. How you get there, from where and how often may lead to an unsustainable situation.

Art and Sustainability

The urge to become sustainable is related to the experience of the earth, cosmos and life itself as an inter-related system. Without the recognition of our planet as a living organism it is difficult to imagine how we can really respect her to the extent that we would alter our activities to benefit her

arts + leisure

processes. It would seem that the call for a more sustainable planet is a result of an intensely spiritual urge.

If arts and leisure are to become instruments of sustainability it is important for us to recognise the spirituality in creativity. There is a transcendent aspect to art in whatever form it takes. In Mexico the Huichol Indians say that art and spirituality are the same thing meaning that the creative act is a spiritual act. The artistic process is one of delving deep into one's own personal psyche and in so doing bringing back something of universal importance. Art can become a tool to access the layers of experience that allow us to once again join the larger Earth community.

The role of the arts in community building is an essential one. Many successful community arts centre projects have increased the quality of life for numerous people; inspiring local enterprises and renewing confidence in the individual's creative ability. The centres act as meeting places in a time where very little consideration is given to community gathering. These centres fill the need for sharing our gifts and our stories. The importance of this cannot be overestimated. From a postmodern perspective it is the multidimensional nature of our collective experience that is pre-eminent and so it is our collective stories that form the ground of human wisdom.

Festivals

In the past festivals were created by the participants who were, by and large, a local community. People came together to ritualise important events in community life and to share in the common bonds that hold community together. The festivals were seen not as a leisure activity that one had to make time for. In fact, they marked the passing of time itself.

Today we spend money to watch others perform and by doing so we remove ourselves from the position of responsible participant. In most large festivals the indications of detachment are clear. There is little knowledge of, or respect for, the land; litter is ubiquitous, and the atmosphere often contains hints of distrust and aggression.

In creating a participatory festival much of this negative energy is avoided. Everybody can feel instrumental in the experience. A shared sense of responsibility is developed, and a new found enjoyment of the diverse range of talents and skills each of us can bring to the event is developed. Connections can be made that would otherwise be missed in our usual day-to-day existence.

Participatory festivals should mark an auspicious time. Our ancestors and many tribal peoples today created ritual events that recognised the important times in both the sun and moon cycles. By reconnecting with the larger cycles that are defined by these planetary bodies we may enter into cosmic time which, in its universal nature, is qualitatively different from human time.

In America in recent years, increasing numbers of people involved in the dance/ rave scene have become aware of the close links between a tribal community gathering and the ecstatic experience of the rave. Groups such as The Moon Tribe and Burning Man in California have realised the power inherent in an event that can bring us out of our closeted mundane existence and launch us into an experience which celebrates the deep connection we have with each other and with the rest of the cosmos.

On this side of the globe, it is the politicisation of the festival scene that is most apparent. Since the birth of the "Reclaim the Streets" movement parties and festivals have been used as a method to educate and inform people on community issues and politics. With the introduction of the criminal justice act more and more people within dance culture have become involved with politics and how it affects people's freedom to choose their own way of life. The distinction between activist and raver has become blurred to the extent that many dance festivals now feature stalls, speakers and installations which aim to promote sustainability and social justice.

If you love nature with all your heart new and unimaginable things in art will occur to you. Because art is nothing more than the transfiguration of nature. Alex Beckman

arts + leisure

ARTS AND LEISURE BOOKS

Drawing on the Right Side of the Brain
Betty Edwards
ISBN: 0006381146, 1993.

Feast of Fools
Harvey Cox
ISBN: 0674295250, 1970.

Green Woodworking
Mike Abbott
ISBN: 0937274828, 1994.

Imagine Inventing Yellow
M.C. Richards
ISBN: 0882681273, 1992.

Jambalaya
Luisah Teish
ISBN: 0062508598, 1991.

Microphone Fiends
Tricia Rose and Andrew Ross
ISBN: 0415909082, 1994.

Senseless Acts of Beauty
George Mckay
ISBN: 1859840280, 1996.

The Artist's Way
Julie Cameron
ISBN: 0330343580, 1995.

The Healing Wisdom of Africa: Finding Life Purpose Through Nature, Ritual, and Community
Malidoma Patrice Some
ISBN: 087477991X, 1999.

The Re-enchantment of Art
Suzi Gablick
ISBN: 0500276897, 1994.

The Temporary Autonomous Zone
Hakim Bey
ISBN: 0936756764, 1991.

The Tribal Living Book
David Levinson and David Sherwood
ISBN: 1555661041, 1993.

The Earthscan Reader in Sustainable Tourism
Lesley France
ISBN: 1853834084, 1997.

Ecotourism: an Introduction
David Fennell
ISBN: 0415142377, 1999.

Tourism, Ecotourism and Protected Areas
Hector Ceballos-Lascurain
ISBN: 2831701244. 1996.

ARTS AND LEISURE WEB SITES

Ecotourism International:
http://www.kcv.com/kcv/eti/
Ecotourism Explorer:
http://www.ecotourism.org/

Reclaim the Streets:
http://www.gn.apc.org/rts/

EnviroArts: Orion Online;
http://www.envirolink.org/enviroarts/

arts + leisure

ECO-TOURISM

BALLYMALOE HOUSE

Contact: Natasha Harty
Shanagarry, Co. Cork

Tel: 021-652531
Fax: 021-652021
E-mail: bmaloe@iol.ie
Website: www.ballymaloe.com

Ballymaloe House is a 30 bedroom guest house with a 100 seated restaurant. Ballymaloe has a wetland for treating wastewater, waste separation and will be installing a wormery for composting organic wastes. An EPA guide for guesthouses is being prepared based on their experience.

BAVARIA HOUSE B&B

Contact: Ilse & Rolf Kiebler
Ballinagh, Co. Cavan

Tel: 049-4337452
Fax: 049-4337452

The eco-friendly home for your holiday, relax in our colourful gardens. Superb home-made food served with own organically grown herbs, vegetables and fruit. Herbal advice, English & German spoken.

BUNNATON HOUSE

Contact: Anne Hewett
Bunnaton, Glenvar, Letterkenny, Co. Donegal

Tel: 074-50122
E-mail: bunnaton@tinet.ie
Website: http://homepage.tinet.ie/~chrishewett

Situated on the outstandingly beautiful Tanad peninsula. Bunnaton House offers the budget conscious tourist quality accommodation at an affordable price. Nearby activities – sailing, fishing, horseback riding, hill walking, golf, pubs and restaurants.

BURREN WALKING HOLIDAYS

Contact: Mary Howard
Carrigann Hotel, Lisdoonvarna, Co. Clare

Tel: 065-7074036
Fax: 065-7074567
E-mail: carrigannhotel@tinet.ie

Burren Walking Holidays is a comprehensive walking programme based at the Carrigaan Hotel. Annual Spring/Autumn guided walking weekends. Self-guided walks from March-October inclusive with detailed maps and notes.

CONNEMARA SAFARI

Contact: Brian Hughes
Abbeyglen Hotel, Sky Road
Clifden, Co. Galway

Tel: 1850-777200
Fax: 095-21797

Email: info@abbeyglen.ie
Website: www.abbeyglen.ie

Unique island hopping holiday off the coast of Connemara, including low-level walks of Killarney Harbour, Inisbofin, Clare Island and the more remote Inishtwir, an experience combining history, archaeology and fun.

CELTIC SPIRIT-CULTURE WEEKS

Contact: Elizabeth Zollinger
Inis Mor, Aran Islands, Co. Galway

Tel: 099-61424 / 0041-1-2520918 (Switzerland)
Fax: 099-61424 / 0041-1-2520918 (Switzerland)

The programme focuses on song and dance, storytelling, nature walks, ardia ecology and Celtic heritage and is mostly guided by the Island itself. We offer a fascinating introduction to the unique tradition of the island.

CROOKSTOWN MILL

Contact: Jim Maher
Crookstown Mill, Ballytore, Athy, Co. Kildare

Tel: 0507-23222
Fax: 0507-23222

Restored cornmill, gift shop, tea room, fairs and exhibitions, Custom built furniture and workshops. Deli foods, pre-fabricated cabins/desogm.

CUSSENS COTTAGE

Contact: Stephen / Ita
West Ballygrennan, Bulgaden
Kilmallock, Co. Limerick

Tel: 063-98926
Fax: same
Email: cussenscottage@tinet.ie
Website: http://homepage.tinet/~cussenscottage

Ireland's only vegan guesthouse. Organic gardening in the lush golden vale. 'Upmarket' describes our facilities. Irish vegan cooking that your meat-eating Granny would enjoy. Telephone for brochure/travelogue/sample menu.

Eco Cottage (Tourism Development) Project

Contact: Terry Cunningham,
Rural Enterprise Adviser, Teagasc
Carrigeen, Clonmel, Co. Tipperary

Tel: 052-21300
Fax: 052-21199
E-mail:c.kenny@tipperarysr.teagasc.ie
Website: www.ecobooley.com

Research eco-friendly technologies that can be used to restore remote rural houses for the eco-tourism market including the restoration of one cottage in South Tipperary. For information, write, fax or check website. To rent see Eamonn Looby (Eco-Booley)

ECO COTTAGE (ECO BOOLEY)

Contact: Eamonn Looby
Ronga, Clogheen, Co. Tipperary
Tel: 052-65191
Email: advisory@clonmel.teagasc.ie
Website: www.ecobooley.com

Eco-cottage self-catering unit at foothills of Knockmealdown mountains direct access to Munster Way. Ireland's first eco-booley, all systems and materials are natural water turbine, wood stove, reed bed etc.

GREEN LODGE

Contact: Chris Domegan
Trawnamadree, Ballylickey, Bantry, Co. Cork
Tel: 027-66146
E-mail:greenlodge@bigfoot.com
Website: http://www.angelfire.com/biz/stayvegetarian

Apartments for the vegetarian traveller. Private entrance. Bathroom and cooking facilities. Peaceful wooded surroundings in the heart of West Cork. Reasonable rates. Organic vegetables. Wholefoods and home baked bread available.

GORTRUA ORGANIC FARM

Contact: Michael Hickey & Ute Brinker
New Inn, Tipperary
Tel: 062-72223

We offer a self-contained chalet (double bedroom, kitchen, sitting rooms, bathroom). Gortrua is a 100 acre organic farm on the banks of the river Suir producing high quality organic meat.

HARBOUR VIEW HOSTEL

Contact: Jim Fitzgerald
Route N70, Kenmare Road
Sneem, Co. Kerry
Tel: 064-45105 / 064-45276
Fax: 064-45105

The Hostel is situated at The Ring of Kerry on the famous Kerry walk. Dorms and private rooms near Sneem, guided tours locally. Bike hire. Private parking. Superb views and good value accommodation. Licenced bar and restaurant. Courtesy minibus available.

HENEGHANS GUEST HOUSE

Contact: Bridget Horkan
Newtown St., Castlebar, Co. Mayo
Tel: 094-21883
Fax: 094-26476
Email: heneghans@tinet.ie
Website: www.castlebar.mayo ireland.ie/heneghan.htm

Old world holistic guesthouse. Relax by the fire in our sitting room or in our library and garden. Extensive breakfast menu using local produce and home grown herbs. We cater for vegetarians and vegans. All rooms with T.V and telephone en-suite.

KILLARY LODGE

Contact: Mary Young / Kathy Evans
Leenane, Co. Galway
Tel: 095-42276
Fax: 095-42314
Email: lodge@killary.com
Website: www.killary.com

Killary Lodge has a stunning location, set in the wilds of Connemara. Freshly produced vegetarian meals, bread, cakes etc. Relax in solitude and nature.

INTO THE WILDERNESS WALKING TOURS

Contact: Johnny Walsh
Climbers Inn, Glencarr, Killarney, Co Kerry, Ireland
Tel: 00353-66-9760101
Fax: 00353-66-9760104
Email: climbers@iol.ie
Website: www.climbersinn.com

Into the wilderness walking tours provide daily walking tours in the Killarney National Park and the highlands of Ireland, tours to Ireland's highest mountain. Individuals, family and groups welcome. Experienced local guide will lead you on an exciting day out exploring the highlands of Kerry and lakes.

MALIN HEAD HOSTEL

Contact: Mary Reynolds
Malin Head, Inishowen, Co. Donegal
Tel: 077-70309

Malin Head Hostel provides clean, comfortable accommodation. It is situated in a sheltered organic garden (produce available to guests) with views of the Atlantic. Mary provides weekend activity breaks in reflexology/aromatherapy.

MOUNTAINEERING COUNCIL OF IRELAND

Contact: Milo Kane
133 Bettyglen, Dublin 5
Tel: 01-8319548
Fax: 01-6707330
Email: dkane@iol.ie
Website: http://www.mountaineering.ie/

As part of our services to members and clubs we preserve access rights and traditional open character of the uplands, monitoring planning applications in upland areas and promoting sustainable tourism and recreational practises. We operate with local community and environment groups in Wicklow and the Mournes and are affiliated to Keep Ireland Open.

ORGANIC FARMING / ECO-CAMPING / APARTMENTS

Contact: Ineke and Theo Peterse
Coomleagh-West, Bantry, Co.Cork

Tel: 027-66171

We wish to stimulate small-scale sensible tourism in the countryside as a green organic environmentally friendly alternative for mass tourism. We have small-scale eco-camping and apartments.

PINK HOUSE

Contact: Corry O Reilly
Brackloon, Westport, Co. Mayo

Tel: (w) 098-28151 / (h) 098-27462
Fax: 098-27462

Stay in a spacious award winning, designed house in a woodland setting situated in the foothills of Croagh Patrick. Perfect hillwalking terrain. Healthy homecooked vegetarian food served. Organic / free range when available.

SUNYATA HOLIDAY & RETREAT CENTRE & HERBAL CLINIC

Contact: Clare & Stanley DeFreitas
Snata, Sixmilebridge, Co. Clare

Tel: 061-367073
E-mail: sunyata_ireland@hotmail.com

The centre provides peaceful space for retreats, workshops and self-catering holiday. Meditation retreats and herbal medicine workshops organised periodically, also herbal clinic run by fully qualified medical herbalist.

TIPPERARY LITTER AND TOURISM INITIATIVE

Contact: Elisha McGrane
TRBDI, Thurles, Co.Tipperary

Tel: 0504-28101
E-mail: emcgranetrbdi@tinet.ie

This project aims to improve tourism and the environment in a number of pilot communities in Tipperary through education, awareness and innovation action-based projects. The project partners are Tipperary (North Riding) County Council, Tipperary (South Riding) County Council, Tipperary Leader Group, An Taisce, Tipperary Rural and Business Development Institute, Tipperary North and South Riding Tourism Forums and The Tipperary Energy Agency. The project is part funded by the Department of Tourism, Sport and Recreation.

TIR NA NOG HOLISTIC CENTRE AND HOSTEL

Contact: Peggy Quirke
Ballyea, Cahir, Co. Tipperary

Tel: 086-8475891 / 052-41962
Fax: 052-41962

Website: http://www.holistic.ie/tirnanog

Dormitory style accommodation, excellent standard, 12 beds. Self-catering or fully catered. Wheelchair friendly. Suitable for families, groups, workshops, individuals.

THE DOWNHILL HOSTEL

Contact: William Gilfillan
12 Mussenden Road
Downhill, Coleraine, Derry

Tel: 0801265-849077
Email: downhillhostel@hotmail.com
Website: http://www.angelfire.com/wa/downhillhostel

Relaxed atmosphere makes this owner-operated hostel an ideal base to enjoy the north coast. Activities include forest / beach walks, bird watching and horseback riding, dorm style and private rooms.

THE COTTAGE

Contact: Roef Fendles
Kilcorney Road, Lissylisheen, Kilfenora, Co. Clare

Tel: 086-8015566

The Cottage is a cosy non-smoking 'low budget' accommodation in the Burren. A lonely place, quiet and relaxing. 4 bunk beds, 2 beds, open all year, open fire in the common room, self-catering facilities, breakfast.

THE PHOENIX

Contact: Lorna & Bill Tyther
Dingle Peninsula, Shanahill East, Boolteens, Castlemaine, Co. Kerry

Tel: 066-9766284
Fax: 066-9766284

Located between Killarney, Dingle, Tralee, close to beaches and mountains. Uniquely restored swimhouse, accommodation with self-catering possibilities. Our restaurant services exotic vegetarian / vegan cuisine. Beautiful gardens, water features pets. A relaxed family run business. Kerry airport nearby.

TRADITIONAL FARM HOSTEL

Contact: Marty Phelan
Farren House, Ballacolla, Portlaois, Co. Laois

Tel: 0502-34032
Fax:0502-34008

Traditional Farm Hostel on a working farm, 35 beds in 10 bedrooms, all en suite, good location to visit most of Ireland or for breaks. Family rooms. Large kitchen and dining room, open fire, relaxed accomodation.

TRISKEL FLOWER FARM

Contact: Margaret Hedge & Joseph Hedge
Cloonagh, Beltra, Co. Sligo

Tel: 071-66714
Fax: 071-66967
E-mail: tourist_hostel@yahoo.com
Website: www.goireland.com
(Click Sligo then horses to find Triskel)

Education - alternative holistic programmes for learning disabilities children and animals (horses). IHO hostel and camping in Ox Mts. on Sligo Way, hill walk. Organic gardens above heritage woodlands. Traditional music / dance sessions. Connemara ponies, £7 & £10 per person. Log fires, women's history.

CRAFTS

ALAN JOHNSTON TRADITIONAL TOOLS

Contact: Alan Johnston
Beagh, Gort, Co. Galway

Tel: 091-631035

Chillington Hoes: The ergonomic alternative to spade and fork. Range of six hoes for heavy to light work. Also versative IBIS hand cultivator, slashers, sickles and blades. SAE for details.

DINGLE CRAFT VILLAGE

Contact: Una Ni She
Ceardlann na Coille, Dingle, Kerry

Tel: 066-9151008

Warm tactile wool, felt rugs and wall hangings. Simple clear designs including bronze-age motifs. Natural colours of rare breed sheep. Oldest manual technique of working wool. Easy to care for.

HANDS ON FURNITURE LTD.

Contact: Hans Leptien
Unit 34, Tramore Road Commercial Park, Tramore Road, Cork

Tel: 021-312695
Fax: 021-312695

Design & Manufacture Furniture.
We design and manufacture commissioned furniture with an emphasis on clean lines and a contemporary appeal for the corporate and domestic markets using only temperate and if possible Irish-grown hardwoods.

INSPIORAID.

Contact: Eimear Hawes
Coad, Kilnaboy, Ennis, Co. Clare

Tel: 065-6837011

Producing ranges of original wood shelves, mirrors, candle holders, bathroom accessories etc. Each piece hand-crafted with a subtle Celtic influence, colour washed and lacquered, catalogue available on request.

LEADLINES STAINED GLASS

Contact: Celia Daly / Hugh Quillinan
Shandon Craft Centre, Cork

Tel: 021-211877 / 021-210767
Fax: 021-210767

Design, manufacture and installation of stained glass for the following markets; domestic, ecclesiastical, commercial, public works. Once-off figurative hand-painted kiln-fired designs a speciality. Renovation works undertaken.

MAD JABOOBA STUFF

Contact: Joanne Faulkner
42 Lower Clanbrassil St., Dublin

Tel: 01-4738017

Joanne Faulkner as "Mad Jabooba Stuff" teaches recycling and environmental issues through paper making. Makes handmade paper lamps and wall hangings available by mail order. Crafts, specialist books handmade to commission.

MILMORANE BASKETRY

Contact: Hans Matthes
Milmorane, Macroom, Co. Cork.

Tel: 026-47230

At Milmorane Basketry we use several different colours and shades of willow to make attractive and strong baskets. The willow is harvested every winter. Our range includes log baskets, linen baskets, cradles, shopping baskets etc. We also make baskets to order.

PAPER MACHE CRAFT

Contact: Krystyna Pomeroy
Kiltrellig, Kilbaha, Kilrush, Co. Clare

Tel: 065-9058364

One-woman studio in West Clare working in paper mache and paper; low-tech, processes using reclaimed materials whenever possible. Cards, bowles, bird sculptures, shop and exhibition displays.

THE CRAFT GRANARY

Contact: Ann Ryan
c/o Southeast Regional Craft Centre
Church Street, Cahir, Co. Tipperary

Tel: 00353-52-41473
Fax: 00353-52-41415

The Craft Granary, based in a refurbished mill, houses a craft retail area, an exhibition gallery and a coffee shop/restaurant. A yearly programme of exhibitions and workshops promoting craft development is co-ordinated from the granary.

ESB Lough Ree

Environmental Summer School and Arts Festival

Come experience the delights of Lough Ree and the surrounding countryside in the company of Ireland's finest environmentalists including Dick Warner, Eanna Ní Lamhna, Richard Collins, John Feehan, Harman Murtagh and Catherine Hannon.

We offer a varied programme of events - field trips on land and water, evening entertainment, an arts festival, lake cruises and walking tours. We also offer tailor made weekends for groups of 10 or more.

WE ARE NOW TAKING BOOKINGS FOR THE SUMMER SCHOOL AND ARTS FESTIVAL 2000 — 9TH - 16TH JULY

We also offer a programme of specialist weekends through out the year such as our Bird Watching Winter School, Tree & Flower Identification Heritage Weekend, Environmental Photography and many more....

Contact **Karen Nolan at 043 27070 for full details on our programme of events for 2000.**

THE IRISH BASKETMAKERS ASSOCIATION

Contact: Martin O'Flynn and Yvonne O'Flynn
Maughanasilly, Kealkil, Bantry, Co. Cork

Tel: 027-66111

The Irish Basketmakers Association is an association of professional and amateur basketmakers and allied crafts people devoted to supporting this traditional craft, running workshops and supporting this truly sustainable craft.

ARTS

ACTIVE ART CREATIONS

Contact: Simon Cocking
42 Lower Clanbrassil Street, Dublin 8

Tel: 01-4738017
Fax: 01-4547026
E-mail: simoncocking@hotmail.com

Mosaics made from recycled and found materials, and workshops given in how to source, design and install weather proof mosaics. Also community art workshops, murals, collages, playground designs and games with a frisbee.

ARTISTS ASSOCIATION OF IRELAND

Contact: Stella Coffey
43 Temple Bar, Dublin 2

Tel: 01-8740529
Fax: 01-6771585

E-mail: artists.ireland@indigo.ie

Resource organisation for professional visual artists. Published art bulletin, bi-monthly: A comprehensive magazine of visual arts. Activity throughout Ireland.

BIG GREEN ART

Contact: Brendan Farren
Mulnamina, Glenties, Co.Donegal

Tel: 075-44027
Email: brendanrua@hotmail.com

Big Sculptures, murals, signs, designs: Eco-house / space design and build: environmental / social / self-consciousness through public art: recycled / sustainable materials.

CALYPSO PRODUCTIONS

Contact: Maria Fleming
7 South Great Georges Street, Dublin 2

Tel: 01 6704539
Fax: 01 6704275
Email: calypso@tinet.ie
Website: http://homepage.tinet.ie/~calypso

Calypso Productions was established in 1993 to make a positive social and theatrical contribution by creatively tackling issues that effect our lives. They commission and produce high profile, innovative and relevant theatre work, accompanied by outreach programmes.

CREATIVE ACTIVITY FOR EVERYONE (CAFE)

Contact: Wes Wilkie
143 Townsend Street, Dublin 2
Tel: 01-6770330
Fax: 01-6713268
E-mail: cafÈ@connect.ie

Creative Activity for Everyone (Cafe) is an all-island network that engages in and promotes creative activities. We provide a voice for cultural change and promote equality through creative action.

DANCING THE RAINBOW

Contact: Anne O'Hanlon
Logatrina, Dunlavin, Co. Wicklow
Tel: 045-401641 / 01-4975921

Dancing The Rainbow. In a fragant, sensual environment, combining dance, yoga, colour-therapy, voice and music, we move through the Seven colours and Seven different atmospheres of the chakras. We work from the still point.

FELIX ECO ART

Contact: Felix Ford
Clarepatrick, Woodside Road,
Sandyford, Dublin 18
Tel: 01-2866609 / 01-2953152
Fax: 01-2866610

For exhibition work, design ideas, colourful, inventive kids parties, serious political artwork, pro-active photography and the passionate, visual response to earth - I am available and ready! Creativity knows no limits.

HYPERBOREA

Contact: Ben Whelan
Booterstown House, Booterstown Ave., Co. Dublin
Tel: 01-2884533
E-mail: hyperboreaevents@esatclear.ie
Website: www.esatclear.ie/~janus/hyperborea

An education and arts collective creating participant orientated festivals and multimedia events. We aim to increase awareness in the areas of spirituality and sustainability and to aid in community building.

NATURE ART WORKSHOP CENTRE

Contact: Thomas & Annette
Ballybane, Ballydehob, Co. Cork
Tel: 028-37323
Fax: 028-37323
Website: www.holistic.ie/nature-art

Self-catering accommodation and camping in remote and natural surroundings. Workshops: African drumming, healing, shamanic journey, painting, dance. Drums and percussion: sales, repair and mail order. Spiritual healing sessions.

Celtic monument tours.

RATH-ART

Contact: Nikki Pod
Rathurles, Nenagh, Co. Tipperary
Tel: 01-6731971
E-mail: coral@iol.ie

Rath-Art is a family run business hand-crafting slate mirrors and ethereal glass candle holders. All our products are intrinsically designed to a very high standard to enrich your home and environment.

SPACE KRAFT

Contact: Mick Curtin & Grainne Mc Entee
1 Hamilton Street, S.C.R., Dublin 8
Tel: 01-4736116 or 086-8231179
Email: spacekraftartlab@hotmail.com

We are a collective of artists, craftspeople and woodworkers who build subterranean earth dwellings, showing how simple structures like these forge links between craft and performance, whilst promoting the use of eco-friendly 'pits' at large events and festivals.

CLOTHING

NATURAL INSTINCTS-ORGANIC CLOTHING

Contact: Jimmy Doogan
Clogher, Carrick, Co. Donegal
Tel: 073-38256
Fax: 073-38258
E-mail: doogan@iol.ie

Natural Instincts produce an extensive range of organic clothes produced from certified organic wool and certified organic cotton. Colour is obtained using reactive biodegradable dyes. Range includes ladies and gents knitwear, shirts, blouses, jackets, skirts, pyjamas, bathrobes and much more.

PATAGONIA

Contact: Enid Woolmington
24-26 Exchequer Street, Dublin 2
Tel: 01-6705748 / 6705749
Fax: 01-6705701
Website: www.patagonia.com

Suppliers of fine ethically produced organic and hemp clothing for indoor and outdoor wear.

SUSTAINABLE PARTY HIRE

3BASS SOUNDSYSTEM
Contact: Frank Ryder
Knockdoe, Claregalway, Co. Galway

Tel: 091-797706 or 087-2290270
E-mail: 3bass@oceanfree.net
We provide sound, light and atmosphere to your
requirement. Indoors and outdoors, festivals, fairs,
garden parties. We can also provide DJs and bands
to suit all tastes.

THE CATALYSER COLLECTIVE
Contact: Ollie
Tel: 086 8047894
E-mail: ollie@emcz3.tp
Small, localised self-sustaining, re-empowering
events by 'catalyzer' - kiddies street parties, fairs
and fundraisers. Have marquess, power and rig,
DJ's profections, furo art, stiltmakers, fire-eaters,
conscious food and information stalls.

SEE ALSO

ECO COTTAGE (TOURISM DEVELOPMENT) PROJECT
Research of eco-friendly technologies that can be
used to restore remote rural houses.
Full listing: Green Building and Eco-design section.

GEORGIAN HOUSE AND GARDEN
Restored Georgian town house.
Full listing: Green Building and Eco-design section.

BAYTONRATH ORGANIC FARM
Self-contained accommodation available.
Camping also.
Full listing: Agriculture section.

GORTRUA ORGANIC FARM
A 100 acre organic farm offering a self-contained
chalet.
Full listing: Agriculture section.

BEV AND DEL RICHARDSON
A pagan spiritual centre on 13 acres of semi-wild
meadow available for others to hold camps and
workshops.
Full listing: Health section.

LISTINGS

SUSTAINABLE EARTH FAIR 1999

This book was an idea that developed from the Sustainable Earth Fairs that were initiated by the editors. The first two took place at Maynooth University, and the third at Trinity. They were titled, 'Co-operating for Sustainability', 'Action for Sustainability' and 'Networking for Sustainability.' The third fair was organised with three Trinity College societies, The One World, The Greens and the Environmental societies. This is a report of the event.

A REPORT OF THE THIRD SUSTAINABLE EARTH FAIR,
'Networking for Sustainability.' By Elaine Carey, TCD.

The Third Sustainable Earth Fair was held in Trinity College Dublin on 6th and 7th of March 1999. This was a grassroots convention with the aim of exploring areas of globalisation such as the Multilateral Agreement on Investment, debt, human rights and genetic engineering. The main objective of the fair was to highlight potential sustainable solutions including local economics, organics, permaculture and sustainable communities. Participants came from all over Ireland attended the Fair, offering a wonderful opportunity to share experiences, ideas and to network. The Earth Fair was taken outside Maynooth University for the first time and held in Goldsmith Hall in Trinity College, a venue that proved ideal for the event.

The event was organised by Low Impact in association with The Trinity College One World Society, Greens and Environmental Societies. It was co-ordinated from the VOICE office and around 500 people attended. Over the two days four main presentations were held. On Saturday the two sessions were on global issues and on the Sunday the two sessions were on local issues. Twenty-one workshops were held over the weekend covering a wide range of topics relating to sustainability, and stalls highlighted the activities of groups and businesses working in this field. The Organic Collective from An t-Ionad Glas hosted the workshops and activities for children over the two days.

MAIN PRESENTATIONS KEYNOTE ADDRESS

Victoria Tauli-Corpuz gave the keynote address; she is from the Tebtebba Foundation in the Philippines. Victoria also represents the Third World Network and the Asia Indigenous Women's Network. She introduced Saturday's theme of globalisation in a speech entitled "The Face of Globalisation Today and Challenges for Sustainable Development." Victoria cited some examples of the negative effects of globalisation on developing countries. She highlighted the problems for indigenous peoples in particular, whose livelihoods and environments were endangered by trends towards market orientated cash cropping, and away from protection of biodiversity and sustainable agriculture. Victoria also detailed inequalities between North and South that were inherent in the global financial system. Victoria ended with a call for action, drawing encouragement from the success of the anti-MAI campaign, and advocating further international solidarity and awareness raising.

BIOTECHNOLOGY: CAN IT FEED THE WORLD?

Saturday afternoon's main presentation was a panel discussion on the topic of biotechnology. The four panellists - Victoria Tauli-Corpuz, Caroline Robinson an organic producer, Dr Ruth McGrath from VOICE and Justin Oram from the Famine Centre in UCC - examined some of the major issues involved in biotechnology. Justin Oram addressed the biotechnology industry's claim that genetically engineered food could solve the food shortages around the world. He argued that it was not the lack of availability of food, but the uneven distribution of power and wealth that caused food shortage and famine. He also spoke about the Green Revolution and its contribution to the concentration of land in the hands of bigger farmers and the increased use of artificial soil additives and fertilisers. Ruth McGrath examined the patenting of organisms, particularly under the World Trade Organisation's TRIPS agreement, and how this too allowed big corporations further control over agricultural production. Caroline Robinson demonstrated the benefits of organic farming over intensive monocultural farming, and noted that high input farms were unsustainable and uneconomic, compared to organic farms which had much more regard for the quality of the soil and much less investment in machinery and fertilisers. Victoria Tauli-Corpuz reiterated the statement that it was unequal distribution of food and not the lack of it that caused famines. She gave examples that demonstrated the unpredictability of genetic engineering, and the dangers of over reliance on biotechnology.

THE FEASTA SESSION; COMMUNITY ECONOMICS.

On Sunday morning, Feasta and the Eco-Village Network gave a joint presentation on sustainable communities and local currencies. Ruth Whitfield from the Scottish Organisational Currency System (SOCs) introduced the concept of the 'Barataria' local currency system and its aim to offer an alternative economic system for, in particular, the community, voluntary groups and small businesses. A short exercise in trading was carried out in the hall where participants imagined they had services to sell and traded in the regional currency. This was followed by a presentation and slide show by the Irish Eco-village Information Network.

DEBT ACTION.

A large number of the participants of the Fair assembled outside Goldsmith Hall on Sunday lunchtime and marched into town to join the Human Chain to Break the Chains of Debt that formed around the Central Bank. This event was organised by Trocaire to mark 300 days to the millennium. Participants included those who had taken part in the Creative Campaigning workshops which had focused on preparing for this action. The event was a great success, attracting hundreds of people with street theatre and music, and receiving coverage on national television.

THE FINAL SESSION; "WHERE DO WE GO FROM HERE?"

The final presentation was an open forum that allowed all participants of the fair to raise points. It turned out to be a lively discussion of the issues that had been raised throughout the weekend and the possibilities for action and co-operation. This was facilitated by Feasta's Peter Dorman who encouraged the participants of the event to share their views, hopes and ideas for the future.

More details and photographs are available on the Sustainable Ireland web site.

http://www.sustainableireland.org

Thanks to NCDE, the Dept. of the Environment for their financial support, to Voice for their help, Trinity college for their co-operation and to all the speakers, workshop facilitators, stall holders and participants who made the event the success that it was.

THE FOURTH SUSTAINABLE EARTH FAIR 2000.

A fourth event focusing on sustainability will be held in the spring of 2000.
To find out more about this event call Davie Philip at SOURCE.

arts + leisure

MEDIA/ INFORMATION George Monbiot

Zoologist, anthropologist, author and journalist, George Monbiot is one of the new breed of opinion makers on the environment. His activist guide to exploiting the media can be found at This Land is Ours website: http://oneworld.org/tlio/index.html

Sending Effective Press releases

Journalists speak only one language, and that's their own. If you're going to reach them you have to speak that language too. This means that your press release should mimic the format and style of a news story. It's a simple and straightforward formula and (sorry to be dictatorial) it MUST be applied. If it isn't, your press release won't work. Period.

Here's how to fill it in, section by section:

[1] Your **contact details.** No journalist will run a story without them.

- The name of your organisation/disorganisation (preferably big, bold and across the top of the page)
- One or more contact names
- Contact number(s): where contacts are DEFINITELY going to be for at least the next two days (mobile phone numbers are useful).

[2] An **embargo** means that you are instructing journalists not to publish or broadcast the information in the press release before a certain time. There are several good reasons for an embargo:

- Journalists will know they aren't going to be trumped by anyone else getting in before them.
- It creates a sense of event.
- Timelines concentrate journalists' minds.
- You know when to expect publicity, so you can plan subsequent news management around it.

This is the usual format:

EMBARGO: 00.01am, Friday 15th May

00.01am is a good time, as the papers can then keep up with the broadcasters, and it's less confusing than 00.00.

- DON'T put on an embargo if you've got some immediate news that you want on the radio or TV straight away.
- Generally, you'd embargo a press release giving advance warning of an event (till about 24 hours before the event is due to start), but not a press release which comes out once the event has started.

[3] The **headline** must be short, pithy and to the point. Avoid mystery, elaborate puns or being too clever. The purpose of the headline is to grab the journalists' attention and give them an idea of what the press release is about. If it doesn't do both of these things, they'll read no further and dump it in the bin. It must be NO MORE than eight words long. Use a big, bold font.

Writing headlines isn't easy, and generally takes a good deal of practice. So practise. Look at how they do it in the papers, then try writing headlines for imaginary scenarios, or real ones which aren't going to happen for a while. Remember: in this as in all writing, a straightforward, plain style is best.

[4] The **first paragraph.** This isn't easy either but, like the headline, it's essential to get it right. You've got ONE sentence in which to tell the whole story. If the journalist doesn't get the jist of it, she or he won't read on.

- There is nothing so complicated that its essential point can't be summarised in a simple sentence. So work out what you're trying to say, then boil it down to its essence. As before, look at the news stories in the papers and see how they do it.

[5] The **rest of the text.** Must be no more than two or three paragraphs long, each of which should be no longer than one or two straightforward sentences. They should expand on what you say in the first paragraph. Keep it simple and avoid jargon. Assume that journalists know nothing. If there is other essential information which you can't fit in, put it in the Notes for Journalists section (see below).

- Above all, make sure that the first and second paragraphs have covered all the five Ws: WHO, WHY, WHAT, WHERE and WHEN.

[6] Your **contact details again.** Remember: most journalists have a three second memory, are wilfully blind and very, very stupid, so you have to keep on their case.

[7] **Notes to journalists.** This is optional. Preferably they should be on a separate page. Journalists have got very little time, and the sight of a huge block of text which is hard to digest will put them off. They want to look at the first page and know that the essentials of the story are there. If they want more, they can turn over and read on. Generally, you'd write no more than four or five paragraphs of notes (and certainly no more than a page). This is the place for the complex information which might put journalists off if it's on the front page.

- Number the paragraphs in this section, as it makes it them look easier to digest.

What makes a press release effective

News, of course, is meant to be all about novelty, so emphasise what's new about your action or event.

If you are organising transport to get to your event or action, say so in the press release, pointing out that journalists are welcome to join you on the coach.

When to send press releases

The most critical press release is the one that goes out about two days before the event. Without it, you won't get much coverage, if any at all. But it's a good idea to put one out much earlier than that as well - about ten days prior to the event - so that when the journalists get the second one they should be ready to respond to it. Check copy deadlines for publications that are not daily.

If it's a one-day action or event and your press person has still got the energy and resources, it's no bad thing to send out a further press release saying how it all went. A journalist's interest is pretty unpredictable, and could be stimulated at any time.

If the action or event lasts longer than one day, send out a new press release every day, as long as you've got something to say. Once the event's in the press already, there'll be plenty of opportunities for follow-ups. This is the time when you can sometimes get them to cover the issue you're trying to highlight, rather than simply the event.

Who to send them to

The secret of all successful press releasing is getting them to the right people - so find out who the right people are. Make a list of:

* Media outlets you want to reach

* Individual journalists who seem to be interested in or sympathetic to your cause

NB: You should adapt the tone and contents of your press release to the media you're trying to reach.

How to send press releases

Faxing is still the best way to send them, and a fax modem is invaluable. Some journalists are beginning to emerge from the Neolithic, so they might be contactable by email, but on the whole the communications industry is the last place to use up-to-date communications. Don't use snail mail: it invariably gets lost/disregarded/placed on the bottom of the pile.

media

To get fax numbers, simply phone the papers, TV and radio stations in question and ask for the fax number of the news-desk. If you also want to send your press releases to named journalists at the same organisation, it's best to get their fax numbers off them: reception will often give you the wrong fax number, or one that's been out of date for months. Keep all the fax numbers you get for future reference. Best of all, load them permanently into your computer, so, once you've decided who should get what, your fax modem can contact them automatically.

Following up

One thing of which you can be absolutely certain is that something will get lost in the newsrooms you're targeting: either your press release, the journalist's concentration or the essence of the story. This means you MUST follow it up with a phone call. Just a quick one will do. Ask: Did you get it? Will you be covering the event? Do you need any more information?

They're likely to be rude, gruff and unhelpful. But don't be put off - they're paid to be like that. Make sure you're ready, if need be, to summarise the story in one or two sentences; the first question the journalist will ask is "wot's it all about then?", and her/his attention will wander if you spend more than ten seconds telling them. However rude they are, never fail to be polite and charming: at the very least, you'll put them to shame.

HERE ARE SOME NEWSPAPER, T.V. AND RADIO CONTACT DETAILS TO SEND YOUR PRESS RELEASE TO:

NATIONAL NEWSPAPERS

Belfast Telegraph
Tel: (0801232) 264000
Fax: (0801232) 554506.
Business: Francess Macdonnell
Health: Nigel Gould

Examiner
Tel: 021-272722.
Fax: 021-275477.
Business: Kevin Mills
Environment: Dan Collins
Health: Caroline O'Doherty

Irish Independent
Tel: 01-7055333.
Fax: 01-8731787
Business: Frank Mulrennan
Environment: Treacy Hogan
Health: Eislish O'Regan

Irish Times
Tel: 01-6792022.
Fax: 01-6772130.
Business: Cliff Taylor
Environment: Frank Macdonald
News Editor: Neil Keilly
Regional Development: Tim O'Brien

Ireland on Sunday
Tel: 01-6718255.
Fax: 01-6718882.

Star
Tel: 01-4901228.
Fax: 01-4902193.

Sunday Business Post
Tel: 01-6026000.
Fax: 01-6796496.

Sunday Independent
Tel: 01-7055333.
Fax: 01-7055779.

Sunday Tribune
Tel: 01-6615555.
Fax: 01-6615302.

Sunday World
Tel: 01-4901980.
Fax: 01-4901980.

PROVINCIAL AND SUBURBAN NEWSPAPERS

Anglo-Celt
Tel: 049-31100.
Fax: 049-32280.

Antrim Guardian
Tel: 0801849-462624.
Fax: 0801849-465551.

Armagh Observer
Tel: 0801-868 722557.
Fax: 0801-868 727334.

Connaught Telegraph
Tel: 094-21711.
Fax: 094-24007.

Connaught Tribune
Tel: 091 -567251.
Fax: 091-567970.

Clare Champion
Tel: 065-28105.
Fax: 065-20374.

Connaught Sentinal
Tel: 091-567251.
Fax: 091-567970.

Derry People and Donegal News
Tel: 074-21014.
Fax: 074-22881.

Derry Journal
Tel: 0801-504 272200.
Fax: 0801-504 272218.

Donegal Democrat
Tel: 072- 51201.
Fax: 072-51945.

Donegal People's Press
Tel: 074-28000.
Fax: 074-24787.

Drogheda Independent
Tel: 041-38658.

Fax: 041-34271.

Dundalk Democrat
Tel: 042-34058.
Fax: 042-31399.

Galway Advertiser
Tel: 091-567077.
Fax: 091-567079.

Kerry's Eye
Tel: (066) 49200.
Fax (066) 23163.

Kerryman/Corkman
Tel: 066-21666.
Fax: 066-21608.

Kilkenny People
Tel: 056-21015.
Fax: 056-21414.

Leinster Express
Tel: 0502- 21666.
Fax: 0502-20491.

Liffy Champion
Tel: 01-6245533.
Fax: 01-6243013.

Limerick Chronicle
Tel: 061-315233.
Fax: 061-314804.

Longford News
Tel: 043-46342.
Fax: 043-41549.

Lurgan and Portadown Examiner
Tel: 0801-868 722557.
Fax: 0801-868 727334.

Mayo News
Tel: 098 25311.
Fax: 098-26108.

Meath Chronicle and Cavan West Meath Herald
Tel: 046-21442.
Fax: 046-23565.

Offaly Express
Tel: 0506-21744.
Fax: 0506-51930.

Roscommon Champion
Tel: 0903-25051.
Fax: 0903-25053.

media

Sligo Champion
Tel: 071-69222.
Fax: 071-69040.

Tipperary Star
Tel: 0504-21122.
Fax: 0504-21110.

Waterford News and Star
Tel: 051-874951.
Fax: 051-855281.

Wicklow Times
Tel: 01-2869111.
Fax: 01-2869074.

RADIO AND TELEVISION STATIONS

96 FM
Tel: 021-551596.
Fax: 021-551500.

Anna Livia FM
Tel: 01-6778103.
Fax: 01-6778150.

BBC
Tel: 0801-232 338000.
Fax: 0801-232 338800.

Clare FM
Tel: 065-28888.
Fax: 065-29392.

Cool FM
Tel: 0801-247 817181.
Fax: 0801-247 814974.

Donegal Highland Radio
Tel: 074-25000.
Fax: 074-25344.

Dublin's 98 FM
Tel: 01-6708970.
Fax: 01-6708969.

East Coast Radio
Tel: 01-2866414.
Fax: 01-2861219.

FM 104
Tel: 01-6686989.
Fax: 01-6689401.

Galway Bay
Tel: 091-770000.
Fax: 091-752689.

Mid West and North West Radio
Tel: 0907-30553.
Fax: 0907-30285.

Radio Kerry
Tel: 066-23666.
Fax: 066-22282

Radio Na Life 102 FM
Tel: 01-6616333.
Fax: 01-6763966.

RTE Television
Tel: 01-2083111.
Fax: 01-2083080.

Teilifis na Gaeilge
Fax: 091-505021.

TV3
Tel: 01-4193347.
Fax: 01-4193322.

Ulster Television
Tel: 0801-232 328122.
Fax: 0801-232 246695.

MEDIA BOOKS

Toxic Sludge Is Good for You! : Lies, Damn Lies and the Public Relations Industry
John C. Stauber and Sheldon Rampton, ISBN: 1567510604, 1995.

Manufacturing Consent
Edward S. Herman and Noam Chomsky, ISBN: 0099533111, 1995.

Global Spin, the Corporate Assault on Environmentalism
Sharon Beder
ISBN: 1870098676, 1997.

MEDIA WEB SITES

Adbusters
http://www.adbusters.org
Kill Your Television Home Page
http://www.netreach.net/~kaufman/
Reclaim the Streets
http://www.gn.apc.org/rts/
SchNews
http://www.schnews.org.uk/
Rachel's Environmental and Health weekly
http://www.rachel.org

MAGAZINES

Permaculture Magazine
Hyden House Ltd, The Sustainability Centre, East Meon, Hampshire GU32 1HR, England
Tel: 0044-1730 823311
Fax: 0044-1730 823322
Email: info@permaculture.co.uk
http://www.permaculture.co.uk/
Overseas:
(international code +44 - 1730)

Whole Earth
P.O. Box 3000 Denville, NJ 07834-9879
Tel: 001-888-732 6739

Email:subs@wholeearthmag.com
http://www.wholeearthmag.com/

The Ecologist
c/o Cissbury House
Furze View,Five Oaks Road,Slinfold, West Sussex, RH13 7RH, UK
http://www.gn.apc.org/ecologist/

Yes, a journal of positive futures:
http://www.futurenet.org/
YES! PO Box 10818,Bainbridge Island, WA 98110-0818

Ecodesign:
EDA, The British School,Slad Road,STROUD
Glos GL5 1QW
http://www.salvo.co.uk/mags/EcoDesign.htm

Resurgence
Subscriptions Manager -
Jeanette Gill, Rocksea Farmhouse, St. Mabyn,Bodmin, Cornwall, PL30 3BR, U.K.
email: subs.resurge@virgin.net
http://www.gn.apc.org/resurgence/

SEE ALSO
HYPERBOREA
Multimedia Creation for Non-Profits
Full Listing: Arts and Leisure Section

media

PRINT MEDIA

AISLING ARANN

Contact: Dara Molloy
Mainistir, Inis Mor, Aran Islands, Co. Galway

Tel: 099-61245
Fax: 099-61245
E-mail: aismag@iol.ie

We are focused on creating a sustainable, just and spiritually rooted lifestyle. Projects: self-sufficiency; hospitality in 'An Charraig' (Spiritual Centre) and Killeany Lodge (Pilgrim Hostel); Celtic Spirituality; Aisling Magazine and other publications.

BLUE

Contact: Robert Allen
Felix Ford, Eanna Dowling
1 Fortfield, Castlebar, Co. Mayo

Tel: 094 -6179
E-mail: Blueplanet@ireland.com

Blue is Ireland's Environmental community and social Newsletter produced by experienced activists and journalists. Contents include Irish and International reportage, features and opinion pieces. Subscription costs £40 per annum.

DULRA MAGAZINE

Contact: Diarmuid MacConville
242 Sunset Drive, Cartron Point, Sligo

Tel: 071-44348
Fax: Ring phone number first
E-mail: diarmo@indigo.ie
Website: www.emc23.tp

Publishing magazine on environmental, social justice and spiritual issues. Combines hard edged investigative stories that the newspapers are too scared to touch, with a round up of environmental campaigns and a strongly upbeat, positive message.

GAY COMMUNITY NEWS

Contact: Michael McGrane
6 South William St., Dublin 2

Tel: 01-6710939/6719076
Fax: 01-6713599
E-mail: gcn@eircom.net

GCN is a monthly publication with a readership of 30,000 and a nationwide distribution network that also extends to Northern Ireland and abroad. Ten years old, it is a non-profit organisation and its principal aim is to reflect the lives and interests of Ireland's gay, lesbian, bisexual and transgendered communities.

DIRECT ACTION AGAINST APATHY

c/o Green Action, QUBSU, University Rd., Belfast BT7 1NF

E-mail: daaa@hotmail.com
Website:
http://www.geocites.com/rainforest/vines/5944

Direct Action Against Apathy aims to inform, empower, entertain, and push aside the tide of apathy that prevents people from actively shaping a sustainable, equitable and positive future. By giving a voice to individuals, groups and organisations marginalised by mainstream media, we are working to improve our environment and community both locally and globally. We produce a quarterly magazine called Direct Action Against Apathy.

POSITIVE NEWS

Contact: Shauna Crockett - Burroughs
5 Bicton EnterpriseClun,Shropshire,
SY7 8NF England.

Tel: 0044-1588 640 022

WALNUT BOOKS

Contact: Rob Hopkins
The Hollies, Castletown, Enniskeane, Co. Cork.

Tel: 023-47001
E-mail: robnemma@iol.ie

Walnut Books is a mail order book service specialising in practical environmental books on subjects such as permaculture, organic gardening, natural building, renewable energy, composting, agriculture, green economics, trees, woodlands and water recycling. We seek out many unusual hard-to-find titles from around the world and offer a selection of books to truly inspire you to change the world for the better! For a comprehensive catalogue please send postage of £2.30 to Walnut Books.

EARTHWATCH MAGAZINE

(Friends of the Earth Ireland)

Contact: Lothar Luken (Editor)
Dromore, Bantry, Co. Cork

Tel: 028-31853
E-mail: foeeire@iol.ie or envmag@mail.tinet.ie

'Earthwatch' has grown into a broad based magazine where different groups and individuals cover all things environmental in Ireland (North and South) and discuss global issues, green politics, technology, philosophy & spirituality.

SOURCE MAGAZINE

166 Lower Rathmines Rd.,
Dublin 6

Tel: 01–4911711
Fax: 01–4911710
E-mail: info@sourcemag.ie
Website: http://www.sourcemag.ie

Source magazine is Ireland's social, environmental

and holistic monthly magazine. It can be bought in newsagents and health food shops nationwide. For subscriptions please contact us at the above numbers.

ELECTRONIC MEDIA

ANU INTERNET SERVICES
Contact: Stepten Wik
James Street, Westport, Co. Mayo

Tel: 098-28300
Fax: 098-28953
E-mail: stephen@anu.ie
Website: www.anu.ie

ANU Internet Services are a full service ISP specializing in quality hosting packages to a wide range of Irish and International clients. Our expertise allows us to efficiently and cost-effectively create solutions to your internet needs.

TECHNE ASSOCIATES
Contact: Dr. Roy Johnston
P.O Box 1881, Rathmines, Co.Dublin

Tel: 01-4975029
E-mail: rjtechne@iol.ie
Website: www.iol.ie/~rjtechne

Architecture, design and maintenance of knowledge-bases, using Web and CD Rom. To apply the results of research by the international information technology community in a friendly and socially useful manner, in all relevant domains.

EMC
Contact: Rob Stocker

Tel: 01-8681466
Email: rpb@mc23.tp
Website: www.emc23.tp

EMC are a collective promoting the use of multimedia and electronic communication amongst the grassroots and artistic communities. The group constructed the stunning website for the Glen of the Downs campaign. EMC work co-operatively with other groups - both in training and in organising exhibitions and multi-media events.

IBC COMPUTER AND INTERNET COMPANY
Contact: Melanie Kovero
19 Ulverton Road, Dalkey, Co. Dublin

Tel: 01-285 0128
Fax: 01-2852463
Email: sales@ibc.ie
Website: www.ibc.ie

Since 1991, IBC has been selling, supporting and upgrading PC and Apple computers, laser internet printers and suppliers, business software, internet website design, hosting and management. Visit www.ibc.ie to see the best environmental options for your office.

MEDIA

PUBLIC COMMUNICATIONS CENTRE
Contact: Geraldine O'Dowd
22 South Great Georges Street, Co.Dublin

Tel: 01-6794173
Fax: 01-6795409
Email: info@pcc.ie
Website: http://www.pcc.ie

Public Communications Centre is a full-service strategy and communications resource servicing exclusively non-profit, progressive forces for change. We encourage and assist groups to examine and set their agenda, to identify their audience and to claim the best possible media and strategies to influence that audience.

MULTIMEDIA

UNDERCURRENTS
16b Cherwell Street, Oxford, OX4 1BG, Britain

Tel: 0044-1865-203662
Fax: 0044-1865-243562
E-mail: underc@gn.apc.org
Website: www.undercurrents.org

Undercurrents challenges the dominant definition of what is newsworthy and provides an alternative to the daily trivial soap gossip fed to us by the mainstream media. Combining our skills with activists and communities in conflicts, the Undercurrents alternative news video reports the news you don't see on the news.

TEMPLE OF DESIGN
Contact: Mary Guinan
9 Parliment Street, Dublin 2

Tel: 01 679 3075

Graphic Design services in the center of Dublin. Specialist in working with campaign groups.

COMMUNITY & FAMILY

page 191 **Introduction** Fr. Harry Bohan

page 194 **Community Development** Josie Fogarty

page 194 **Sustainable Rural Development** Marie O'Malley

page 196 **Social Economy** Tallaght Social Economy Unit

page 197 **Eco-Villages** Rob Hopkins

page 198 **Co-Housing** Robert Alcock

page 199 **Local Agenda 21** Peter Doran

page 221 **Children** Susan Von Mohlmann

page 222 **Education** Pearse O'Shiel

page 222 **Natural Birth** Judith Crow

page 223 **Home Birth** Marie Ni Chonchubhair

page 225 **Breastfeeding** Margaret McGuigans

COMMUNITY AND FAMILY Fr. Harry Bohan

Fr. Harry Bohan is the current chair of the Rural Resource Development Ltd. He is a priest of the Diocese of Killaloe, based in Shannon. 'People are crying out for meaning and community,' is the message he takes from his work. He has written widely on the subject of Christianity, spirituality, community and economic development, his books include 'Ireland Green', 'Roots in a Changing Society' and 'Hope Begins at Home.'

'Balancing the local with the global'

It is sometimes hard to see the present for what it is. However, some things are becoming clear. The 20th century began with the great hope that the world would be a brighter and happier place and, of course, in many ways it is. We are the best fed, best housed, best educated generation ever to have lived in the Western world. In many ways we are living through a golden era.

On the other hand there are great fears. We have seen our society uprooted. Our pattern of living and behaviour, formed over centuries, has changed dramatically. Many of the old sign-posts are disappearing, and old loyalties questioned. This has become very much a secular age. The loss of meaning, loneliness, aloneness, crime, individualism, family and community breakdown are all indications that we must restore the balance.

Restoring the Balance

We are now part of a global economy and in a very significant way we are shaped by the global. Corporate values are setting the agenda for many areas of life. We have tended to measure success, for the most part, in monetary terms.

There are indications that the breathtaking developments of modern science may have exhausted their potential. When 'security' becomes one of the fastest growing industries in a society then it is clear that the process of modernisation is creating as much fear as hope. Commerce does not necessarily bring peace.

One of the hottest topics in leadership circles today is creating a sense of community. There is now a serious interest in the need to balance concern for people with concern for profits.

While this is a huge challenge there are clear indications that whereas the 20th century has been the century of great material success in the West, the next century and the new millennium could see a major return to things of the spirit. There are signs that the response could come through institutions working in partnership with one another and with the local community.

The two systems of family and community are "essentials" when it comes

community + family

to developing the local. Could the values we are searching for be more easily found 'where people are', with the local?

Family and Community

It is not easy to define "family" at the end of the century. One thing is certain, however, the family has experienced massive change in a short period of time. It has moved from the extended to the nuclear to the single parent grouping in a short period of time and to some extent, there are shades of all three still around.

In this article, I will simply confine myself to touching on two phases of family and some characteristics of family life worth holding onto.

The family

1st phase:

Up to the 1960s, Irish life revolved around the two systems of family and community. The family of the 30's, 40's, 50's had a number of very powerful characteristics.

The traditional family was uncompromisingly dominated by the "boss". Sons even into their middle age, were given little authority. There were clear sets of male and female tasks. Most of the heavy work was done by the male whilst the woman dominated activities within and to some extent around the house.

Marriages were often arranged. The "match" was seen as a social and economic vehicle for survival and in a society where physical survival was a constant preoccupation.

It was very much an enterprise unit with clear sets of male and female tasks but within which children played an important part. Practically every family had other adults, apart from parents, associated with it - grandparents, unmarried uncles, aunts, neighbours and friends.

The whole family was conscious of their dependence on God. Prayer was important, necessary and habitual. A lot of learning took place within the home and there was a lot of sharing.

Because future occupational positions were more or less fixed, parents thought more of their children's future character than careers - will they be honest, level-headed, honourable - bringing esteem to the family? Will they respect us in our old age?

2nd Phase:

This phase began in the 1960's with an unprecedented and ever growing level of prosperity and with the rise of mass electronic communications which has introduced powerful images, ideas, values and authority figures. There was a definite pattern in the decline of the large three generation household. The position of the elderly altered radically with the decline of the extended household. The number of single parent families became a definite phenomenon. In 1980, the nuclear family accounted for only 45% of all households. The most radical changes took place during this period.

If family life is to be as significant as it was in the past or as many people would want it to be, we must be clearer about the external structures which will enable us to meet these objectives. Generally, the work practices which have developed and the broader social structures do not facilitate the kind of togetherness and growth conducive to a healthy family life.

However, even as things are, there are more opportunities than we realise. Certainly, a lot of schooling could go on in the home, or in a small local setting run by parents not working outside the home. The whole of the leisure industry could become more family oriented. A lot of work carried out in offices and factories could be done in the family home.

Community

The emergence of individualism and competition from the profit and market values of the commercial world have led to a lack of sharing and an increase in loneliness. Community and family breakdown have also increased.

This may be why we are beginning to see the re-emergence of the community in many areas. We now have community watch, community colleges, community health care, and community hospitals. These initiatives coupled with a new energy at the local level are achieving an assertiveness in a manner which challenges everybody involved in development.

By rediscovering a pride in place and locality local people are empowered and moved to the centre of the stage. In the cultural field community issues are finding a whole new expression, but in many areas of life they are moving to the fore.

I believe the fundamental challenge now is to restore the balance between the local and the global. To contribute to this, our organisation has set up an applied research centre. The purpose of the centre is to focus on the local community, to identify the factors which go to shape it such as the family, local resources, the corporation, education, spirituality/values, sport: To research, highlight and work at restoring these is vital in determining our future. Our conference last November (up to 1,000 attended) "Are We Forgetting Something?" highlighted some of these. Our next conference will focus on balance.

community + family

> **The pressure on resources does not come from numbers it comes from killing the relationship of nurturence communities have with their ecosystems.** Vandana Shiva

COMMUNITY DEVELOPMENT

Josie Fogarty Southside Partnership

Community development supports people to work collectively to bring about social change – it is not an individual response to crises as they emerge. It is about enabling people to be active in the development of their own local areas and the wider society of which they are a part. It enables and supports people to challenge inequalities and power imbalances that they are experiencing. Community development is concerned with achieving tasks such as managing local community resource centres, establishing community responses to drugs or engaging in estate management initiatives. It is also concerned with the process of how all these are achieved, i.e. the need to involve local people, especially those most excluded, at all stages of the project, providing opportunities for community leaders to network and learn from each other, the sustainability of the actions being undertaken and a focus on the empowerment of local people doing things for themselves.

Community development is a key action under the Local Development Programme. It is playing a lead role in building local organisations and local leadership so that socially excluded communities can impact on the development agenda for their areas and the wider policy arena that directly affects their lives. The Department of Social, Community and Family Affairs also supports it. But more importantly, it is supported by hours of voluntary activity that local community activists engage in because they want to improve the quality of life in their community and to actively engage in a struggle to bring about structural change.

Josie Fogarty, community development co-ordinator, Southside Partnership. Tel: (01) 2963660

Sustainable Rural Development

Ms. Marie O'Malley Manager of the Rural Development Unit, Faculty of Agriculture, UCD

The term "rural development" can better be understood by defining it as the development of rural areas and the people who live therein. This simple interpretation helps us to realise that rural development is ultimately about people and communities. Primarily it is about people who live in rural areas but not exclusively so, as the relationships and interdependence between rural and urban become more and more apparent in an era of commuting workers. Development of rural areas is multi-sectoral in that it views the progress not just in terms of better health or better roads but as the whole system, with the success of one sector closely associated with success in another. For example, rural development depends just as much on improvements in the health sector as it does on progress in areas of education, income/employment and roads infrastructure.

There is no common definition of the term 'rural' within Europe. However, in Ireland the Census of Population defines rural as all areas outside towns of more than 1,500 people. Using this criteria, Ireland has 43% of its total population classified as rural.

While rural development is ultimately about people, a central element is sustainability. The terms 'sustainable development' originated in the 1970s and was popularised in the 1980s by international environment and development concerns. The Bruntland Report (developed by the UN General Assembly's Commission on Environment and Development) in 1987 has been an influential document in defining sustainable development and in proposing a strategy to achieve it. The report defines sustainable development as 'Development which meets the needs of the present without compromising the ability of future generations to meet their own needs'.

Although rural is often identified with agricultural, the economic and social development of rural areas is no longer synonymous with agriculture and agricultural development. The rapid economic growth experienced in Ireland in recent years has not been evenly distributed throughout our society and for many rural areas disadvantage and marginalisation remain significant problems. Rural communities are currently facing a number of particular challenges such as depopulation, declining agriculture, lack of employment opportunities, social exclusion, poor infrastructures and the protection of the environment.

The recent European Union Agenda 2000 agreement which has an increased focus on rural development and acknowledges it as the second pillar of the Common Agricultural Policy (CAP), may have an impact on European policy in the future.

The Irish Government's White Paper on Rural Development (1999) commits itself to a long-term vision of Irish rural society and formulates a variety of strategies to ensure the maintenance of vibrant, sustainable rural communities in the future. Policy makers have a responsibility to ensure that the diversity and quality of the rural countryside is maintained and preserved for the benefit of future generations. However, this can only be ensured by revitalising and sustaining rural economies through the implementation of policies which permit the social, economic and environmental development of rural areas and takes into account the changing aspirations and priorities of their inhabitants.

References:

Department of Agriculture & Food, 1999. *Ensuring the Future - A Strategy for Rural Development in Ireland; White paper on Rural Development*. Dublin: The Stationery Office.

European Commission, 1996. *The Cork Declaration; A Living Countryside*. Brussels: Commission of the European Communities.

European Commission, 1988. *The future of Rural Society*. Bulletin of the EC. Supplement 4/88. Brussels: Commission of the European Commission.

National Economic and Social Council, 1994. *New Approaches to Rural Development*, Report. No.97. Dublin: NESC.

National Economic and Social Forum, 1997. *Rural Renewal - Combating Social Exclusion*, Forum Report. No.12. Dublin: NESF.

Report of the Review Group, 1993. *Strategy for Rural Development Training*. Dublin: Teasgasc.

Web Sites

1 LEADER II Irish National Networking Service: www.leaderii.ie
2 "Rural Innovation" Dossier No.4, LEADER European Observatory: http://www.rural-europe.aeidl.be/rural-en/biblio/spec/contents.htm

Social Economy Tallaght Social Economy Unit

The Social Economy has been described as "That part of the economy which operates between the market economy (private sector) and the non-market economy (public sector)". It has also become known as the 'new' Social Economy, the 'Third sector' or 'Third System'. The Social Economy offers potential to communities in delivering services which are not met by the private market sector and are not provided by the public sector.

The Social Economy operates where the market has failed to respond to the demands of citizens both for the provision of services and for employment needs. So the Social Economy is an effective way to respond to specific local needs and to involve those otherwise excluded from mainstream economic activity in the provision of these services. This is only one aspect of the importance of the Social Economy.

In fact the Social Economy represents a continuum of possibilities of alternative economic and social organisation. This idea of the Social Economy as occupying a spectrum between the private (profit driven market) economy and the public (tax funded) sectors, is reflected in the variety of definitions offered to describe this sector. In other words the Social Economy has a far from limited scope.

The Social Economy can be seen as a community response to exclusion and unemployment in the form of initiatives which combine social and economic objectives, geared towards sustainability and which have the capacity to make a significant contribution to increasing the quality of life. This form of organisation has existed throughout human history based on the principles of collective action, participation, autonomy, and local self-help. It is as much about social objectives as economic ones, in fact the achievement of social objectives is a means of achieving economic ones. Developing the Social Economy requires a holistic approach to social and economic objectives and can be part of a joint community development and enterprise programme.

> **Development is a process in which culture and nature are made to conform to the needs of technology and the economy.**
> Helena Norberg-Hodge

Eco-Villages

Rob Hopkins is the founding Director of Baile Dulra, the company behind The Hollies Sustainable Village in Enniskeane, Co. Cork. He is a Permaculture designer and also jointly runs Eco-Village Design Services, a consultancy for all areas of eco-village design, planning and implementation.

All the elements for a sustainable society are now tried and tested; affordable homes can be built with natural materials needing little or no heating, reed beds can treat sewage effectively, renewable energy systems are now cost-effective and efficient, and low-labour, high-yield food gardens have been shown to work in this climate. The logical next step is to draw all these elements together to create human settlements which demonstrate not only how sustainable living can be achieved, but also how it can create livelihoods, abundance, diversity and the strong sense of community so rapidly disappearing from our society.

Ireland is now seeing a number of eco-village initiatives springing up around the country (networked via The Irish Eco-Village Information Network) which have, in turn, been inspired by other, longer established developments elsewhere in the world. So far the only generally accepted definition of an eco-village is that it is "a human scale, full-featured settlement in which human activities are harmlessly integrated into the natural world in a way that is supportive of healthy human development and can be successfully continued into the indefinite future" (Gilman 1991).

community + family

From Crystal Waters, the first permaculture designed eco-village in Queensland, Australia with 83 residential sites on 640 acres, to Davis Homes in California, an urban estate of passive solar houses set among Garden-of-Eden-like groves of fruit trees, the idea has spread around the world and has been absorbed into different societies and ecologies with great vision and imagination. No two eco-villages are the same. There is a broad spectrum of projects from 'tribal villages' such as Earthaven in America which makes all its decisions by consensus, to more 'community' projects with a spiritual focus (such as Findhorn in Scotland), to what essentially are green housing developments. Within that spectrum is a huge diversity of approaches, beliefs, legal structures and scale.

Eco-villages have much to offer in Ireland at this time. The larger cities are becoming prohibitively expensive for most of those who wish to house themselves, rural areas are becoming depopulated, fewer and fewer farms employ less and less people and the need for sustainable development is now recognised in Government policy. Rural eco-villages have the potential to bring people back to these areas, creating employment, education and training opportunities while also creating oases of biodiversity and restoring landscapes. They also have the potential to revive urban areas, creating settlements which meet more of their residents' needs than just a roof over their heads; well designed urban eco-villages can produce fruit, vegetables, energy for the settlement itself and beyond, employment, beautiful green space, having a truly revitalising effect on the city around them. Eco-villages are not a retreat from the world, rather they embrace the world with a vision of how things can be and, in many ways, how things must be if we are to make it through the next century in abundance and harmony.

Co-Housing Robert Alcock Dublin Co-housing Group

For many people, the city is a place of isolation and sterility. Few know their neighbours, and getting out to meet friends and family can be expensive, tiresome and, for the old and the immobile, near-impossible. Genuine neighbourhoods, places where "community" is more than a political buzz-word, are being replaced by apartment blocks that look like luxury jails, with barred windows and electronic gates. Meanwhile, in the suburbs, identical rows of ugly boxes are spreading across the countryside in every direction. Both are cold, heartless and outrageously expensive places to live. Whatever this fury of construction is doing, it certainly isn't bringing housing within the reach of ordinary people. But what alternative is there?

One alternative is co-housing. In a co-housing development, prospective residents design and manage their own housing, whether from the ground up or from existing buildings. Instead of getting a place that seems to have come off an assembly line, you get a development tailored to your own needs and those of your neighbours. Co-housing also tries to build real neighbourhoods by placing emphasis on common spaces, such as pedestrian streets, meeting rooms, cooking and dining and laundry facilities, while retaining the privacy of your own home. In other words, it strives for a balance between privacy and community. It may not sound earth-shattering, but compared with the way our towns and cities are built at the moment, it represents an enormous improvement.

Typically, given their history of innovative yet practical social ideas, it was the Danes who came up with co-housing. Twenty years ago, the first co-housing development, Saettedammen, was completed. Since then, the number of new developments has increased exponentially. The first ones were expensive places to live: some called them "dentists' communes." But increasing numbers of affordable and rental co-housing communities have also been built. There are now over 1000 co-housing developments in Denmark alone. The idea has also spread to other Northern European countries, and in 1988, through the book "Co-housing" by Catherine McCamant and Charles Durrett, to the English-speaking world. North Americans, in particular, have embraced the idea, and the number of groups there has doubled every year since its introduction. Here in Ireland, you might think that a society at once conservative, communal and fiercely individualistic would not be quick to embrace such a novel idea. In fact, since Dublin Co-housing was founded in April 1997 there has been a great deal of interest in the idea perhaps because any alternative to the housing crisis is worth exploring.

Local Agenda 21

Peter Doran is a writer and editor for the International Institute for Sustainable Development's Earth Negotiations Bulletin at United Nation Conferences on environment and development. He is also a member of Northern Ireland's Local Agenda 21 Advisory Group.

What is Local Agenda 21?

Local Agenda 21 is about bringing the United Nations 'Earth Summits' (Rio de Janeiro 1992, and New York 1997) home to our communities. In Agenda 21, the global action plan agreed at the 1992 United Nations Conference on Environment and Development, one of the shortest chapters is dedicated to the enabling role of local authorities. The brevity should not deflect from the importance of local community participation in transforming the dominant unsustainable patterns of development. The era of globalisation is unfolding side by side with an urgent need to empower local communities.

community + family

Caught between the near collapse of economic sovereignty brought about by the acceleration of transnational forms of governance, nation-states have responded to the challenge of sustainable development with contradictory policy initiatives and rhetoric. Five years after the first 'Earth Summit' the United Nations Environment Programme reported that the global outlook remained precarious. The Global Environment Outlook Report (1997) reported that "the global environment has continued to deteriorate and significant environmental problems remain deeply embedded in the socio-economic fabric of all nations in all regions".

In Ireland, as in much of the rest of the world, politicians have been slow to wake up to the challenges posed by the 'Earth Summits'. Only towards the close of the millennium are we beginning to detect an undercurrent of change, driven by legislation from bodies such as the European Union and by an active citizenry who increasingly demand goods and services produced with equity and environmental impact in mind.

The quality of Local Agenda 21 processes varies enormously from one local authority to another. Where local authority officers are left to get on with designing their Local Agenda 21 strategies and brochures without an active citizens' network to monitor and participate, the process will sometimes amount to little more than a re-packaging of existing environmental responsibilities.

Here is a fourteen point checklist of achievements to help citizens ensure that a Local Agenda 21 is addressing all the most important elements:

- Resources are used efficiently and waste is minimised.
- Pollution is limited to levels which natural systems can cope with all the while ensuring that damage is eliminated.
- The diversity of nature is valued and protected.
- Where possible, local needs are met locally.
- Everyone has access to food, water, shelter and fuel at reasonable cost.
- Everyone has the opportunity to undertake satisfying work in a diverse economy.
- People's good health is protected by creating safe, clean, pleasant environments and health services which emphasise prevention of illness.
- Access to facilities services, goods, and other people is not achieved at the expense of the environment or limited to those with private motor cars.
- People live without fear of violence from crime or persecution because of their personal beliefs, race, gender or sexuality.
- Every citizen has the skills, knowledge and information needed to

enable them to play a full and active part in society.

- All sections of the community are empowered to enable them to play a full part in society.
- All sections of the community are empowered to participate in decision-making.
- Opportunities for culture, leisure and recreation are readily available to all.
- Places, spaces, and objects combine meaning and beauty with utility.

At the second 'Earth Summit', a special session of the United Nations General Assembly held in 1997, the Irish Government underlined the far reaching political implications of the sustainable development agenda. The Irish delegation told the international gathering that "A new partnership to advance sustainable development must be driven by a number of key imperatives. It must put people at the centre of development policy and practice. It must empower women and major social groups".

If Local Agenda 21 is to become an effective tool for community empowerment and a genuine forum for unlearning the errors of unthinking development, politicians must bring their rhetoric home from the 'Earth Summit' and translate it into a commitment to putting people at the centre of the development process for the first time. The days of running the economy on auto-pilot must be consigned to the bin in favour of a quiet revolution in the lives of individuals, institutions and cultures.

Children Susann Von Mohlmann the Family Centre, Rialto.

Children offer their parents and society one of the greatest opportunities to reflect upon and create the kind of environment which supports each child to develop into its fullest potential. In a quiet way, yet so powerful, a child challenges us to become clearer and more directive in naming and acting upon what we think is important.

Carers have the opportunity and responsibility to make choices as to what is in the best interest of the developing child and family life. The parent's unique life experiences and individual circumstances, cultural, religious and social settings can inform their guiding decisions, highlighting the parent's values and concerns about bringing up a child.

Each choice, or lack of, can present a challenging responsibility. This can be confusing times since child development and parenting styles is a topic much written about and spoken of. The range of views and approaches, the ongoing research into what affects children is vast and often diverse. What may have been considered a good way of responding to a child in the past may seem unacceptable today. These personal attitudes, factual knowledge and new ideas concerning the well being of children directly influence the child and family, child care practice and the education system.

community + family

Children's growth and education remain an ongoing opportunity to sustain what we consider to be of highest value to the individual person and the wider society. Sustainability begins with the birth of each child.

> **The human being is less a being on the earth or in the universe than a dimension of the earth and indeed of the universe itself**.
> Thomas Berry, The Dream of the Earth

Education Pearse O'Shiel Coolenbridge Steiner School

Education is a central concern for each community. A community becomes sustainable only so long as it can articulate its values and allow these values to underpin the education of its children. When a community allows values that do not take account of its own particular ethos it relinquishes responsibility for its own survival as a distinctive community, allowing outside forces to impose their agenda.

The Irish Constitution (Bunracht na hEireann) permits an extraordinary degree of community control over education. Parents who make a conscientious choice have the right to educate their children according to their own values. Moreover, if we are to retain our community's unique spiritual, environmental and ethical values we are compelled to exercise this right. We can do this by starting schools, changing schools and by playing a full and active role in the education of our children.

Natural Birth Judith Crow childbirth educator, yoga teacher and rebirther

What do you think about when you see the word "Birth"? Images of pain, danger, blood? Or do you revel in the opportunity for enrichment, inspiration, empowerment and the understanding that comes with the tenderness of seeing a new life begin? The way we were born shapes our perceptions and expectations of birth and of life. What happens at birth imprints itself very deeply into our psyches, into our very way of being in our bodies on the earth. So it follows that to create a sustainable, peaceful society we change the way we do birth.

In our Western culture we have misunderstood and mishandled birth in so many ways. Physiologically, having women lie on their backs has been a disaster, causing painful, long, dangerous labours and leaving us with an inheritance of fear and distrust of the natural process. Psychologically and spiritually we have failed our babies by accepting the prevailing belief that they don't feel pain and have no memory, allowing us to cause them panic, horrendous pain and the heartbreak of separation from the only source of comfort and nourishment they know.

community + family

Thankfully we now know that babies who are born gently into a loving receptive environment don't need to screw up their eyes and faces in panic, but open like flowers and bond ecstatically with their parents in awe and wonder, just as nature intended. Anthropologists tell us that warlike societies the world over separate their newborns from their mothers, while peaceful societies who live in harmony with the earth insist on the sacredness of the bond between mother and baby.

We have a wonderful future before us when babies are born without fear and collectively we can step out of our addictions and defences. When what we bond with at the moment of birth is not a drugged state or a panicked state but an experience of the sacredness of relationship, we can begin to explore the true nature of our connection with each other and our planet.

Home Birth

Maire Ni Chonchubhair a sociologist specialising in birth, is the author of Birth Tides (Pandora)

Home birth? Hello?

No rush to get to hospital on time!
No hospital gowns. No identity crisis.

No clocks. No drips. No drugs.
No rush to produce this baby.

No poking or prodding. No stirrups.
Just privacy. And freedom.

No superbugs. No strangers.
No waiting-rooms.

No wiring your womb up to a foetal heart monitor.
No screwing electrodes into your baby's scalp.

No false positives, no rush to get the baby out.
No 'emergency' section.

No theatre lights, no high trolleys.
No metal, no Dettol.

Only the peace of your own bed in your own room.
And your own germs.

No amniotomies, no episiotomies.
You want your perfect body intact.

No rush to take your baby away.

community + family

No nurseries.

Early labour? Go for a walk. Go for a swim.
Clean out the cutlery drawer.

Call the shots. Call your midwife. Play music.
Make coffee. Sit in the bathroom. Be on your own.

Knowing your midwife is half the battle.
You know your midwife for nine months.

She tells you to take your time.
No rush, no fear.

Lie in a hot bath, or sit in a birth pool.
Water eases the stress of labour.

He holds your hand, makes hot toast,
Massages your back, boils water.

Your midwife listens to the baby's heartbeat.
You trust her, and feel safe.

No pushing, no pulling, no panic.
No rush to get the baby out.

You give birth standing up, or sitting down.
Body wide open, baby slips out.

You come back from earth.
No rush to cut the cord.

You watch it together, admire its rainbow colours.
Marvel at this pulsating thing which has kept your baby alive.

Three hearts beat in time.
There is no rush. Only time.

While it is true that the various members of the natural community nourish each other and that the death of one is the life of the other, this is not an enmity, it is an intimacy. Brian Swimme and Thomas Berry, The Universe Story

Breastfeeding Margaret McGuigan the LaLeche League

Breastmilk is the superior infant food. It protects children from illness and ensures their healthy physical and psychological development. For mothers, breastfeeding provides health benefits such as reducing the risk of breast and ovarian cancer. Breastfeeding also empowers women by increasing their self-confidence in their capacity to nourish and protect as well as nurture their babies and by decreasing their dependence on commercial products.

The health benefits of breastfeeding for babies are now well documented. These include a more efficient immune system, prevention of disease, decreased risk of allergies, and better dental development than their formula fed counterparts.

Breastmilk is a natural and renewable resource, entirely free of waste. It does not have to be shipped anywhere - every mother has a ready supply wherever she goes and it needs no packaging! It is always the right temperature, does not need sterilisation and causes no pollution. Breastmilk is also free to every mother and baby!

By breastfeeding her baby a mother is not using any extra water, packaging, transportation, fuel or energy. Breastfeeding benefits all sectors of society economically, ecologically and socially. Breastfeeding is unique - it is the best example of how humanity can sustain itself through provision of the first and most complete food for humans.

community + family

Choices for Change

The responsibility for changing to a more sustainable lifestyle - one which respects the ability of future generations to meet their needs, rests with everyone of us, either as an individual or as a member of an organisation.

As a consumer, i.e. a purchaser of goods and services or an investor in business, you are in a very strong position to make choices which are more in harmony with the limits of the Earth to provide us with raw materials.

You can make a difference to the global situation by your everyday decisions, i.e. by making informed choices for sustainability.

Sustainable consumerism or investment is not about a set of rules for what we buy or invest in but is an approach to making such decisions.

Issues to Consider for Consumers

Before making any purchases you should find out about the
- source of raw materials and efficiency of use of natural resources
- environmental impacts of the production process and transport over long distances
- energy consumption and durability of the product
- extent of packaging and whether the product and / or packaging can be reused or recycled
- social and working conditions under which the product was made or grown
- environmental performance (e.g. compliance with environmental legislation), of the producer, processor or the service provider
- environmental impacts on developing economies
- impact of under-pricing on the ability of developing countries to fund sustainable development (e.g. to install pollution prevention or control systems)
- need for balance so that trade and environmental policies are mutually supportive, e.g. reduced demand for tropical timber or related products may simply encourage forest clearance in developing countries and the diversion of land from sustainably managed forests to cash crops.

**EOLAS AR AN gCOMHSHAOL
INFORMATION ON THE ENVIRONMENT**

17, St Andrew St., Dublin 2, Ireland
Tel 1890 200 191 or 01 888 3001
Fax: 01 888 3946
e-mail: info@enfo.ie
Website: www.enfo.ie

It's easy to make a difference.
Extracts from the forthcoming ENFO SUSTAINABLE LIVING GUIDE for shoppers and investers.

community + family

COMMUNITY BOOKS

Spiritual Politics
Corinne McLaughlin and Gordon Davidson
ISBN: 0905249623, 1994.

The Ecology of Place: Planning for Environment, Economy and Community
Timothy Beatley and Kristy Manning
ISBN: 1559634782, 1997.

Communities Directory
The Fellowship for Intentional Community
ISBN: 0960271430, 1995.

Designing Ecological Settlements - ecological planning and building: experience in new housing in the renewal of existing housing quarters in European countries
Margrit & Declan Kennedy
ISBN: 3496026308, 1999.

Directory of Eco-Villages In Europe
Barbro Grindheim & Declan Kennedy
ISBN: 3980218430, 1999.

Facilitator's Guide to Participatory Decision-Making
Sam Kaner, Lenny Lind, Catherine Toldi, Sara Fisk and Duane Berger
ISBN: 0865713472, 1996.

FAMILY BOOKS

Immaculate Deception 11: Myth, Magic and Birth
Suzanne Arms
ISBN: 0890876339, 1994.

Songs from the Womb: Healing the Wounded Mother
Benig Mauger
ISBN: 1898256543, 1998.

The Midwife Challenge
Sheila Kitzinger
ISBN: 0044408455, 1991.

Where to be Born?
Rhona Campbell, and Alison Macfarlane
ISBN: 095124051X, 1994.

Birth Tides
Maire O' Connor
ISBN: 0044409168, 1995.

COMMUNITY AND FAMILY WEB SITES

The Village - Sustainable Projects Ltd, developing sustainable community
http://www.sustainable.buz.org

Eco-village Directory
http://www.ecovillages.org/

Irish Eco-Village Information Network
http://www.ecovillages.org/ireland/

community + family

patagonia®

Clean Air,
Earth, Water

24-26, Exchequer Street.
Dublin 2, Ireland.

Tel: +353 (01) 6705748 / 6705749
Fax: +353 (01) 6705701

Website: www.patagonia.com

COMMUNITY DEVELOPMENT

SUSTAINABLE NORTHERN IRELAND PROGRAMME (SNIP)

Contact: Heather Moorhead
75a Cregagh Road, Belfast, Co. Antrim BT6 8PY

Tel: 0044-28-9050 7850 or 0801-232 507850
Fax: 0044-28-9050 7851
Email: info@snip1.freeserve.co.uk

SNIP is an organisation set up in 1997 to catalyse the local Agenda 21 process in Northern Ireland. We work with communities, with local authorities, and intersectorally to encourage people to use sustainable development principals in their daily activities.

FOYLE BASIN COUNCIL

Contact: Peter Doran
22 Bishop Street, Derry, Co. Derry

Tel: 0801-504 377970
Fax: 0801-504 377970
Email: fbc@sustainableireland.org
Website: www.sustainableireland.org

To promote and support local Agenda 21 through education for sustainable and equitable development.

DUBLIN HEALTHY CITIES

Contact: Ray Bateson
Carmichael House, North Brunswick Street, Dublin 7

Tel: 01-8722278
Fax: 01-8722057
Email: dhcp@indigo.ie

Health is both an important objective for people and a main component of the process towards achieving sustainable development as emphasised by Agenda 21.

DUBLIN CITY AGENDA 21 CITIZENS NETWORK

Contact: Bernie Walsh
Mandela House, 44 Lower Gardner Street, Dublin 1

Tel: 01-8788897

Dublin City Agenda 21 Citizens Network aims to promote and encourage the local Agenda 21 process for Dublin City through partnership with local community stakeholders.

COMMUNITY ACTION NETWORK

Contact: Cecilia Forrestal
24 Gardiner Place, Dublin 1

Tel: 01-8788005
Fax: 01-8788034
E-mail: canadmin@eircom.ie

CAN is committed to promote and contribute to greater equality in Irish society by developing policy and good practice.

DUBLIN INSTITUTE OF TECHNOLOGY

Contact: Gill Weyman
Department of Built Environment, Bolten St., Dublin 1

Tel: 01- 4023717
E-mail: gillweyman@hotmail.com

Research into local agenda 21 and local community indicators of sustainable development.

SOUTHSIDE PARTNERSHIP

Contact: Neal Newman
Upper Georges St. Dun Laoghaire, Co. Dublin

Tel: 01-2301011
Fax: 01-2301713

Southside Partnership is the local social and economic development organisation in Dun Laoghaire-Rathdown, specialising in growing strong and sustainable community based organisations working for social & economic justice.

MUINTIR NA TIRE

Contact: Roisin Stapleton
Canon Hayes House, Tipperary Town, Co. Tipperary

Tel: 062-51163
Fax: 062-51200
E-mail: muintirtipp@tinet.ie

A national voluntary community development organisation set up to promote the principles of self-help and self-reliance; principles promoted through the model of the democratically elected, representative community council.

RURAL DEVELOPMENT

DEPARTMENT OF AGRIBUSINESS & RURAL DEVELOPMENT

Contact: Marie O'Malley
University College Dublin, Belfield, Dublin 4

Tel: 01-7067858
Fax: 01-7061101
E-mail: marie@agriculture.ucd.ie

As part of the Department of Agribusiness Extension and Rural Development at the faculty of Agriculture in UCD, the unit provides a top-level training, research and consultancy service in Ireland and abroad.

RURAL RESOURCE DEVELOPMENTS LTD

Contact: Gerald Kennedy
Town Hall, Shannon, Co. Clare

Tel: 061-361144
Fax: 061-361954
Email: rrd@tinet.ie

Rural Resource Development Ltd. is a rural and community development organisation, based in

Shannon. It administers the EU Leader programme in Co. Clare. It offers a wide range of supports to community groups.

TIPPERARY RURAL AND BUSINESS DEVELOPMENT INSTITUTE

Contact: Kate Dwyer, Racecourse Road, Thurles, Co.Tipperary

Tel: 0504-28000
Fax: 0504-28111
Email: info@trbdi.ie

A lifelong learning and rural development body working to improve the economic and social conditions in rural Ireland, based on a philosophy of sustainable rural community and business development.

COMMUNITY EDUCATION

CENTRE FOR ADULT CONTINUING EDUCATION

Contact: Denis Staunton
The Laurels, Western Road, Cork

Tel: 021-902301 / 021-902302 / 021-902789
Fax: 021-276619
Website: http://www.ucc.ie/ucc/depts/ace

The Centre is a bridge between the resources of the University and the wider community. This year, the centre is responsible for 1800 adult learners in 42 centres of learning in 10 counties as well as centres in Northern Ireland and the U.K. Range embraces 30 different certs., diplomas, and degrees in community based and continuing education and provision.

NORTH WALL WOMEN'S CENTRE

Contact: Pauline Flynn & Marina Doody,
Lower Sheriff Street, North Wall, Dublin 1

Tel: 01-8365399
Fax: 01-8365452

We are a women's centre located in the heart of the Docklands. We provide recreational and second chance educational courses to local women with the provision of child care. Participants on our CE scheme work and train in areas of childcare. Youth work and administration. We are responding to the changing needs of the community.

AONTAS

Contact: Berni Brady
22 Earlsfort Terrace, Dublin 2

Tel: 01-4754121
Fax: 01-4780084
E-mail: Aontas@iol.ie

Aontas is the Irish National Association of Adult Education, a voluntary membership organisation. It exists to promote the development of a learning society through the provision of a quality and comprehensive system of adult learning and education that is accessible to and inclusive of all.

ECO-VILLAGE / SUSTAINABLE COMMUNITY

IRISH ECO VILLAGE INFORMATION NETWORK

Contact: Stephen & Mieke Wik
Steamstown, Westport, Co. Mayo

Tel: 098-28423
Fax: 098-28593
E-mail: mieke@anu.ie or stephen@anu.ie
Website: www.ecovillages.org/ireland/

The aim of the IEVIN is to assist in the exchange of information about the development of sustainable human settlements in Ireland and to make more information widely available about eco-village concepts and demonstration sites.

ECO-VILLAGE AT BURDAUTIEN

Contact: Graham Strouts / Marcus Mc Cabe
The Ark, Burdautien, Clones, Co.Monaghan

Tel: 047-52295
E-mail: burdautien@Anv.ie
Website: http://www.ecovillage.org/ireland/burdautien

The Eco-Village is designed as a model of a socially, economically and ecologically sustainable human settlement. We are building a village of low-impact dwellings and environmentally conscious businesses. Eco-Village at Burdautien Business Centre. Native Irish trees and permaculture plants nursery. Forest garden design. Willow sculpture and earth education, courses: permaculture, strawbale houses, gardening.

THE HOLLIES SUSTAINABLE VILLAGE

Contact: Rob Hopkins
Castletown, Enniskeane, Co Cork.

Tel: 023-47001.
E-mail: robnemma@iol.ie

The Hollies Sustainable Village is a development by Baile D'Ira Teo., the first eco-village development company to get charitable status in Ireland. It is based on a 56 acre farm in West Cork which was purchased in October 1998. It is intended to be a 16 house eco-village with a study centre and a visitors centre with a café and a shop, all set in a highly productive permaculture landscape.

SLI AN UISCE

Contact: Julia Kemp, Fred la Haye
Toreenlahard, Ballingeary, Bantry, West Cork

Tel: 027-52136 or Tel: 027-52136
E-mail: julia_kemp@hotmail.com

30 acre permaculture project / eco-hamlet, occasional weekend courses including organic gardening, coppicing, green building, reed beds and LETS. For more information send a SAE to Sli an Uisce, Tooreenlahard, Ballingeary, West Cork.

LISTINGS

BALLAMORE DEVELOPMENT GROUP

Contact: Rachel O'Grady,
Pratts, Askeaton, Co. Limerick

Tel: 061-394190
Fax: 061-394190
Email: arena@indigo.ie

Feasibility study completed on sixty-acre site at
Ballamore, Askeaton in 1998. Three other reports
relevant to Askeaton completed in 1999: Tourism,
alternative energy, eco-village /sustainable
development. Reports and studies are now on
public view at five centres. Next stage finance and
planning.

SUSTAINABLE PROJECTS LTD

Contact: Gavin Harte
19 Grantham St, Dublin 8

Tel: 353 01-4781216 / 088-2522880
website: http://www.sustainable.buz.org

Sustainable Projects Ireland Ltd. aims to create a
unique ecological village of about 40 houses, with
a community building, and an enterprise centre on
a 100-acre rural site, about one hour from Dublin.
The company requires a capital investment fund of
about £1.2 million, requiring 40 investors at
approximately £30,000 each.
When an investor holds £30,000 in loanstock they
can convert their stock and acquire a housing plot
with outline planning permission and full services
provided.

DUBLIN CO-HOUSING GROUP

Contact: Rachel Ludlow
35 Parliament St., Dublin 2

Tel: 01-2988500
E-mail: amjoyce@iol.ie

An expanding group of people with a shared vision
of creating a sustainable housing community in
the city, pulling resources and facilities to create a
stable, secure, healthy living environment.

EARTH WISDOM FOUNDATION

Contact: Kevin Hayes
64 Acorn Road, Dundrum, Dublin 16

Tel: 01-2951562

Earth Wisdom Foundation is a non-profit
organisation building community, embracing
people of all ages, ethnic origins and social
origins. It is independent of all political or
religious persuasions. The foundation's aim is to
identify new ways and opportunities for social
empowerment and economic development that
meet the needs of the present without
compromising the ability of future generations to
meet their own needs.**Trees are Life** compilation CD
available.

TUILE TEANGA

Contact: Isolde Carmody
Teach Shinanna, Shanraw, Keshcarrigan,
Co. Leitrim

E-mail: isoldec@yahoo.com
Website: www.homepages.iol.ie/~sinann

To create a sustainable, minimal impact living and
working environment. The employment will be
focussed on the Centre for Oral Arts and
Traditional Crafts, which will be a community-
based, sustainably run centre, open to the public.

TIR AN DROICHEAD

Contact: Jose Ospina
13 Glengarriff Road, Bantry, Co. Cork

Tel: 027-52416
Fax: 027-52415
E-mail: ospina@indigo.ie
Website: http://www.novas.freewire.co.uk

Development of social housing for excluded groups
through an integrated approach that delivers
services, training and economic integration.

COMMUNITY CENTRES

OUTHOUSE

Contact: Joe Harnett
6 South William St., Dublin 2

Tel: 01-6706377
Fax: 01-6791306
E-mail: outhouse@indigo.ie

LISTINGS

Website: www.http//indigo.ie/~outhouse/

The community centre for the members of Dublin's Lesbian/Gay/Bisexual/Trans communities, provides meeting space for thirty plus different groups and organisations, an information and referral service, a coffee shop, and offices of the gay men's health project. Open Mon-Sat, noon-6pm.

IONAD 'BUAIL ISTEACH' NA GAEILGE'

Irish Language Drop-in Centre

Contact: Cris Ni Choisdealbha
f/ch Connolly Books, 43 Sraid Essex Thoir Baile Atha Cliath

Tel: 01-4024807

CIORCAL COMGach Aoine, 1-2.30 pm (Tae & Caife Saor in aisce)
IMEACHTAI (tri Ghaeilge): Siuloidi Sleibhe, Turasanna Canala, Imeachtai Glasa/Comhshaoil, Tacr le Cearta Sibhialta agus Cearta Daonna, Cuairt ar Ionaid Stairiula. Irish Converstaion, Fridays 1-2, free tea and coffee EVENTS (through Irish): Mountain walks, canal trips, organic farming, events, support for human and civil rights, visits to historical places.

HOMELESS

CASTLEBLAYNEY TRUST FOR HOMELESS NEEDY AND UNEMPLOYED

Contact: Sr. Celine McArdle
Beech Corner, Castleblayney, Co. Monaghan

Tel: 042-974 0909
Fax: 042-974 0710

Castleblayney Trust consists of seven voluntary Trustees who work with Homeless, Needy & Unemployed people to improve their care, support, rehabilitation, accomodation and employment opportunities.

FOCUS IRELAND, RD+E DIVISION

Contact: Public Awareness Manager
1 Lord Edward Court, Bride St., Dublin 8

Tel: 01 4751955
Fax: 01 4751972
E-mail: focusirl@indigo.ie
Website: http://www.focusireland.ie

Focus Ireland is a voluntary organisation that works to prevent, alleviate and eliminate homelessness in Ireland. Focus Ireland provides housing and other services to people out of home.

CHILDREN

MAAM CHILDREN'S PLAYSCHEME

Contact: Jean Parker
The Old school-Kilmilkin, Maam, Co.Galway

Tel: 091-571157
Email: sor@iol.ie

A community run playscheme for young people, five to twenty years, co-operative play and games, art, children's rights, environmental awareness, music, drama, story telling. Talks and training for groups/organisations.

ISPCC

Irish society for the prevention of cruelty to children

Contact: Ann O'Malley, National Research Officer
20 Molesworth St., Dublin 2

Tel: 01-6794944
Fax: 01-6791746
Website: www.ispcc.ie

The ISPCC is a national children's rights and child advocacy agency. It provides child-centred services for children and their families and campaigns on behalf of children. It runs four direct access services: childline (freephone), STEPS (youth advice and counselling service), CRIB(childrens rights information bureau), Leanbh (child begging project).

BARNARDOS

Contact: Margaret Dorgan
Christchurch Square, Dublin 8

Tel: 01-4530355/087-2454500
E-mail: info@barnardos.ie

Barnardos is an independent Irish childcare organisation. At Barnardos we believe that all children have a right to achieve their full potential. We also believe that prevention is better than cure and that giving children a good start in life is an investment that benefits society as a whole. We receive funding from health boards and other government bodies which we supplement with income from our own fund-raising initiatives. We currently provide services in Dublin, Cork, Limerick, Offaly, Tipperary, Waterford and Westmeath.

BARNARDOS SERVICES INCLUDE

1. Family support services, aimed at vulnerable children and families in disadvantaged areas.
2. Solas - bereavement counselling service for children.
3. Adoption advice service which provides information and counselling on all aspects of adoption.
4. The National Children's Resource Centre - a one-stop resource of information on childcare issues for parents, professionals offering information, training and research on all matters concerning children.
5. Guardian, ad, litem service, providing independent reports on children who are involved in legal proceedings.

EDUCATION

COOLEENBRIDGE STEINER SCHOOL

Contact: Pearse O'Shiel
Tuamgraney, Co. Clare

Tel: 061-921253
Fax: 061-921253
E-mail: cooleen@iol.ie
Website: www.cooleenbridge.home.dhs.org

Cooleenbridge Steiner School was founded in 1986. It was the first Steiner school in the Republic of Ireland and now provides holistic Steiner based early childhood education and primary education to over 120 children.

CORK WALDORF STEINER INITIATIVE

Contact: Eoin MacCuirc
Cahergal House, Ballyhooley Rd. Cork City
Tel: 021-359000 ext.5637
Fax: 021-318335
E-mail: mccuirce@csu.ie

The school is a parent initiative offering the choice of Waldorf Steiner education for your child. From parent toddler group through kindergarten, to the class structure. The child-centered educational system offers a real educational alternative.

THE SPEEDWELL TRUST

Contact: Jean Kely
Parkanaur Forest Park, Dungannon,
Tyrone BT70 3AA

Tel: 0801-868-767392
Fax: 0801-868-761794
Email: speedwell.trust@btinternet.com
Website: www.speedwell-trust.com

Speedwell brings Catholic and Protestant children together to have fun exploring the forest and making new friends through, our environmental education programmes they learn respect for each other and the community.

HOME EDUCATION NETWORK (HEN)

Contact: Leoine Baldwin

Tel: 054-55717
E-mail: lbaldwin@tinet.ie
Home education is a legal and viable right in Ireland. HEN offers a forum for home educators; support and information on resources and techniques; social gatherings, regional meetings and a quarterly newsletter.

BIRTH AND PARENTING

HOME BIRTH ASSOCIATION

Contact: Stephanie Casey
Triton Lodge, Neranord Dalkey, Co. Dublin

Tel: 01-2853264
E-mail: steficasi@iol.ie or hba@iol.ie
Website: http://www.iol.ie/~hba

Voluntary group aims to increase public awareness and information about home birth, provide practical support and assistance to parents seeking home birth, and to promote domiciliary midwifery. Quarterly newsletter / group meetings.

MIDWIVES ASSOCIATION OF IRELAND

Contact: Kay O'Sullivan
49 Markland Woods, Maryborough
Hill, Douglas, Co. Cork

Tel: 021-363377
The MAI recognises that childbirth is a normal process for the vast majority of women. We are committed to the safety and welfare of both mother and baby. The aims and activities are to encourage midwives in their support of women's active participation in preconception, pregnancy, birth and parenthood.

LALECHE LEAGUE

Contact: Margaret McGuigan
Cremartin, Castleblayney, Co.Monaghan

Tel: 047-80922
Fax: 047-80922
Website: http://homepage.tinet.ie/~lalecheleague

Helping mothers to breastfeed through mother-to-mother support, education, information and encouragement. Increasing awareness of the role of breastfeeding in the healthy physical and emotional development of babies.

ECOBABY LIMITED

Contact: Renate von Dreusche
39 Pembroke Gardens, Ballsbridge, Dublin 4
Tel: 1850-52-52-53
E-Mail: natalls@iol.ie

Ecobaby delivers eco nappies direct, anywhere in Ireland. They are unbleached, hypoallergenic and made with recycled plastics. These disposables cost less than you think! Call now for your free sample.

TREOIR

Contact: Margaret Dromey
36 Upper Rathmines Rd., Dublin 6
Tel: 01-4964155/01-2821258
E-mail: treoir@indigo.ie
Website: www.indigo.ie/treoir

Treoir is a national body representing statutory and non-statutory organisations that provide services to unmarried parents and their children and it's aim is to improve the position of unmarried parents and children in Ireland. It offers an information, referral and library service and publishes extensively including an information pack for unmarried parents.

GINGERBREAD IRELAND

Contact: Carmel Clarke-Mudrack
29/30 Dame St. Dublin 2
Tel: 01-6710291
Fax: 01-6710352

Gingerbread one-parent-family organisation help-line, Monday-Friday 9.30am-5.00pm. Child and adult professional counselling, family mediation, family law information and advice. Regular support groups and family fun events for members.

ADVICE CENTRES

VICTIM SUPPORT

Contact: Rachael Shevlin
Halliday House, 32 Arran Quay, Dublin 7
Freephone: 1800-661771
Tel: 01-8780870
Fax: 01-8780944
E-mail: info@victimsupport.ie

Victim support is a community based organisation of trained volunteers, dedicated to the service of all victims of crime, who provide emotional and practical support to those affected by crime.

SEE ALSO

ACTIVE ART CREATIONS

Community art workshop, murals, collages, playground designs and games.
Full listing: Art and Leisure section.

CALYPSY PRODUCTIONS

Theatrical work tackling issues that effect our lives.
Full listing: Art and Leisure section.

THE RURAL INNOVATION CENTRE

A productive means of meeting the education and training needs of rural dwellers.
Full listing: Agriculture section.

BABY MILK ACTION

Campaigning for ethical marketing or baby milk.
Full listing: Global and Local section.

JESUIT CENTRE FOR FAITH AND JUSTICE

Engages in action and reflection to counter injustice in Ireland. Issues include homelessness, mental illness and crime.
Full listing: Global and Local section.

page 216 **Introduction** to health Judith Hoad

page 218 **Homoeopathy** Decland Hammond

page 219 **Reiki** Gwendoline McGowen

page 219 **Shiatsu** Diana Cassidy

page 220 **Aromatherapy** Mary Grant

page 222 **Acupuncture** C. Harrison and M. Muldowney

page 222 **Craniosacral Therapy** Marion Bellow

page 223 **Reflexology** Irish Reflexologist Institute

page 221 **Hynotherapy** Dr Joseph Kearney

page 223 **Feng Shui** Carmel O'Connor

page 224 **Yoga** The Irish Yoga Association

page 224 **Tai Chi** Jan Golden

page 224 **Spirituality** Darra Malloy

HOLISTIC HEALTH / MIND BODY SPIRIT

Judith Hoad Dip. SHEN TAO, I.T.E.C.

Judith Hoad is a vibrational medicine practitioner, writer and teacher, living in Inver, Co Donegal. Her recent books include 'Healing with Herbs' and 'Need or Greed? Our Practical Choices for the Earth.' Judith is a founding member of the Irish Council of Vibrational Medicine.

West of the Shannon, many people will 'go for the cure', or 'get a bottle' from someone who has inherited that remedy as a secret recipe. This recipe is usually handed down from father to son, or from mother to daughter. Sometimes the 'cure' arrives by the circumstantial fact of someone's parents bearing the same surname, both before and after marriage - for example, the oldest son of a Gallagher/Gallagher union will have the cure for mumps. In such a culture, The fact that any individual that has earned a Diploma to practise a non-conventional medical discipline is scarcely acknowledged, so long as they can 'cure'. In some societies it takes the literate middle-classes to provide the clientele for non-conventional practitioners, whereas in Ireland everyone is a potential client.

For this reason, it is possible to find practitioners of most disciplines working throughout rural as well as urban parts of Ireland. Until the publication of this directory, it has been advisable to go to the nearest wholefood shop to discover such a practitioner. Those people focusing on health maintenance - such as the growing number who seek and organise the natural foods available in these shops - are also likely to be on the lookout for some holistic practice to assist them, which may be listed here.

We are what we eat and good food is the basis of good health, along with appropriate exercise and peace of mind. Millennia have passed during which humanity trusted food producers to produce reliable, wholesome food. Only in the last forty years or so has it become increasingly common to have that trust violated. The blatant manipulation of food plants and animals has come on top of the realisation that most allergies are due to the chemical pollution of food, by residues from agricultural practices.

The purchasing public has also made the connection between the agri-chemical corporations and the pharmaceutical corporations - so often one and the same - and the allergies to conventional medicines. We are all aware that the profits made by these corporations are their prime concern. Many of us are also making another connection: commerce and industry has close, symbiotic relationships with politics. There is a public perception of how the so-called 'revolving door' works to provide executives and directors from the agri-chemical and pharmaceutical industries with seats on government commissions and committees, while politicians and senior civil servants are offered directorships and employment in those industries.

Growing awareness that holism takes in the physical, emotional, mental and spiritual aspects of being - what Machalle Small Wright calls the 'pems' – has brought yoga, aikido, qi gong, tai chi chuan, circle dance, meditation groups and so on within the ambit of people seeking to restore or maintain a healthy balance in their lives. Most of these practices require the individual to work daily, at home, as well as within the group on a regular basis of group meetings. Thus self-responsibility manifests itself, and dependence on 'experts' and the passive receipt of remedies is wearing away. Many teachers of these disciplines work in conjunction with non-conventional practitioners, or are themselves practitioners who encourage this growth of the individual's participation in their own recovery and health maintenance.

These groups, along with workshops and training schemes, have brought remedial skills into the community in a wonderful way, so that hands-on methods of health maintenance and recovery can now be found in almost every parish. Aromatherapy, massage, reflexology, reiki, aura-soma, flower and gem essences, colour, light and sound therapies are increasingly commonplace. One day soon, I hope, some of these skills, such as reiki, for example, will be taught in schools to children, so that ultimately every family will have a practitioner.

Those skills that contain a diagnostic as well as remedial basis are the true medical alternatives, or sometimes adjuncts – in the 'complementary' sense – to conventional medicine. Such practices include homoeopathy, acupuncture or acupressure – such as shiatsu or shen tao – as well as herbalism, chiropractic, cranial osteopathy and osteopathy.

In a society so numerically small as Ireland, it is hard to find enough practitioners to form professional associations, although a few do exist. In 1988 the Irish Council of Vibrational Medicine was formed at the first public meeting, held in October of that year. Discussions are on-going about the formation of a professional body to register and regulate the practitioner section. These discussions, which take place every six to seven weeks (each time in a different part of the island of Ireland), are open to anyone who has an interest, professional or lay, in any aspect of vibrational medicine. Speakers are invited to describe their practices and informal discussions often ensue. Subjects have ranged from equipment for light therapy, (including light treatment for the S.A.D. phenomenon), to the making of flower essences, to biodynamic gardening techniques used by the Irish Seed Savers. The Irish Council of Vibrational Medicine, therefore, is also holistic in that it encompasses the whole of Ireland, all aspects of vibrational medicine and all degrees of expertise of anyone who is interested.

holistic health

Most non-conventional practitioners provide life-style and eating pattern advice to their clients, along with their particular area of expertise. Workshops and talks help to advance awareness of how the human body functions; what the environmental threats are; how to withstand them and encouragement to participants to make their needs known whenever an opportunity arises. The non-conventional practitioners and practices listed in this directory are offering their information as a tool for people developing self-responsibility for their own and their families' natural good health.

> **Scientific medicine has arrived at an invidious position. It now imagines that it is the only medical system in existence. Modern medical principles have turned from a theory to a dogma, and those who wonder what has been left behind are branded as heretics.**
> Stephen Fulder, The Tao of Medicine

Homoeopathy

Declan Hammond LCH, ISHom Director, The Irish School of Homoeopathy

Homoeopathy is a therapeutic medical science which holistically treats physical, emotional and mental illness by applying the principle of 'like cures like'. It is a powerful, yet gentle, form of healing that respects the wisdom of the body/mind and recognises that symptoms of ill health are expressions of an underlying imbalance in the patient's energy. Cure and ultimately a state of health are attained by using individually prescribed and minute quantities of specially prepared natural remedies. These are capable of stimulating deep healing responses, without any of the worrying toxicity of conventional medication.

Although the basic concepts of this form of therapy have been known and used, at least, from the time of Hippocrates in ancient Greece, it was a German doctor, Samuel Hahnemann (1755-1843), who systematised its medicinal use. His work forms the basis of the science which is still practiced today. He stressed the importance of treating the source of a patient's illness, rather than just suppressing its symptoms, and the necessity of dealing with the patient's mental and emotional state, dietary factors and environmental influences.

Over the last 200 years, homoeopathy has proved itself extremely effective in the treatment of all the major infectious diseases. Chronic illnesses such as arthritis, asthma, allergies and immune disorders, as well as a wide range of psychiatric states and psychological problems are regularly treated by homoeopaths.

Homoeopathy is a safe and effective form of medicine which, in the hands of a qualified professional, offers a real alternative for those looking for a gentler approach to healing, for themselves and their families.

Reiki **Gwendoline McGowan** Reiki Master and Teacher

Reiki is a 'hands on healing' technique that traces its roots to Japan and the late 1700s. This method of relaxation and de-stressing has been welcomed into many Irish homes and has more recently found it's way into the business environment.

Dis-ease and dis-harmony are said to be the main causes of stress in our everyday lives. A course of eight reiki sessions can bring about a clarity and awareness which are sometimes lacking.

In the business environment reiki practitioners are being called into office complexes to give treatments on a weekly basis. This is believed to enhance the productivity of business.

The support reiki offers the overworked mind and body is a non-intrusive method of addressing these imbalances, ideally bringing about a calmer and more relaxed attitude to today's busy schedule.

Whilst reiki is known as a 'hands on healing' technique, in all cases the client stays fully clothed, simply removing his or her shoes.

Reiki has proven to be a wonderful, supportive, non-intrusive and gentle way of bringing Ki (or Chi) back into the human body form. Reiki offers excellent relief from pain or lack of sleep. It can also aid in regaining lack of energy and can encourage one to regain that 'joie de vivre', that so many people tell me they are missing today.

One does not have to be ill to receive healing. Some of us receive healing to maintain a healthy mind, body, soul and spirit.

Shiatsu **Diana Cassidy** shiatsu practitioner

Shiatsu is a Japanese word meaning finger pressure. In practice, the giver uses fingers, thumbs, sometimes elbows and knees, and always concentrated focus and sensitivity, to ensure that the treatment will accurately meet and enhance the receiver's life-force.

Usually the recipient lies on a futon and wears comfortable clothing. The therapist applies appropriate pressure to tsubos (acupressure points), and smoothes the flow of Ki (energy), in the meridians (charted energy pathways).

With most oriental practices including shiatsu, the emphasis is on maintaining health and thus help to prevent physiological disorders. So, in

holistic health

effect, one doesn't have to be ill to receive shiatsu. However shiatsu can help return the receiver to a better state of health, increase relaxation, circulation, vitality, breathing, pain relief and mobility. Some of the many problems that can be helped include migraine, IBS, tension, depression, certain types of epilepsy, anxiety, menstrual disorders, M.E. and sports injuries.

> **A culture that alienates itself from the very ground of its own being – from wilderness outside (that is to say, wild nature, the wild, self-contained, self-informing ecosystems) and from that other wilderness within – is doomed to a very destructive behaviour, ultimately perhaps self-destructive behaviour.** Gary Snyder

Aromatherapy

Mary Grant of Lifespring and chair of Register of Qualified Aromatherapists.

Aromatherapy involves the use of distilled aromatic essential oils obtained from plants. These work with the body's natural processes: as pro-biotic agents; through the limbic system and the sense of smell; on a spiritual level, through action on the energetic field or aura of the person.

While practices surrounding the use of essential oils go back at least 5,000 years, the term was coined by a French chemist, Gattefosse (cf.: Aromatherapie, 1928.) Scientific aromatherapy grew from his pioneering work, today it bears little resemblance to the original as research involves synthetic and 'nature identical' oils.

Aesthetic and current forms described as clinical, holistic aromatherapy drew it's inspiration from the work of Madame Marguerite Maury, in the field of cosmetology and translated into short, popular, beauty therapy type training with their own associations. In practice, oils developed scientifically for the cosmetic and perfumery industry are generally used.

In the U.K. The Aromatherapy Organisations Council, was formed in the early 1990s, to regulate and represent the emerging profession. Membership of the linked Aromatherapy Trade Council is confined to the use of products obtained directly from nature. The Register of Qualified Aromatherapists, in Ireland, subscribes to the norms and ethics as understood by these organisations.

Psycho-social aromatherapy combines clinical, holistic and broad view of scientific aromatherapy, through transdermal, aromatic and transpersonal application on the physical, mental, emotional and spiritual levels simultaneously. Essential oils as described by the Aromatherapy Trade

Council are used.

This approach sees aromatherapy as a healing art linked to cultural and spiritual roots. All cultures used plant essences: explicit references are made in the earliest writings emanating from Ireland.

Pioneered by Mary Grant, this exploration is linked with universal archetypical understanding, delving beyond recorded history to the origins of our myths and legends. As we explore our familial roots, we open up to new levels of meaning contained in our common histories. This gave birth to her synergistic, alchemical psycho-mythological blending which is a very powerful force in evoking self knowledge.

> **In the last analysis, the psychological roots of the crisis humanity is facing on a global scale seem to lie in the loss of the spiritual perspective.** Stanislav Grof

Hypnotherapy
Dr Joseph Kearney from the Irish Association of Hypnotherapists

Hypnosis is an altered state of consciousness in which the client is both alert and aware, and in full control of his or her words and actions at all times. It is a means of by-passing the conscious mind's critical factor with its argumentative nature and directly contacting the subconscious mind where modifications in attitude and behaviour can be achieved. The experience is enjoyably relaxing and effective and safe.

Habit control forms a dominant part of hypnotherapy. Two entirely different treatments are available. Suggestion therapy is used on the simpler problems: smoking, nail-biting, pre-test nerves, slimming etc., and usually requires only one session. Analytical therapy is used to discover the underlying causes of psychological problems.

Hypnotherapy is a wonderful tool to be used for our benefit. It is a complementary therapy and is not an alternative to seeking medical care. Enjoy hypnosis and learn how to use it in your life.

Acupuncture

C. Harrison and M. Muldowney, acupuncture practitioners based at The Drogheda Acupuncture Clinic

Acupuncture originated in China more than 3000 years ago and is a complex medical system used to treat illness, prevent disease and improve well-being. Holistic in approach, it focuses on all aspects of the person.

It involves the insertion of fine pre-sterilised needles, at predetermined points on the surface of the body, in order to restore health.

Acupuncture can be used alone or combined with other forms of traditional Chinese medicine (TCM) e.g. moxibustion: a form of heat treatment; dietary therapy; herbal medicine and life style advice.

It is a comprehensive system of healthcare, used to treat a wide range of medical conditions and is also compatible with western medicines.

Before considering a visit to an acupuncture practitioner, one should ensure that the practitioner is fully qualified and insured, is a member of a reputable acupuncture organisation and uses sterile disposable needles.

Thus, the patient can be confident that the treatment is safe and free of any harmful effects.

When a civilisation lacks rites of passage, its soul is sick. The evidence for this sickness is threefold: first, there are no elders; second, the young are violent; third the adults are bewildered. Malidoma Some

Craniosacral Therapy **Marion Bellow** a Craniosacral therapist.

Craniosacral therapy acknowledges the deepest roots and highest potentials of the human system. Within this system is the concept of an intelligent life force, transmitted throughout the body via its fluid systems. The rhythmic tide-like fluctuation of cerebrospinal fluid and body fluids generally is known as the Craniosacral Motion or Primary Respiratory Impulse. This maintains the body's vitality and constitutional energy and its healing resources.

The practitioner is working with the health of the system to be expressed within even the most chronic patterns of restriction and resistance, encouraging new levels of order, balance and harmony in mind and body. This is done via gentle hands-on contact with the tissues and fluids of the body. The heart of Craniosacral Therapy is a depth of listening and stillness, with a profound trust that the client's system has the inherent intelligence to heal itself.

holistic health

> Sustainable development involves devising a social and economic system which ensures that these goals are sustained i.e. that real incomes rise, that educational standards increase, that the health of the nation improves, that the general quality of life is advanced.
> Pearce et al, Blueprint for a Green Economy

Reflexology Irish Reflexologists' Institute

Reflexology is a simple, non-evasive and effective form of healing. It is a science that rests on the principle that there are reflexes in the feet and hands which correspond to all the glands, organs and parts of the body. By applying pressure with the thumbs or fingers to these reflex points, a qualified practitioner can alleviate or treat a range of conditions – stress, sinus problems, back pain, irritable bowel syndrome, migraine etc. Each reflex point reflects the state of the body part by its feel and condition. An experienced practitioner of reflexology can detect potentially weak areas before they start to cause problems thus helping a person to remain fit and healthy. Reflexology is not a substitute for medical care and is not an alternative medicine, rather a complementary therapy which complements medical practice. Reflexology therapy is excellent as preventative healthcare in bringing about deep relaxation and assisting the body in cleansing itself of toxins and impurities. Energy pathways which have become blocked over many years are cleared of blockages and all body parts are allowed to have free flow of energy. Circulation is improved with each treatment and the body's own defence system is activated. Reflexology is a holistic therapy and it balances the body physically, mentally and emotionally.

An Introduction to Feng Shui Carmel O'Connor Feng Shui Consultant.

Feng Shui [fung shway] 'wind and water'

Based on oriental practices over 4000 years old, feng shui is now becoming more recognised in the West as an art which creates balance and harmony in the environment. Feng shui has mistakenly been seen as another form of interior design. It is much more than this. It is the understanding of the flow of energies in our home and workplaces and how these affect our lives. In feng shui the home is seen as a mirror, reflecting our states of mind, past experiences, aspirations and current life situations. After all a cluttered home leads to a cluttered mind! Using the principles of feng shui we can learn to identify an imbalance of energy and set about healing it with specific enhancements. By re-balancing energies and implementing changes feng shui can help bring harmony, abundance and joy to those who use it.

holistic health

What is Yoga? The Irish Yoga Association

Yoga is the holistic development of the individual. It has been called awareness of life, personal development, the journey into Self or to be simply human. The word yoga is taken from the Sanskrit meaning union with the source... to unite, to join, to integrate. We need to become aware that as human beings we are made of dimensions. We have a body that needs developing, a mind that needs nurturing and an inner space that needs exploring. To live fully in one's being, to experience this human life in its entirety, to reach our full potential as human beings, is the journey of Yoga.

What is Tai Chi? Jan Golden tai chi teacher and acupuncture practitioner

Tai chi is a powerful series of interconnected flowing martial techniques performed slowly that have significant and long-lasting benefits for the body and mind. The essence of tai chi is relaxation through gentle bending, twisting, contracting and extending movements combined with deep diaphragmatic breathing to pump oxygen and blood more efficiently around the body leaving the practitioner feeling vibrant, light, and free from fatigue. With practice, the adept will have excellent coordination, a dramatically improved posture, greater sense of balance, and a heightened sense of vitality without exhaustion.

Tai chi is for all ages. It can be practised by the very young and the very old. All body types can take it up, whether overweight or slim, without any adverse effects. It also complements very well any other form of exercise. The entire bodily nerves are relaxed to promote more efficient dispersal of energy, and the postures are not static, but are constantly shifting from one to another.

Tai chi can be practised at any time of the day or night, in loose clothing. It refreshes you for the day ahead, and calms you down after the strains of a day's toil. It is a perfect way to prepare for old age, as you get stronger, not weaker, as you age. Practised well, it can slow the ageing process down, and deflect some of the unpleasant side effects of modern city life.

Spirituality Darra Malloy

Today there is a paradoxical shift away from organised religion yet towards spirituality. The growth of interest in Celtic spirituality, not just in Ireland but also around the world, has been phenomenal. Many people who continue to go to church feel dissatisfied and undernourished spiritually and are searching for something compensatory. Others have left their traditional religious practices and are either floundering in a wilderness searching for an oasis, or are piecing together bits from various traditions, both Eastern and Western, and creating their own spiritual collage.

It is my view that humanity has reached a crucial moment in human consciousness. The old religions no longer answer all the questions we now ask. Like the lobster who sheds her shell to grow a new one, we are in the process of shedding a shell we have worn for centuries that is no longer adequate. While we grow a new shell, we are vulnerable. The shape and form of the new spirituality to emerge is not yet clear, but the process requires courage, imagination and tolerance of diversity.

A spirituality for today must be capable of underpinning modern life in all its facets: lifestyle, consumerism, the environment, nature, food, market forces, technology, genetics, waste, personal development, cultural identity, women – as well as offering a perspective on the great issues of war and peace, rich and poor, slave and free.

Going back to the indigenous spiritualities of the Celts or the Native Americans will never be the total answer. These spiritualities were for their people and for their time. And yet people are drawn to them today perhaps precisely because they were indigenous. These spiritualities grew out of the people, their culture and their landscape. This is what we need today. Modern religions are like multinational products, exportable anywhere and impervious to culture or place. The search, I believe, is for something more connected.

holistic health

NATURAL MEDICINE COMPANY

The Natural Medicine Company is one of the leading suppliers of health products and natural medicines in Ireland with a history going back 20 years. We specialise in food supplements, and herbal and homoeopathic medicines which you will find readily available in all health stores and in most pharmacies. If you have any problems obtaining supplies or would like further information on either the products or the companies we represent, we would be very pleased to hear from you.

PRODUCT RANGES REPRESENTED BY THE NATURAL MEDICINE COMPANY:

BRAND	RANGES
Weleda	Homoeopathic Medicines, Natural Medicines, Toiletries
Tisserand Aromatherapy	Essential Oils, Toiletries, Accoutrements
Bach Flower Remedies	Rescue Remedy, Individual Bach Flower Remedies
Salus Haus	Herbal Tonics, Herbal Teas
Schoenenberger	Herbal Juices
Lifeplan	Vitamin & Mineral Supplements, Multinutrients
Nelson's	Homoeopathic Medicines, Herbal Specialties
Nature's Own	Food State Supplements
Finders	Dead Sea Magik & Spa Magik Mineral Bath Salts & Skincare, Juices, Gels & Skincare
De Vere Aloe Vera	

Our telephone lines are open **Monday** to **Friday** from **9.00am** through to **5.00pm**.

Tel: 045 865575   Fax: 045 865827

The Natural Medicine Company Ltd., Burgage, Blessington, Co. Wicklow

MIND, BODY, SPIRIT BOOKS

The Web of Life- Fritjof Capra
ISBN: 0006547516, 1997.

The Turning Point- Fritjof Capra
ISBN: 0553345729, 1988.

A Walk Through Time: From Stardust to Us
Brian Swimme and Elizabeth Sahtouris,
ISBN: 0471317004, 1998.

Planet Medicine-
Richard Grossinger
ISBN: 1556431791, 1985.

The Web that has no Weaver
T.J. Kaptchuk,
ISBN: 0809228033, 1984.

Asian Health Secrets
Letha Hadady
ISBN: 0517700557, 1998.

Yoga, the Iyengar Way
Mira Silva and Shyam Metha
ISBN: 0863184200, 1990.

Ecstatic Body Postures
Belinda Gore
ISBN: 1879181223, 1995.

The Tao of Natural Breathing
Dennis Lewis
ISBN: 0965161102, 1996.

Anam Cara - Spiritual Wisdom from the Celtic World
John O'Donohue,
ISBN: 0553505920, 1998.

The Dance of the Dissident Daughter - A Woman's Journey from Christian Tradition to the Sacred Feminine
Sue Monk Kidd
ISBN: 0060645881, 1996.

The Heart Aroused - Poetry and the Preservation of the Soul in Corporate America David Whyte
ISBN: 185835885X, 1999.

God In All Worlds - An Anthology of Contemporary Spiritual Writing
Lucinda Vardey ed.,
ISBN: 0679745432, 1996.

Care Of The Soul - A Guide for Cultivating Depth and Sacredness in Everyday Life -
Thomas Moore
ISBN: 0722599048, 1997.

Cathedrals of the Spirit - The Message of Sacred Places
T.C. McLuhan
ISBN: 0722533659, 1996.

Eternal Echoes - Exploring Our Hunger To Belong
John O'Donohue
ISBN: 0593044932, 1999.

Uncommon Wisdom - Conversations With Remarkable People
Fritjof Capra
ISBN: 0006543413, 1989.

The Feng Shui Handbook - How to Create a Healthier Living and Working Environment
Master Lam Kam Chuen
ISBN: 0805042156, 1996.

MIND, BODY, SPIRIT WEBSITES

Homeopathy Online
http://www.homeopathyhome.com
Resonate Spiritual-Transformational Resources
http://www.resonate.org/
Awakenings: Tools for psychological and spiritual growth
http://www.lessons4living.com/index.htm
Awakening Earth
http://www.awakeningearth.org/
One World On-Line
http://www.oneworld.org/
U.S. Celtic Church Communities
http://www.tcac.com/~allan/accc.html
An Fainne, Earth Based Spirituality in Ireland:
http://indigo.ie/~imago/moot.html

holistic health

holistic health

ACUPUNCTURE

ACUPUNCTURE & CHINESE MEDICINE ORGANISATION

Contact: The Secretary
111 Walkinstown Rd., Walkinstown, Dublin 12

Tel: 093-25180

Largest independent acupuncture organisation in Ireland. BUPA approved. Members are fully qualified and insured and adhere to a code of ethics and practice. Use sterile disposable needles.

MARY KEATING B.Sc. Lic.Ac M.A.I.A
Coolaleen, Broadford, Limerick

Tel: 063-84040
Fax: 063-84040
E-mail: mgcremin@tinet.ie

For pain, asthma, insomnia, sinusitis, menstrual treatment and menopausal problems, infertility, fatigue, arthritis, migraine, depression, digestive problems, general aches and pains.

LETTERKENNY ACUPUNCTURE & HERBAL CLINIC

Contact: Murrough Birmingham
Ramelton Rd., Letterkenny, Co. Donegal

Tel: 074-24559

Acupuncture Mb.AcA (Member of British Acupuncture Association) Chinese herbal medicine M.R.C.H.M.(Member of Register of Chinese Herbal Medicine in Britain and Eire).

NATURAL HEALTH

Contact: Catherine Ansbro
155 Seafield Road, East Clontarf,
Dublin 3 and Boyle, Co. Roscommon

Tel: 01-8331313
Fax: 01-8331313
E-mail: cansbro@eircom.net

Health care for forward movement on all levels: physical, emotional, mental and spiritual. Acupuncture (with or without needles), zero balancing, flower essences, microbial balancing & other nature-friendly processes. Fully qualified.

DROGHEDA ACUPUNCTURE CLINIC

Contact: Mary Muldowney
84 West St., Drogheda, Co. Louth

Tel: 041-9843162/01-2863233/01-6685173

Traditional Chinese medicine, acupuncture, maxibustion, cupping, Tui Na, dietary therapy, herbal prescriptions. Members of the Acupuncture and Chinese Medicine Organisation.
Appointments: 041-9843163.

DUNGARVAN ALTERNATIVE HEALTH CLINIC

Contact: Orla Casey
Pookeen Lane, Main St., Dungarvan, Co. Waterford

Tel: 058-44299
E-mail: dahc@cablesurf.com

Acupuncture & traditional Chinese medicine aromatherapy, chiropractic, hypnotherapy, neurolinguistic programming, Indian head massage, massage, reflexology.

LINDA HEFFERNAN ACUPUNCTURE PRACTICE AND THE COLLEGE OF INTEGRATIVE ACUPUNCTURE.

Contact: Linda Heffernan
6 St. Brendans Rd., Woodquay, Galway

Tel: 091-561676

Linda Heffernan runs an acupuncture and herbalism practice in Galway since 1984. Linda is also director of the College of Integrative Acupuncture which runs a 3 year part-time professional training course commencing each September. App/Eng 091-561676

SEAMUS LYNCH Lic.Ac.M.B.Ac.C.A.M.B.R.A.
17 Alma Rd., Monkstown Co., Dublin

Tel: 01-2846073

Practitioner of acupuncture and zero balancing, a new form of bodywork which focuses on the skeletal structure. Does not use joint manipulation. Teacher of Indian head massage. Weekend workshop and yoga.

GOLDEN ENERGY ARTS

Contact: Jan Golden
Garden Flat 2, 76 Frankfort Ave. Rathgar Dublin 6

Tel: 01-4968342
e-mail: jang@indigo.ie
Website: www.goldenenergyarts.com

Acupuncture is an ancient medical method of restoring health to the body. It can be used by anybody at any age for almost anything and it has no side effects.

AROMATHERAPY

ANAMCARA

"Caring for those who care for others"

Contact: Marguerite Brady
48 Garville Ave., Rathgar, Dublin 6

Tel: 087-8274508 or 01-4971454
Email: yourmystar@ireland.com

Promoting and maintaining health & well-being of individuals using the above mentioned therapies in combination with AnamCara. Aromatherapy handmade products as well as conducting regular workshops in aromatherapy and reflexology.

LIFESPRING

Contact: Mary Grant SRN MEd MRQA
111 Cliftonville Rd., Belfast, N. Ireland
Tel: 087-2436496 / 08 01232-753658
Fax: 08 01232-748236
E-mail: aromatonem@fsbdial.co.uk

Radiance therapy & transpersonal psychotherapy: (UKCP); psycho-social aromatherapy; personal growth, Anam Chara (1978) programmes; family healing; Irish mythology. RQAI accredited Diploma courses: Supervision. Professioal development. Essential oils, ATC therapist quality.

THE REGISTER OF QUALIFIED AROMATHERAPISTS, IRELAND

111 Cliftonville Rd. Belfast, N. Ireland
Tel: 087-2436496 / 08 01232-753658
Fax: 08 01232-748236
E-mail: aromatonem@fsbdial.co.uk

This is a democratic professional association of aromatherapists who have undergone training of the highest possible standards, honouring a mulit-disciplinary approach at consultancy level. Members promote research, supervision, multi-disciplinary work.

ATAR - COMPLEMENTARY THERAPY CENTRE & AROMATHERAPY SUPPLIERS

Contact: Nick & Catherine George
Selskar Avenue, Wexford town, Wexford

Tel: 053-21755 / 087-6759233
Fax: 053-21755
E-mail: atar@indigo.ie
Website: http://indigo.ie/~atar

We manufacture a range of pure esential oils, body care products and base ingredients, our complimentary therapy centre in Wexford town specializes in Swedish massage.

NATURALLY AROMATHERAPY/ REFLEXOLOGY BEAUTY CLINIC

Contact: Siobhan Purcell
The Villa, 42 Morrisons Ave., Waterford
Tel:051-379939

As a professional aromatherapist, reflexologist and beauty therapist. I use these therapies to promote good health, relaxation, and reduce stress caused by the increasing pressure in our personal and professional lines.

ANNAPURNA NATURAL HEALTHCARE

Contact: Anne Cronin
6 Sidney Place, Wellington Rd., Cork
Tel: 087-2255831

As a member of the international federation of Aromatherapy, Anne Cronin offers aromatherapy and reflexology treatments to the highest standards using highest theraputic oils from sustainable sources. Courses given.

MARTINA NEVIN RGN IAPA

The Nature Store
324A North Circular Road, Phibsboro, Dublin 5.
Tel: 01-8304904 / 088-2188033

Aromatherapy massage using essential oils. Swiss reflex massage. Remedial head, neck and shoulder massage. Pregnancy & baby massage. Available Tuesday and Friday at The Nature Store. For other days, phone the above number.

THE AROMATHERAPY & REFLEXOLOGY CENTRE

Contact: Ann Corcoran
Camden Court Hotel, Camden Street, Dublin 2
Tel: 01 4759666

Aromatherapy massage. Healing massage. Reflexology, Indian head massage. Remedial back massage & remedial neck and shoulder massage.

NUALA WOULFE BEAUTY SALON LTD

Contact: Nuala Woulfe
4c Glasthule Road, Sandycove Co. Dublin
Tel: 01 2300244

Beauty therapy / aromatherapy & reflexology. Beauty therapy - Matis & Areda treatments, day spa therapy treatments, aromatherapy, reflexology, massage, manicures, pedicures etc.

SILVERCREST CLINIC

Contact: Martina Piper
Perceval Street, Kanturk, Cork

Tel: 029-51338

I work in the areas of aromatherapy, reflexology, therapeutic massage. All therapies can be beneficial and maybe a help to treat all ailments especially stress, back pain, headaches etc.

MARGARET CONNOLLY

31 St. Columbanus Rd., Milltown, Dublin 14

Tel: 087-2392313 / 01-2960220

Aromatherapy, reflexology, massage and stress management (professional qualifications and insurance). Clinics: Baggot St. and Dundrum. Also: wellbeing@work, on-site treatments and stress management in the work place.

MARY GRANT

Lifespring SRN. M Ed. MRQA

RADIENCE THERAPY INCORPORATES:
TRANSPERSONAL PSYCHOTHERAPY:

UK Registered Psycho-Social Aromatherapy,

Personal Growth Programmes,

Anam Chara (1978) Programmes.

FAMILY OF ORIGIN HEALING, IRISH MYTHOLOGY TODAY:

RQAI Accredited Diploma Courses: Post basic supervision and

professional development.

Books: Psyco-Mythological Blending, Guidlines for P-S

AROMATHERAPY IN HOSPITALS AND INSTITUTIONS:

Essential oils-ATC Therapist quality.

Tel: 087 2436 496 or 0801 232 753658
Fax: 0801 232 748236
Email: AromatoneM@FSBDial.co.uk

COUNSELLING

MAURA HORKAN

Rathmines, Dublin 6, Counselling and Reiki

Tel: 086-8237230

Counselling & Reike for individuals in a confidential and safe setting. Dublin 6 area.

JACQUIE BURGESS

Slaney House, Tullow, Co. Carlow

Tel: 0503-51057

Fax: 0503-51641
E-mail: jacquie@eircom.net Website:
http://homepage.eircom.net/~herbie/jackbio.html

Therapist in personal development, crystal healing, body work, meditation and counselling.
Workshops in meditation, crystals and spiritual development. Author of Healing with Crystals and Crystals for Life (Gill and Macmillan).

KERRY COUNSELLING CENTRE

Contact: Mary Reale
D17 Edward Court, Edward St., Tralee Co. Kerry

Tel: 066-7122931
Fax: 066-7122931

Supply of individual, couples and family counselling, supervision. Counsellor training, assertiveness and parenting courses and staff maintainance.

AIDS HELP WEST

Contact: Nicholas P. Fenlon
Ozanam house, St. Augustine St., Galway

Tel: 091-566266 / 091 562213 / 086-2325129
Fax: 091-564708
E-mail: aidswest@iol.ie

We provide education, workshops about HIV/ AIDS and STDs.
We provide a help-line (Mon-Fri 10a.m to 5p.m)
We provide support services to those infected with HIV and their families

CHIROPODY

STEPHANIE BEASANT

18 Georges St., Tramore, Waterford or Queens St.,Tramore Co. Waterford

Tel: 051-841772

Chiropody/podiatry practitioner approved by the Department of Health for treatment and advice regarding a wide range of foot and related problems.

CHIROPRACTORS

ARKLOW CHIROPRACTIC CLINIC

Contact: Peter Reade B.App.Sci (Chiro) M.C.A.I.
6 Inbhear Mor Square, Templerainey,
Arklow, Co. Wicklow.

Tel: 0402-91133
Fax: 0402-91133
E-mail: arklowchiro@tinet.ie

Gentle alleviation of spine-related disorders e.g. (back, neck, leg, arm, pain, migraine, headaches, indigestion, pain, dysmenorrhoea, asthma, colic, recurrent ear infections and more. Therapeutic massage also available. Highly qualified practitioners.

THE CHIRO CENTRE

Contact: Feargal Tobin BSC DC MBAAC MIAI
3 The Cova, Whitehall Rd Terenure Dublin 12

Tel: 01-4650030
E-mail: fergaltobin@tinet.ie

The Chiro Centre - a health cure clinic specialising in natural solutions to health problems. Incorporating backcare using McTimerery Corley, chiropractic. Asthma care using the Bateyko method. Natural health care using applied kinesiology.

MAYNOOTH CHIROPRACTIC CLINIC

Contact: Linda Finley-McKenna, Dublin Road, Maynooth Co. Kildare

Tel: 01 628 5962

Gentle manipulation of spinal misalignments for the restoration of health.

CHINESE MEDICINE

CHINESE TRADITIONAL MASSAGE (TUI NA)

Contact: Tim Li
3 Moatland Road, Navan.

Tel: 086-8470912

Tim Li is a fully qualified practitioner in Tui Na, a deep tissue massage, including manipulation which works on acupoints and pain relief points, leading to better circulation, sleep and toxin removal.

SUE HARVEY Lic TCM MORTCM

4 Dartmouth Road, Dublin 6, Co. Dublin

Tel: 01 6685987

Traditional Chinese medicine. Chinese medicine dates back over 2,000 years. It aims to prevent illness, promote health and ensure a long life, it is a holistic medicine which looks to the root cause of illness.

CLINIC OF ORIENTAL & TRADITIONAL CHINESE MEDICINE

Contact: Deirdre Mackesy
9 Oakfield Green, Glanmire, Co. Cork

Tel: 021-866607
E-mail: cotcm@indigo.ie

Specialising in all aspects of traditional chinese medicine: acupuncture, chinese herbal medicine, tuina, homoeopuncture. Excellent results in asthma, irritable bowel syndrome, insomnia, anxiety, impotence, female gynaecological disorders etc. Reduces injury time in sports injuries by 50%.

NATURAL MEDICINE CENTRE

Contact: Gemma Dillon
Kells Road, Navan, Co. Meath

Tel: 046-27156
Fax: 046-27156

Gemma Dillon Lic.Ac., Dip.Ac. MAFI ACMO. Traditional Chinese medicine, acupuncture, herbal medicine, vega testing – organs and food sensitivities, complex homoeopathy.

GUANGMING

Contact: Betsy Didderions
Townshend Street, Skibbereen, West Cork

Tel: 028-22616
Fax: 028-36381
E-mail: betsydidderiens@tinet.ie

Treating many ailments with acupuncture and Chinese herbs. Also specialising in children's ailments and sports injuries. By appointment only.

CHINESE MEDICAL CENTRE

Contact: Wenmi Mohaci
47 Upper Georges Street, Dun Laoghaire, Co. Dublin

Tel: 01 2800268
Fax: 01 2809160

Traditional Chinese medicine regulates the meridians of the body to unblock the stagnation of Qid. The Chinese doctors are from Beijing and are fully qualified in both Chinese and Western disciplines. Heal all ailments for patients.

TRADITIONAL CHINESE MEDICAL CENTRE

Contact: Noeleen Slattery
T.C.M Centre, Main Street, Rathcoole Co. Dublin.

Tel: 01-4589672
Fax: 01-4589705

Traditional Medical centre offering a wide range of therapies.

CRANIOSACRAL THERAPY

GERALDINE NOLAN

53 Binn Eadair View, Sutton, Dublin 13

Tel: 086-8187249
E-mail: geraldine@72ndst.com

Craniosacral therapy is a subtle light-touch therapy based on evaluation and correction of the craniosacral rhythm. It facilitates the body's own healing process and leads to the deep tissue healing through therapeutic process of Somato emotional release.

THE ENERGY MANAGEMENT PROGRAMME

Contact: Joseph McGuire, The Healing Place, 61 St. Assam's Park, Raheny, Dublin 5

Tel: 01-8484270 / 087-2461853
E-mail: josmcg@adent.ie

Treatments and readings: Craniosacral therapy, Shiatsu hands on healing. What the face reveals. 9 Star Ki oriental astrology. Also available to give workshops throughout Ireland. Gentle - safe - powerful - effective.

CLINICS AND HEALING CENTRES

'SUAIMHNEAS' HOLISTIC HEALTH CLINIC

Contact: Kim Byrne, Alva Fitzgerald, Marie Fitxpatrick. Main St., Buncrana, Co. Donegal

Tel: 077 63550 or 087 2814870

Aromatherapy, reflexology and holistic massage provided. By appointment only. Ladies and Gents of all ages are welcome.

REGENIUS HEALTH CARE & CLINIC

Contact: Rosaleen Kelly, RPN, MSRI, CPI
Kiltabee, Ballyhaunis, Mayo

Tel: 0907-30022 / 086 8188123

Rosaleen is a former nurse who treats all illnesses combined with food testing, nutritional testing, stress work, educational kinesiology. All courses are approved by International Kinesiology College and Gateways College, California.

COLLEGE OF NATUROPATHIC COMPLEMENTARY CLINIC

Contact: Herman Keppler
73 Gardenwood Road, East Grinstead, West Sussex RH19 1RX.

Tel: 0044-1342 410505
Fax: 0044-1342 410909
E-mail: info@bestcareuk.com
Website: http://www.naturopathy-uk.com

3-4 year diploma-course in Belfast and Dublin in naturopathy, homoeopathy, Chinese medicine, herbal medicine, iridology. For more details call Belfast 0801238-532464 or above.

THE RHIANNON CLINIC

Contact: Karen Ward
Rhiannon, St. Pauls' Grands, North King Street, Smithfield, Dublin 7

Tel: 087-2399571
Fax: 01-670 4905
E-mail: kward@ie.packardbell.org

Holistic clinic offering Ki massage, diet consultations, stress management, psychotherapy, yoga. Treating clients perspective to enhance their health energy vitality and life.

RATHMINES CLINIC OF NATURAL MEDICINE

Contact: Gary Collins
14 Rathgar Road, Rathmines, Dublin 6.

Tel: 496 1316
Fax:459 1155
E-mail: lgc@clubi.ie

Traditional Chinese medicine. Acupuncture, herbs, Tuina massage, Shiatsu. Pranic healing (energy healing for pity and emotional disorders), cellular healing (healing emotional and behavioural patterns to develop clarity, confidence and self-empowerment).

COISCEIM NATURAL THERAPY CENTRE

Contact: Anne M. O'Donnell
8 Church Street, Tralee, Co. Kerry.

Tel 066-7181855
Fax: 066-7181855

Treatments in massage therapy, reflexology and body work: Bio-resonance testing. Evening classes, workshops. We also stock a range of self-help books, supplements and aromatherapy oils in our shop.

AS SOLAS HEALING CENTRE

Contact: Anne Boyle & Phil Moloney
"The Hermitage" Mt. Anglesby, Clogheen, Co. Tipperary.
Tel: 052-65566

Diploma courses in:
Energetic massage therapy, ITEC Diploma in anatomy & physiology. Reflexology - registered with BCMA (British Complementary Medicine Association). Post Graduate and counselling. Evening classes in yoga, meditation, self-healing. Summer courses: Holistic holidays and Mini breaks.

SHAMROCK HEALTH CLINIC

Contact: Robert Dowdall, 12 Birchyien Close, Kilnamanagh, Tallaght, Dublin 24.

Tel: 01-4510212 / 087-2025179

Sport therapy, reflexology, Indian head massage. The treatment I give is aimed towards prevention, thus maintaining an overall health and fitness level. Injury is also treated when it occurs.

SANDYCOVE HEALTH CLINIC

Contact: John Peter Caviston
57a Glasthule Road, Sandycove ,Co. Dublin

Tel: 01-2845287

Chiropody, reflexology, aromatherapy, Ki-massage, Swedish massage, physical therapy incorporating myofacial, neuromusculary and muscle energy techniques. Indian head massage, mobility chair massage, on-going myofacial workshops. Reflexology and aromatherapy workshops, ITEC Reflexology Diploma courses.

UNLIMITED BODY HARMONY

Contact: Rosemary Khalifa or Marge Casey
65 Park Lawn, Clontarf, Dublin 3.

Tel: 087 2077393
Fax: 01 8330656

Unlimited body harmony; listen to the body which, after all, knows best, allowing the body to unwind and let go of old traumas which encourages more movement and harmony in oneself.

ODESSY HEALING CENTRE

Contact: Brenda Doherty
15 Wicklow St.,Dublin 2

Tel: 01 878 6454
Fax: 01-6771021

An oasis of peace amidst the hustle and bustle of city life offering: acupuncture, aromatherapy massage, bio-energy healing, body harmony, homoeopathy, hypnotherapy, Indian health massage, rebirthing, reiki, Swedish massage.

BEARA CIRCLE NATURAL MEDICINE

Contact: Ula Kimon
Beara Circle, Castletownbere, Co. Cork

Tel: 027-70744 / 027-70595
Fax: 027-70745

Beara Circle, founded 1988 in a former convent, combines: clinic for natural medicine, accomodation, wholefood restaurant, lectures, workshop facilities. Treating: Allergies, arthritis, candida, depression, hyperactivity, immune-deficiency, overweight, stress.

ALTERNATIVE LIFESTYLES HEALTH CLINIC

Contact: Oilbhe O'Donoghue.
Unit 3, Market Court, Town Hall, Bray, Co. Wicklow.

Tel: 01-2762095/2866396
Fax: 01-2869788
E-mail: eod@indigo.ie

Centre for natural therapies. Services include aromatherapy, allergy testing, dietary therapy, nutrition, holistic massage, homoeopathy, iridology, life coaching, reiki etc.

BOOK CONNECTION

Holistic Bookstore

Extensive range of Self-help, Alternative Medicine, Positive Living & Spiritual / Personal Growth titles

Solarlight T/A Book Connection, Convent Lane, Bloomfields Shopping Centre, Dun Laoghaire, Co. Dublin. Ph / Fax: (01) 2300447 email: eeg@esatclear.ie

HOLISTIC THERAPY CENTRE

Contact: Eileen Clair
Carrowncalla, Kilrush, Co. Clare

Tel: 065-9052239

Bio-resonance medicine- A computerised test which can show what is out of balance on a physical, emotional and psychic level and what remedies, dietary changes or therapies are appropiate to restore balance.

PANDJI NATURAL THERAPIES INTERNATIONAL

Contact: Stephen Bulmer
2 Ormond Rd., Drumcondra, Dublin 9.

Tel: 01-3576649 / 086-8708996
Fax: 01-3576649
E-mail: pandji@irelands-web.ie

A Vajrayana Buddhist healing centre offering

Chinese and Balinese therapeutic massage; rebirthing; traditional Thai massage; Shiatsu nutrition; chakra balancing; trance therapy; reiki healing and atunements; acupoint and acupressure therapy; meditation.

THE HEALING OASIS

Contact: Anne O'Neill RGN, MIHCA
Ranelagh, Dublin 6.

Tel: 01-4970774; 087-2225283

Combination of Ki/Indian head/Swedish/ancient Thai massage, counselling, colour therapy, healing, kinesiology, Australian bush flower remedies - intuitively working with the individual in the most appropiate way for them.

SHOSELISH HOLISTIC CENTRE

Contact: Joseph McCormack
Blenheim, Cross Dunmore Rd., Waterford

Tel: 051-875444
Fax: 051-875444

Shoselish Holistic Centre uses holistic (physical, mental, emotional) approach to promote and maintain good health by activating the bodys' own power and accelerating its natural ability to heal itself.

CHRYSALIS HOLISTIC CENTRE

Contact: Claire Harrison
Donard, Co. Wicklow

Tel: 045 404 713
Fax: 045 404713
E-mail: peace@chrysalis.ie
Website: www.chrysalis.ie

A registered charity based in West Wicklow, founded in 1989 specialising in residential courses in personal growth and in spirituality with facilities for private group bookings and hermitage retreats.

THE HEALING HOUSE

Contact: John Kenny
24 O'Connell Ave, Berkeley Road, Dublin

Tel: 01 8306413
Fax:01 8306060
E-mail: info@healinghouse.ie
Website: www.healinghouse.ie

The Healing House provides space for healing by enabling spiritual healers, counsellors, therapists and practitioners of complementary medicine to run courses and give individual sessions.

CORK FLOATS

Contact: William Ahern
70 Douglas St., Cork

Tel: 021-321857

Cork floats is an holistic health centre offering flotation therapy, massage, aromatherapy, reiki, homoeopathy and astrology. Floating is zero gravity relaxation...the new answer to stress management for the millennia.

HARVEST MOON CENTRE

Contact: Peter Kane or Wendy Hickey
24 Lower Baggot Street, Dublin 2

Tel: 01-6627556
E-mail: peterjkane@hotmail.com
Website: http://www.avcweb.com/harvestmoon

Flotation / massage / holistic stress management / healing. Many holistic therapies including various types of massage, flotation tank, chiropractic, shiatsu, psychic readings, spiritual healing meditation, yoga, open 6 days 11am till late. Special offers and gift vouchers available.

NATURAL HEALING CENTRE

Contact: Rose/Terry Byrne
22 Derrynane Gardens, Bath Ave.
Sandymount, Dublin 4.

Tel: 01 6681472

Iridologist, herbalist, aromatherapy, reflexology, stress management, massage.
Our aim, combining herbs and iridology, is to treat the individual in a more holistic approach. Looking at every aspect, job, diet, home, exercise routine, sleep patterns as well as general health background etc.

CATRIONA DOYLE
Main St. Kiltimagh, Mayo.
Tel: 094-82010/087-2369702

As an Holistic therapist I welcome you to avail of reflexology, therapeutic massage using essential oils and clinical hypnotherapy. Ring for free explanatory brochures.

CROÍ
Deborah O'Neill
Gurteenroe, Bantry, Co. Cork
Tel: 027-52193

Exciting new centre in beautiful West Cork, offering a blend of therapies for groups and individuals; psychotherapy, imagery, bio-energy, reiki. Retreat breaks and training in energy healing

EDUCATION

CONTINUING EDUCATION CENTRE
Contact: Sr. Kathleen Moran
Sion Hill, Blackrock Co. Dublin
Tel: 01 2886831 or 01 288 2075
Fax: 01 288 5260

Education, spirituality, culture and leisure. This centre is educationally and pastorally oriented. It provides broadly-based courses which may not be available elsewhere. Courses catering for cultural, personal, emotional and spiritual development – fees relatively small.

LIVING EARTH APPRENTICESHIPS-ROOM FOR HEALING
Contact: Judith Hoad
Inver, Co.Donegal
Tel: 073 36406

Health maintenance / repair / education.
Living Earth apprenticeships require commitment to a year studying herbalism, healing arts and the Living Earth at physical, emotional, mental and spiritual levels during 13 separate weeks at Inver. Fees negotiable.

JANUS
Contact: Ben Whelan
Booterstown House, Booterstown Ave., Co. Dublin
Tel: 01-2884533
E-mail: janus@esatclear.ie
Website: http://www.esatclear.ie/~janus

Janus is primarily a learning community which aims to provoke public discussion in the areas of spirituality & sustainability. We are currently developing a curriculum for a "Modern Mystery School" modelled after Plato's academy.

THE LIVING WATER WORKSHOP
Contact: Grahame Whitehead
8 Kilmacrannell, Castlebalfour, Lisnaskea, Co. Fermanagh, N. Irl.
Tel: 0801-365 722902
Fax: 0801-365 722902
Website: Holistic.ie/lastchanceclinic

The Living Water Workshop is a group of healers / diviners who are re-educating the public about water health. What is living water? Good water, bad water, vortex technology - the key to living water. See advert p.225.

HEALTH PRODUCTS AND SUPPLIERS

YELLOW BRICK ROAD
Contact: Robert Neilson
8 Bachelors Walk, Dublin 1.
Tel: 01-873 0177
Fax: 01-873 0177
E-mail: bobn@iol.ie

Specialists in healing crystals, feng shui, accessories and books for alternative lifestyles. Regular classes and workshops. Also stockists of quality beads, jewellery making equipment and jewellery. Friendly, helpful, expert service.

GAIA ESSENCES
Contact: Ann Callaghan /Antionette O'Connell
Rockingham House, Newcastle, Co. Wicklow
Tel: 01-2863222 / 01-2819705
Fax: 01-2811931
E-mail: anto@indigo.ie

Co-creative essence making and sale. Workshops in co-creative use of essences for health and environment. Making your own essences co-creatively. Co-creative care for the new children. Life skills for the 21st century.

AVEDA

Contact: John McNicholas
Main St., Kiltimagh, Co. Mayo

Tel: 094-9481005
Fax: 094-9481005
E-mail: carmacltd@eircom.net

A complete range of skincare, hair, make-up and lifestyle products all manufactured from pure plant ingredients – organically grown wherever possible and totally without petrochemicals. We have an active policy to reduce, re-use and re-cycle.

WELL DISTRIBUTION

Contact: Ronnie Cox
33 Knockbraken Rd., Belfast, Co. Antrim BT86SE

Tel: 0801 232-815996
Fax: 0801 232-815996

Tahitian Noni Juice. The best kept secrets of supplementary medicine. Sold as a food supplement understates this phenomenal product, which helps in arthritis, blood presure diabetes (1 and 2), depression and many major ailments.

ACUPUNCTURE AND ALTERNATIVE SUPPLIES LTD.

Contact: Noeleen Slattery
T.C.M. Centre, Main Street, Rathcoole, Co. Dublin

Tel: 01-4589672
Fax: 01-4589705

Supply of Chinese herbal remedies and acupuncture equipment. Traditional medical centre offering a wide range of therapies.

PHILIP NEWELL

Bridge-a-Crinn, Dundalk, Co. Louth.

Tel: 042-9377328

Yoga teacher - reiki, Seichem master – independent distributor of Neways personal cure and health products. Products you have always wanted, but could never get. Products that really work. Effective natural solutions – bridging the gap between science and human needs.

ATLANTIC AROMATICS

Contact: David Kelly
9 Ardee Court, Bray, Co. Wicklow

Tel: 01-2865399
Fax: 01-2865414

Aromatherapy (essential oils) supplies. Supply of pure essential oils for aromatherapy - specialising in oils distilled from organically grown plants obtainable at health food stores countrywide.

LISTINGS

TIR NA NOG OILS

Contact: Maria Kinsella
Limerick, Ireland
Tel: 087 2203980
E-mail: essentialoil@tinet.ie
Website: http://homepage.tinet.ie/~kinco

Alternative health – aromatherapy.
We offer essential oils, carrier oils, natural
cosmetics, wooden oil storage boxes, wall charts
and pottery burners. We sell in the Limerick Milk
Market every Saturday until 1.30 pm.

HEALERS

TOM COLEMAN

Harolds Cross, Dublin 6W.
Tel: 01-4966215

I am a natural healer and as such have the gift
from the Spirit to serve as a sensitive channel for
light, love and healing. Registered healer: British
Register of Complementary Practitioners.

HEALTH FARMS

HAGEL HEALING FARM & ANAM CARA NATURAL HEALTH CENTRE

Contact: Contact: Janny Wieler
Coomleigh, Bantry, Co. Cork
Tel: 027-66179
Fax: 027-66438

A special healing place to retreat from daily stress
offering a wide range of natural therapies. Detox
week/weekend, health week, retreats, home-grown
food. Also individual treatments by appointment.

CLOONA HEALTH CENTRE

Contact: Dhara Kelly
Westport, Co. Mayo
Tel: 098-25251
E-mail: cloona@anu.ie
Website: http://www.holistic.ie/cloona

Specialising in cleansing and relaxation, we run
original, invigorating programmes combining
simplicity, depth and beauty,. Residential courses
with daily yoga, walks, sauna, massage and
cleansing diet. Peaceful countryside. Stunning
views.

AN TEARMANN BEAG, HEALTH & HOLISTIC CENTRE,

Contact: Sally McCormack / Mary Condron.
Moorsfort, Kilross, Tipperary
Tel: 062-55102
Fax: 062-55102
E-mail: antearmannbeag@tinet.ie
Website: www.avcweb.com/tearmannbeag

This health farm offers a wide range of therapies,
delicious home cooked food, emphasis on
vegatation. A comprehensive library for books and
tapes in an atmosphere of peace and tranquility.

HERBALISTS

IRISH ASSOCIATION OF MEDICAL HERBALISTS

Contact: Carole Guyett, MIAMH,
Derrynagittah, Gaher, Co. Clare.
Tel: 061-924268
Fax: 061-924182

Leading professional body of Medical Herbalists in
Ireland. Members have completed a rigorous four
year training and adhere to a strict professional
code of ethics.

MEDICAL HERBALIST

Contact: Helen McCormack
186 Philipsburgh Ave, Dublin 3.
Tel:01-8368965

A medical herbalist is trained to diagnose ailments
both of a chronic and acute nature and to
prescribe a range of medicinal herbs tailored to a
patients need to provide relief.

THE DISPENSARY: MEDICINAL HERBS AND THERAPY ROOMS

Contact: Mimm Patterson
Derry City Herbal Clinic, 7 London Street,
Derry BT486RQ.
Tel: 0044-2871 271500 / 0801-504 271500
Fax: 074-28074
Website: www.thedispensary.co.uk

Retail shops & therapy rooms.
Dispensaries retail area is the only Northern
Ireland distribution of Napeers herbal products.
We also have 5 therapy rooms offering
acupuncture, herbal medicine, sports massage and
therapy, homoeopathy and osteopathy.

ANGELINA KELLY ITEC MIRI

20 Forest Park, Kingswood Estate, Dublin24
Tel: 01-451 9283
Fax: 01-451 9283

Bach Flower Remedies(R), reflexology, Bioforce
herbal medicines, complementary health
consultants, talks, seminars, workshops. Safe
haven to explore and discuss problems in
sympathy, every consultation is conducted
professionally and confidentially.

NICOLE TREACY IAMH

6 Sandycove Avenue East, Sandycove, Co. Dublin
Tel: 01-2301841
Fax: 01-2805284

As a qualified medical herbalist, I have spent four
years training in diagnosing, prescribing and
dispensing herbal medicines. Every prescription is

tailored to suit your individual needs, after consultation.

HOMOEOPATHY

IRISH SOCIETY OF HOMOEOPATHS
Contact: Karen Doherty
35/37 Dominick St., Galway
Tel: 091 565040
Fax: 091 565040
E-mail: ishom@eircom.net
The Irish Society of Homoeopaths works to promote and advance homoeopathy in Ireland. We represent student and practicing homoeopaths, foster high standards of practice, and advise members of the public seeking referral. Contact us Monday to Thursday (mornings).

IRISH SCHOOL OF HOMOEOPATHY LTD.
Contact: Angie Murphy
Admin office, 47 Ratoath Estate, Cabra, Dublin 7
Venue for courses, Milltown Park College, Ranelagh, Dublin 6
Tel: 01 868 2581
Fax: 01 868 2581
E-mail: ishom@indigo.ie
The Irish School of Homoeopathy is affiliated to the Irish Society of Homoeopathy, the regulating body of professional homoeopathic practitioners. We are committed to homoeopathic education in Ireland and to this end we provide several courses in Milltown Park College.

HELEN SWEENEY
11 St. John's Road, Clondalkin, Dublin 22
or 15 Wicklow St. Dublin 1
Tel: 01 878 6454
Fax: 01-6771021
Classical homoeopath and reiki master. Practising in the Odessy Healing Centre and Clondalkin.

GILLIAN DUNLOP
Youngstown, Taghmon, Co. Wexford.
Tel: 053 39151
Gillian trained with the Irish School of Homoeopathy in Dublin. After 2 years in practice she became a registered homoeopath and now works from home and in the Centre for Natural Therapies in Wexford.

LILIAN VAN EYKEN
14 Pairc na gCa, Moycullen, Co. Galway
Tel: 091-555810
Lilian Van Eyken is a member of the Irish Society of Homoeopaths, trained at the Dutch Academy of Natural Medicine and the European University For Traditional Chinese Medicine.

SABINE KAEMPFE
Old Post Office, Rosturk/Mulranny, Co. Mayo
Tel: 098-36247
Homoeopath (Heilpraktikerin) - Classical homoeopathy.

RUTH DUNNE
3 Lakewood Park, Dyke Rd., Galway.
Tel: 091-760592
Homoeopathy is a holistic medicine which facilitates the body to heal itself using minute doses of carefully selected remedies to activate the body's own natural healing force.

DAVID JEFFREY
36 Gilabbey Street, Cork.
Tel: 021-501600
To use Homoeopathic medicine as an aid to restoring harmony by removal of disease and, through education, to facilitate an understanding of the role life experience plays in the disease process.

PAULINE O'REILLY
11 Edenvale Rd., Ranelagh, Dublin 6.
Tel: 014976553
Fax: 014976553
E-mail: deirdre0@gofree.indigo.ie
Classical homoeopathy. Homoeopathy is a holistic medicine which takes the persons mental,

emotional, physical symptoms into account and, using minute doses of carefully selected remedies, facilitates the body to heal itself naturally.

DONAGHMEDE HOMOEOPATHIC CLINIC

Contact: Dianne Sims Lic ISH
The Donahies, Dublin 13.

Tel: 01 848 4868

Classical Homoeopathic Clinic. Homoeopathic clinic in Dublin Northside. Ring for appointment.

GILLIAN WRAY I.S.Hom
101 Collins Park, Dublin 9.

Tel: 8316269
Fax: 8316269
E-mail: gwray@tinet.ie
Website: http://homepage.tinet.ie/~gwray

Classical homoeopath. Homoeopathic medicines are made from natural sources, either plant, animal or mineral. They are extremely safe and efficient when used correctly. All consultations are by appointment.

PAULA BYRNE LBSHOM ISHOM
Kilvahan, Portlaoise, Co. Laois

Tel: 0502-27181
Fax: 0502-27225
E-mail: kilvahan@tinet.ie

Classical homoeopath. Byrne is a classical homoeopath who practices in Portlaoise (0502-22239) and Carlow (0503 40118). A graduate of the Burren School of Homoeopathy and registered with the Irish Society of Homoeopaths, she holds a post-graduate Diploma from the Dynamis School of Homoeopathy.

ANNE WALKER Lic. ISH I.S.Hom
Carrigeen, Kilglass, Co. Roscommon.

Tel: 078-37221
Fax: 078-37221

Homoeopath. Homoeopathy is an effective and scientific system of healing which assists the natural tendency of the body to heal itself. It recognises that the whole person needs treatment not the disease.

HYPNOTHERAPY

APPLEBY HYPNOTHERAPY CLINIC

Contact: John J. Kelly
Camolin, Enniscorthy, Co. Wexford

Tel: 054-83425
Fax: 054-83425
E-mail: hypnosis@indigo.ie
Website: http://indigo.ie/~hypnosis

We treat panic attacks, insomnia, stress, confidence building, smoking, weight reduction, memory and concentration, exam nerves, stage

fright, personal development, shyness, blushing, enchancing creativity, bereavement, phobias, bed-wetting and public speaking.

MARY MITCHELL

Ammarose, Derryharriff, Castlebar, Co. Mayo.

Tel: 094-23654 / 086-8490823
E-mail: marymitchell@eircom.net

Using hypnoanalysis and holistic therapies can help you with conditions of body, mind & spirit, such as depression, anxiety, stress, out of balance etc. Mary Mitchell Adv. Dip. MIAH, holistic therapist and teacher.

WEXFORD HYPNOTHERAPY CLINIC

Contact: Bernadette Murphy Adv. Dip. Hyp. MIAHH
Stavsnas, Coolcotts, Wexford

Tel: 053-42269
Fax: 053-42269
E-mail: hypnotherapy@excite.com

Hypnotherapist, psychotherapist, a member of the Institute of Clinical Hypnotherapy and Psychotherapy and also a member of the National Guild of Hypnotists (USA Inc). Release from physical, social and psychological problems.

PEGASUS HEALING CENTRE

Contact: Michael Hyland MDU DIP HYP MSNLP MAHP MSNU UK
17 Leiklip Park, Leixlip, Co. Kildare.

Tel: 01-6247219

Emotional and psychological health care. Professional hypnotherapist, trained in the UK by Richard Bandler as neuro linguistic programmer, American trained thought field therapist, trained counsellor, UK spiritual healer, neurologist.

INSTITUTE OF CLINICAL HYPNOTHERAPY-PSYCHOTHERAPY

Contact: Dr. Joe Keaney
Therapy House, 6 Tuckey St., Cork.

Tel: 021-273575
Fax: 021-275785
E-mail: hypnosis@iol.ie
Website: www.iol.ie/~hypnosis/ichp

Hypnotherapy training – Irish School of Ethnical and Analytical Hypnotherapy. Professional hypnotherapy training course, open learning diploma. Includes modules and advanced practical training held at Griffith College, South Circular Road, Dublin 8.

KINESIOLOGY

TONIA BRIONES

21 Silverdale Rd. Ballinlough, Cork City

Tel: 021-293978 / 021-293978
Fax: 021-293978

Kinesiology: Testing muscle finds if imbalances are physical, emotional, mental, nutritional, electro-magnetic, structural, energy or stress related. **Educational kinesiology & brain gym:** Works for learning difficulties, concentration, co-ordination & raising self-esteem. **Craniosacral:** A gentle method to encourage proper flow of spinal fluid through our nervous system. **Reiki:** Gentle and relaxing energy balance. **Acupuncture & homoeopathy:** A combination of two very powerful techniques that has an effect of cleansing and allows Qi to circulate. **Seiki:** A profound Japanese method to enable the body to unwind and relalign itself.

EOIN MACCUIRC
8 Geraldine Place, Albert Rd., Cork City

Tel: 021-318335
E-mail: mccuircee@csu.ie

Courses and therapy in kinesiology, traditional Chinese medicine, homoeopathy. Bio point testing, Craniosacral therapy. Touch for health, applied physiology. Alternative treatment for all age groups, babies through to pensioners.

ELLIE KEATING
25 Eyre Square, Galway.

Tel: 091-564244

Body balance/allergy testing, reflexology, kinesiology, counselling. Lose weight, relieve stress and increase your energy by using a combination of kinesiology, allergy testing, reflexology, counselling, psychotherapy and hypnotherapy.

MASSAGE THERAPY

IRISH HEALTH CULTURE ASSOCIATION
Contact: Barry Devlin DIP Ki massage MIHCA
11 Grove Ave, Blackrock, Co. Dublin

Tel: 086-814 6511

Ki massage therapy can aid back, neck and shoulder pain. Help recovery from injury, improve elimination of wastes and toxins from the body, increase energy levels both physically and mentally.

ABSOLUTELY ESSENTIAL
Contact: Shiona Watson
Circular Rd., Kilkee, Co. Clare

Tel: 065-9060055
Fax: 065-9060055
E-mail: abess@indigo.ie
Website: http:// indigo.ie/~abess

Offering a range of therapeutic treatments to assist the individual in their own healing and well-being. Holistic massage. Aromatherapy. Sports injuries.

ACCREDITED BOWEN THERAPISTS, IRELAND
Contact: Lesley Harvey
230 Scrabo Road Newtownards, Co. Down

Tel: 0801-247 826164
E-mail: intouchalternatives@nireland.com
Website: www.homestead.com/bowenireland

Bowen is a gentle, effective muscle release therapy. By enabling the body to re-balance, it can help with back, neck, shoulder, knee, breathing, digestive, fertility problems and more.

GEORGINAS INTERNATIONAL COLLEGE OF THERAPY
Contact: Georgina Price, 37 Shop St., Galway.

Tel: 091-564796

Georginas international college of therapy offers courses in beauty therapy, body massage, aromatherapy, sports massage and electrolysis. All courses are registered with the following examining bodies: I.T.E.C, C.I.B.T AC and C.I.D.E.S.C.O For details contact Georgina @ 37 Shop Street Galway 091 564796

BONNIE CONNOLLY
Newtown, Castlebar, Co. Mayo.

Tel: 094-22588

Shem is an emotional release therapy. Therapeutic massage. Reflexology. Indian head massage. Pranic healing is a safe, effective method of energy healing. These holistic therapies help to balance and maintain a healthy body.

EMILY MIGGIN Lic TCM MPRTCM
5 Morehampton Road, Donnybrook, Dublin 4
Tel: 01-6683132
Fax: 01-6680012

Traditional Chinese massage / massage therapy. As a member of the Professional Register of Chinese Medicine (BUPA approved), I practice TCM-acupuncture, moxibustion, dietary therapy, herbalism. As a certified massage therapist – deep connective / sports, shiatsu / acupressure, Amadeus healing.

KI MASSAGE THERAPY
Noreen Barry
Sandycove Health Clinic
57a Glasthule Rd., Sandycove, Co. Dublin
Tel: 01-2782278 first for appointment

Ki massage is a natural way of alleviating the accumulation of stress and tension in the body. Gives relief from asthma, arthritis, neck and shoulder tension and long back discomfort.

AMERICAN HOLISTIC INSTITUTE OF IRELAND
Contact: Maureen Maloney & Jimmy Faherty
73 Claremount, Circular Road, Galway, Co. Galway
Tel: 091-525941
Fax: 091-529807
E-mail: faherty@iol.ie

Scholl provides holistic diploma courses in therapeutic massage - 2 year Diploma. Also, continuing education for holistic practitioners. International recognition modules in personal development in Connemara, the inner healing journey. Join us.

INNIU SCHOOL AND HEALING CENTRE
Contact: Martina Coyne RN SCM
11 Main Street Lucan, Dublin.
Tel: 01-6283467 / 086-8213808
E-mail: info@holistic.ie
Website: www.holistic.ie/inniu

Private, sessions in massage, reiki, reflexology, stone therapy. Multi-dimensional cellular healing. Ongoing training in reiki and intuitive massage. Special focus on personal development and professional training.

I.H.C.A.
Contact: Elizabeth Homan
6 Orchardstown Ave Rathfarnham Dublin 14
Tel: 01-4943101

Ki massage, aromatherapy, Indian head massage, spiritual healer. Having qualified and worked for many years as Ki massage, aromatherapy and Indian head massage therapist, I recently

expanded my practice to include spiritual healing – healing of mind, body and spirit.

MEDITATION

DUBLIN MEDITATION CENTRE
Contact: Pauline McGuire
2 East Essex St., Temple Bar, Dublin 2.
Tel: 01-6713187
Fax: 01-6705717
E-mail: fwboir@iol.ie
Website: www.iol.ie/~fwboirl

Teach meditation, yoga and buddhism. Dublin Meditation Centre is a state registered charity, we teach practical, jargon free effective Buddhist meditation to all interested. Practicing such meditation soon leads one beyond theory into deep personal experience of interconnectedness.

METAMORPHOSIS

METAMORPHOSIS
Contact: Eithne O Mahony
'Shiloh', Clondulane, Fermoy Co. Cork.
Tel: 025-31525 / 025-32966
Fax: 025-33751
E-mail: shiloh@iol.ie
Created by Robert St. John.
Influences out of the past arrive at conception and the memory is stored unconsciously. This affects our attitudes and behaviour. Metamorphosis is a very effective means of helping one to erase these limiting patterns.

THE METAMORPHIC TECHNIQUE
Contact: Eddie O'Brien
8 Cliff Road, Tramore, Co. Waterford.
Tel: 051-386531
Fax: 051-390266
E-Mail: weobrien@esatclear.ie

The Metamorphic Technique is a unique approach to our need for self healing. Because the technique is completely non-invasive physically and psychologically, it is found that healing can emerge in a totally natural way.

MIND/BODY/SPIRIT

BALANCING LIFE'S ENERGIES
Contact: Anna Cooper or Sarah Boyd
28 Belfast Rd., Holywood, Co. Down BT18 9EL
Tel: 01232-425307
E-mail: sana@freeworld28.freeserve.co.uk

These workshops are particularly valuable for people under stress. They include breathing, bodywork, music, relaxation and awareness of body energies. Especially applicable for groups of colleagues in businesses, schools, institutions etc.

STRESS ELIMINATION TECHNOLOGY LTD.

Contact: John Flynn
Doonard, Tarbert, Co. Kerry.

Tel: 068-36586
Fax: 068-36378

Geopathic stress detection using the most modern equipment available and geopathic stress, suppression using the German range of "Duplex" devices, electro-magnetic stress suppression devices also in stock.

NORDIC NATURAL ENERGY AND TECHNOLOGY

Contact: Ciaran Graham
Cullen Upper, Wicklow

Tel:0404-48204
Fax: 0404-48295
E-mail: ciaran@nordic.ie

Working with natural vibrational energy, we create atmosphere that allows the human body, plant and animal life to live in harmony and heal itself. We also raise the living energy in water.

THE GRAIL MOVEMENT IN THE BRITISH ISLES

Contact: Mairead Daly
5 Kingston Crescent, Dundrum, Dublin 16.

Tel: 01-2984108

New spiritual knowledge. The Grail Movement is responsible for the dissemination of the work *In the Light of Truth*, the Grail message by Abd-ru-shin. Introductory literature and details of public activities will gladly be supplied upon request.

THE BEECHES HEALING CENTRE

Contact: Pat & Bernie Glennon
The Beeches, Kilconnell, Ballinasloe, Co. Galway.

Tel: 0905-86800

Bio-energy therapy and bio-resonance. Medicine, suitable for all conditions and diseases - very high success rate.

DANCES OF UNIVERSAL PEACE

Contact: Bev Doherty
Glentogher, Carndonagh, Co. Donegal
Tel: 077-74581
Fax: 077-74581
E-mail: ronaislg@iol.ie

Qualified leader of the Dances of Universal Peace. The Dances of Universal Peace are multi-faith sacred circle dances that honour all spiritual traditions, through movement and chanting, offering a path to inner peace. Workshops are held nationwide. **For private appointment contact Pat/Bernie at 0905-86800.**

JAIME MCGRANE

Prospect Bungalow, Knocklyon, Dublin 16.
Tel: 01-6627556

Fax: 01-4943503
E-mail: jmcgrane@yahoo.com

My work is focused on assisting people to heal all aspects of themselves by providing a safe, supportive space for release and empowerment.

BRAHMA KUMARIS

(World Spirituality University)

Contact: Janet Sylph / Margaret O'Sullivan
6 Woodhaven, Bishopstown, Cork.

Tel: 021-341297
Fax: 021-341297 (ring first)

Brahma Kumaris - World Spirituality University. Free courses in meditation. Learn to appreciate yourself, gain peace of mind, deal with stress and understand yourself on a deeper level. No physical exercise involved.

AN SANCTOIR LTD.

Ballydehob, West Cork.

Tel: 028-37155
E-mail: Sanctoir@tinet.ie
Website: http://www.westcorkweb.ie/ansanctoir

An Sanctoir is a beautiful octagonal building and is home to weekly classes in yoga, tai chi, dance and qi gong. It hosts workshops in a wide range of holistic practises, as well as concerts and other events. Set in 30 acres of peaceful nature reserve, it's also a perfect setting for camps, retreats and gatherings.

THE GROVE OF SINANN

Contact: Chris Thompson
Teach Shinanna, Shanraw, Keshcarrigan, Co. Leitrim.

Tel: 078-42154
E-mail: sinann@iol.ie
Website: homepages.iol.ie/~sinan

Within our calendar tree circle, labyrinth and other sacred spaces, we offer workshops on all aspects of Celtic and pre-Celtic spirituality/ self-development. We also host seasonal gatherings and rites of passage.

PRANIC HEALING CHAKRA

Contact: Geraldine Nolan
53 Binn Eadair View, Sutton, Dublin 13

Tel: 086-8187249
E-mail: geraldine@72ndst.com

Pranic healing is a powerful core method of cleansing and removing diseased energy from the aura and the chakras; it strengthens the body's defense system by balancing its vital energy.

GENTLE WIND PROJECT

Contact: Kitty Kaos-Hornsby
Cool Mountain West, Dunmanway, Co. Corcaigh.

Tel: 026-49306
E-mail: kittykaos@tinet

Healing to restore and regenerate a person's energetic structure when experienced once in a person's life. Work on hurt and damage at its source. Positive, lasting life improvements. This works by donation.

ROSIE DEVITT ESSENCES

Contact: Rosie Devitt
20 Glencraig Park, Holywood Co. Down.
Tel: 0044-2890 422628 / 0801-232 422628
E:mail: rosiedevitt@nireland.com

Flower, gem and other vibrational essences.
A very ancient therapy, the vibrational essences of flowers, gemstones, various metals and minerals have been found to be of benefit to body, mind and spirit.

CASTLEPOOK

Contact: Bev & Del Richardson
Castlepook, Doneraile, Co. Cork

Tel: 022-24339
Email: del@paganireland.com
Website: www.castlepook.com or
www.paganireland.com

We are an earth based, pagan spiritual centre on 13 acres of semi-wild meadows incorporating meditation space, and private work-space. We provide life rites celebrations including handfastings, namings and all other Rites of Passage. Our facilities are available for others to hold camps and workshops. We are always open to visitors, asking only prior contact.

NATURAL VISION IMPROVEMENT

NATURAL HEALING CENTRE

Contact: Gisela Jurgen
Carclough, West Belmullet, Co. Mayo.

Tel: 097-82065

Through different holistic methods you can learn to make your life better for yourself. Gisela specialised in natural vision improvement. Take off your glasses and see clearly, using vision games to reactivate stiff eye muscles and brain gym to encourage both hemispheres to co-ordinate in harmony. Palming and breathing to relax your eyes and make you feel more comfortable in life.

NURSING HOMES

FLORENCE GARDEN NURSING HOME

Contact: Maire Woods
5-8 Florence Garden Nursing Home, Bray, Wicklow

Tel: 01-2863900/01-4901368.
We provide a warm and relaxing environment for the elderly and people suffering from Alzheimers disease. Where possible, we use complementary medicines including herbal and homeopathic treatments.

OSTEOPATHY

BLACKROCK OSTEOPATHS

Contact: Simon Curtis
11 Proby Sq., Blackrock, Co. Dublin.

Tel: 01-2886514
Fax: 01-2781292
E-mail: simoncurtis@esatclear.ie

Blackrock Osteopaths is staffed by fully qualified registered osteopaths who are all members of the Irish Osteopathic Association. Special interest in sports and dance injuries and trained in craniosacral osteopathy.

PSYCHICS

MOIRA ALLEN
Hillview House, Prosperous, Naas, Co. Kildare.

Tel: 045-868252
Fax: 045-892305
E-mail: hillview@eircom.net

Psychic readings, psychic development lessons, reiki healing and teaching to master level available.

REFLEXOLOGY

IRISH REFLEXOLOGISTS' INSTITUTE

Contact: Maria B. Pundyne
15 Chatsworth, Bangor, BT19 7WA, Co. Down

Tel: 0801-247 466995

Contact: Lua McIlraith (Southern Ireland)

Tel: 086-8138446
Website: www.avcweb.com/reflexology

Irish Reflexologists' Institute is a non-profit making body regulating the professional and ethical standards of reflexology in Ireland - North and South. Has a code of practice and ethics and uses a holistic approach.

AILEEN O'CONNOR
2 County View Terrace, Ballinacurra, Limerick

Tel: 061-228860
Fax: 061 342923
E-mail:aileenoc@iol.ie

I practice reflexology, reiki, colour therapy, Bach flower remedies. I use a rayometer to balance the body's natural energies and douse for geopathic stress. I teach a Diploma course in reflexology.

HEALTH THERAPIES CLINIC

Contact: Rose McDonald RPN, SRN, SCM, MIRI, ITEC, OSM Dip
13 Gladstone St., Waterford
Tel: 051-858584 or 051-423736(hm)
E-mail: judmar@indigo.ie

Professional practitioner in reflexology. Reiki-seichem energy, magnified healing, metamorphic technique, massage-therapeutic; on site massage; Indian head massage; sports injury; polarity therapy - craniosacral balancing counselling. Courses/talks on reiki, reflexology, massage. Magnified healing.

DR. ANTHONY J. WALSH

Robertstown, Carrigaline, Co. Cork.
Tel: 021-771551

Reflexology is a form of complementary medicine that activates the healing process within the body by a special pressure technique on the feet and hands.

YVONNE O'RIORDAIN

St. Judes, Old Brick Road, Templeogue, Dublin 16.
Tel: 087-6761971

Three Complementary Therapies. For further information contact: Yvonne O Riordan, ITEC Diploma in: Reflexology & ITEC Tutor, reflexology, holistic massage, aromatherapy, Member of IRI, and MAR.

MARY MOLLAGHAN

6 Moonlaun, Tramore, Co. Waterford.
Tel: 051-391112

Practitioner of reflexology, which stimulates reflexes on the feet to increase the bodies own healing abilities and reiki, which uses universal life energy to promote balance, healing and consciousness.

REBIRTHING

ASSOCIATION OF IRISH REBIRTHERS

Contact: Catherine Dowling
33 Inchicore Rd., Dublin 8.
Tel: 01-4533166
Fax: 01-4533166

Rebirthing is a breathing technique rooted in the ancient traditions of the Far East and shaped by the discipline of eastern and western psychology. It is a holistic mind-body therapy that allows people access to the world inside themselves and provides a means of resolving internal difficulties that is deep, lasting and energising. Rebirthing is for people who want to transform their inner world gently but powerfully, and who want to take charge of their lives with confidence.

REIKI

MAUREEN GILLEN

Fernbank, Point Rd.,Crosshaven, Cork.
Tel: 021-831991
Fax: 021-831991

Reiki/seichem is universal energy which is used to heal on all levels. A one day teaching enables you to do healing on yourself and others. It's simple for everyone.

STRESS MANAGEMENT CONSULTANT

Contact: Annette Smyth MASC (Corp,)
4 Donegall Crescent, Whitehead, Carrigfergus, Co. Antrim BT38 9LS
Tel: 0044-2893 378070

I offer reiki, seichem, reflexology and aromatherapy. Also available are reiki and seichem workshops (prepared to travel). Gift vouchers are available.

BROOKFIELD PHYSIOTHERAPY CLINIC

Contact: Teresa Collins
Ardmanning Ave, Togher, Co. Cork
Tel: 021-962268
Fax: 021-312488
E-mail: brookfieldphysio@tinet.ie

Reiki individual treatments and Level I, II, and III classes. I have taught USUI reiki for 6 years – Levels I, II and III. I am the author of the first book on reiki published in Ireland, *Reiki at Hand* which is used as a text book in all classes. Monthly follow-up classes are included with all levels to further develop reiki in the practitioners life. Individual treatments are also available.

REIKI / AURA-SOMA

Rosaleen Tobin
1 Butterfield Crescent, Rathfarnham, Dublin 16.
Tel: 01-4933964
Fax: same
E-mail: tobin@tinet.ie
Website://homepage.tinet/~tobin

Reiki master, teacher and healer. Counselling diploma. Cutting of ties. Aura-soma colour therapy individual sessions, workshops and aura-soma products. Workshops on growth and spirituality.

THE DIVINE CHALLICE SCHOOL OF REIKI HEALING AND ANGELIC INVOCATIONS

Contact: Gwendoline McGowan
"Hamilton Lodge", Turvey Avenue, Donabate, Co. Dublin
Tel:087-2448545
Fax: 01-8407904
E-mail: gwendolinemcgowan@tinet.ie
Website: www.avcweb.com/gwendoline

Healing therapist, chakra balancing, distress. Dis-harmony and dis-ease appear to cause most of todays stresses, reiki offers support for the over-worked mind, body and feeds the soul. Reiki brings a more released energy to todays busy life.

CATHY STANTON
Macroom & Cork City, Co. Cork
Tel: 086-8326475/026-46128

Cathy specialises in couselling for bereavement, seperation and relationship problems, supporting clients through times of change. She is a reiki therapist. Reiki being a relaxing stress therapy without words.

SHEN

IRISH SHEN THERAPY ASSOCIATION
Contact: Maureen Maloney & Jimmy Faherty
73 Claremount, Circular Road, Galway Co. Galway
Tel: 091 525941
Fax: 091 529807
E-mail: faherty@iol.ie

Because shen works directly with the emotions, shen's clinically established procedures can bring rapid and dramatic changes to conditions that often take years with more traditional methods. Contact above for your own area practitioner.

SHEN TAO

ROOM FOR HEALING
Contact: Judith Hoad
Inver, Co. Donegal
Tel: 073-36406

Vibrational medicine practitioner & teacher of shen tao acupressure, essences and native herbs in one-to-one consultations. Guide of the Living Earth apprentices. All my work is for voluntary contribution. Details on request.

SHIATSU

CORK SCHOOL OF SHIATSU
Contact: Diana Cassidy RPSSI
61 Westcourt Heights, Ballincollig, Co. Cork
Tel: 021-572324 / 087-2070132

Cork School of Shiatsu. Introductory and professional part-time training courses available in Cork. Approximately three years in duration.

SHIATSU PRACTITIONERS

DIANA CASSIDY
RPSSI, 61 Westcourt Heights, Ballincollig, Co. Cork
Tel: 021-872324 / 087-2070132
Professional appointments available in Ballincollig

and Cork. Specific treatments for anxiety, scar tissue, problems and certain back pains.

TAI CHI

TAO SCHOOL OF TAI CHI
Contact: Laetitia Collins
52 Monastery Gate Ave, Clondalkin, Dublin 24
Tel: 01 459 1990(hm),
Fax: 459 1155
E-mail: lgc@clubi.ie

Tai chi and qi gong, gentle Chinese mind-body exercises. Improves posture and energy; reduces stress; enhances awareness concentration and confidence, regular classes and seminars. Private tutition in company training.

GOLDEN ENERGY ARTS
Contact: Jan Golden Garden
Flat 2, 76 Frankfort Ave., Rathgar, Dublin 6.
Tel: 01-4968342
Fax: 01-4968342
E-mail: jang@indigo.ie
Website: www.goldenenergyarts.com

I teach a WU style tai chi form to business and to the public. This form and the Taoist standing meditation are specifically designed for today's stressful technological society.

YOGA

IRISH YOGA ASSOCIATION
108 Lower Kimmage Rd.,
Harolds Cross, Dublin 6W.
Tel: 01-4929213 (answering service only)
Fax: 01-4929213
Website: http://indigo.ie/~cmouze/yoga.htm

Three year part-time course which includes asanas, pranayama, philosophy, meditation, anatomy and physiology, first-aid. Commencing September. Please send A5 s.a.e. for further information and application form.

IRISH YOGA ASSOCIATION
108 Lower Kimmage Rd.,
Harolds Cross, Dublin 6W.
Tel: 01-4929213 (answering service only)
Fax: 01-4929213
Website: http://indigo.ie/~cmouze/yoga.htm

Established 1978 to promote yoga in Ireland. Activities: teacher training course; seminars; members newsletter; membership 270; subscription £20p.a. Our diploma holding teachers are teaching countrywide. For further information please send s.a.e.

WOMEN'S HEALTH

WELL WOMAN CENTRE
Contact: Angela Kenn
67 Pembroke Rd., Dublin 4.
Tel: 01-6609860/01-6681108
Fax: 01-6603062

Centres also at 35 Lower Liffey St., Dublin 1
Contact: Jennifer Feighan, **Tel:** 8728051, 8728095, 8728466 and Northside Shopping Centre, Coolock, Dublin 5. **Tel:** 8484264, **Fax:** 8484264, **Contact:** Imelda Healy. Well Woman Centres provide a comprehensive women's health service including general health check-up, family planning, menopause clinics and counselling.

ANIMAL CARE

ALTERNATIVE ANIMAL CARE
Contact: Tom Farrington
Allswell, Barley Hill East, Rosscarbery, Co. Cork
Tel: 087-2494059
Fax: 023-48811
E-mail: alternanimalcare@eircom.net

Alternative animal care is run by Tom Farrington, a vetinary surgeon of twenty years experience who uses both homoeopathy and conventional veterinary in a complementary fashion in the treatment of animals.

ALTERNATIVE ANIMAL CARE FARRINGTON & MEADE
Contact: Tom Farrington
30 Whitehall Rd. Terenure, Dublin 12
Tel: 01-4555362/ 087-2494059
Fax: 01-4557102
E-mail: alternanimalcare@eircom.net

Alternative animal care is run by Tom Farrington, a vetinary surgeon of twenty years experience who uses both homoeopathy and conventional veterinary in a complementary fashion in the treatment of animals.

ANIMAL CHIROPRACTIC
Contact: Dr. Abby Hassan
4 Farrer Street, Braddon 2612,
Canberra, Australia
Tel: 0061-2-62626472

Gentle and effective chiropractic whole body treatment which includes assessment of the spine, pelvis and joints for any misalignment or muscle spasms. Suitable for all animals.

BURNS PET NUTRITION
Contact: Sheena Burns
Killonan, Ballysimon, Co. Limerick
Tel: 061-330534
Fax: 061-335678
E-mail: dsb@gofree.indigo.ie

Burns Real Food for Dogs. Complete, natural, no GM ingredients. Brown rice, fish or chicken, vegetables preserved with vitamin E. Also Burns Real Food for Cats available from veterinary surgeons.

SEE ALSO

FENG SHUI
Carmel O'Connor
A design consultant encorporating the practical principles of feng shui into her work.

Catherine Larkin
Feng shui practicioner

Feng Shui Design
Feng shui design for harmonious living.

Elizabeth Studenski
House feng shuied for more harmonious living.

Jaya Moran
Millennium feng shui frogs for house, garden and business.

Full listings for Feng Shui:
Green Building and Ecological Design section.

MALIN HEAD HOSTEL
Provides weekend breaks in reflexology and aromatherapy.
Full listing: Eco-tourism in Art and Leisure section.

DANCING THE RAINBOW
Dance in a fragant, sensual environment.
Full listing: Eco-tourism in Arts and Leisure section.

SUNYATA HOLIDAY & RETREAT CENTRE & HERBAL CLINIC
Meditation retreats and herbal medicine workshops.
Full listing: Eco-tourism in Arts and Leisure section.

NATURE ART WORKSHOP CENTRE
African drumming, healing, shamanic journey, painting, dance.
Full listing: Arts and Leisure section.

NEANTOG ORGANIC FARM
Reflexology and reiki practicioners.
Full listing: Agriculture section.

AISLING ARANN
Focused on creating a sustainable, just and

spiritually rooted lifestyle.

Full listing: Media and Information section.

THERAPEUTIC DIETITIAN
Cecilia Armelin

Advises adults and children on a wide variety of
illnesses.

Full listing: Food and Drink section.

PURE H20, STEAM DISTILLED WATER

Domestic and commercial steam water distillation
untis.

Full listing: Food and Drink section.

IRISH DOCTORS ENVIRONMENTAL ASSOCIATION

Highlights the link between health and the
environment.

Full listing: Environmental section.

TEACH BAN, THE HOME OF HEALTHY LIVING

Shiatsu courses available to release blocked
energy.

Full listing: Food and Drink section.

LISTINGS

ADVERT INDEX

Aisling Magazine1	86
Anam Cara M. Brady	232
Anti-Vivisection Society	51
Auro Paints, Healthy Building	136
Biochrome	139
Book Connection/Solarlight	234
Comhar	94
Department of the Environment	24
Development Studies, Kimmage	93
Eco Baby	233
Ecovillage Ltd.	231
ESB Lough Ree1	75
F.H. Wetland Systems	125
Feasta	164
Food for Thought	45
Forrest Friendly Floors	140
Full Life	46
Full Spectrum Lighting	138
Irish School of Homoeopathy	237
Just Forrests	142
Keras Wholefoods	46
Kinesiology Institute	239
Lifesprings Group	231
Lillyput Press	162
Living Water	225
Mayo Energy Agency	105
McSeans Herbal	235
Natural Medicine Company	226
New Vistas	228
O'Tooles	47
On the Case	49
Patagonia	228
Petra Berntsson	141
Register of Qualified Aromatherapists	230
Repak	124
Simply Water	50
Sustainable Earth Fair	178
The Healing House	241
The Hopsack	47
Triscle Heating	108
Unicorn Products	236
Voice (of Irish Concern for the Environment)	20

LISTINGS INDEX

3Bass Sound System	177
Absolutely Essential	241
Absolutely Organic	45
Accredited Bowen Therapists, Ireland	241
Actionaid Ireland	89
Active Art Creations	175
Acupuncture & Alternative Supplies	237
Acupuncture & Chinese Medicine Organisation	229
Adrian Joyce Architects	141

AEGIS	163
African Cultural Project	95
Aids Help West	231
Airogen Ltd.	108
Aisling Arann	188
Alan Johnston Traditional Tools	174
All That's Green	91
All@Sea	108
Allen, Moira	244
Alternative Animal Care	247
Alternative Animal Care, Farrington and Meade	247
Alternative Lifestyles Health Clinic	234
American Holistic Institute of Ireland	242
Amnesty International Irish Section	92
An Gríanan	46
An Sanctoir Ltd.	243
An t-Ionad Glas	69
An Tairseach	69
An Taisce	27
An Tearmann Beag	238
Anam Cara	229
Andrew Croft	145
Animal Chiropractic	247
Annapurna Natural Healthcare	230
ANU Internet Services	189
Aontas	210
Appleby Hypnotherapy Clinic	240
Aran Salmon Ltd.	47
Arklow Chiropractic Clinic	231
Armagh City and District Council	32
Aromatherapy&Reflexology Centre, The	230
Arramara Teoranta	68
Artists Association of Ireland	175
Ás Solás Healing Centre	233
Association of Hunt Saboteurs	32
Association of Irish Rebirthers	245
Association of Refugees and Asylum Seekers (ARASI)	89
Atar	230
Atlantic Aromatics	237
Atlantis Foundation Action Network	92
Attac-Ireland	162
Aveda	236
B9 Energy (O&M) Ltd	108
Baby Milk Action	93
Badgerwatch Ireland	32
Bagáiste-Cotton Bags	125
Balancing Life's Energies	242
Ballamore Development Group	211
Ballybrado Organic Farm	71
Ballymaloe House	171
Ballyphehane Credit Union	163
Bantry LETS	163
Banulacht	89
Barnardos	212

Bavaria B&B	171
Bealtaine Ltd.	109
Beara Circle Natural Medicine	234
Beara Local Economy System	162
Beasant, Stephanie	231
Beeches Healing Centre, The	243
Belfast Food Co-op	48
BEOFS Bio Energy and Organic Fertilisers Services	68
Better by Nature	47
Between	89
Beulah Plumbing, Heating, Solar Services	106
Bia Arann	66
Big Green Art	175
Bio-Cara Ltd.	68
Biochrome Ltd	143
Blackrock Osteopaths	244
Blue	188
Bord na Mona Environmental ltd.	126
Boytonrath Organic Farm	66
Braade/Carrickein Conservation Group	30
Brahma Kumaris	243
Briones, Tonia	240
Brookfield Physiotherapy Clinic	245
Bunnaton House	171
Burgess, Jacqui	231
Burns Pet Nutrition	247
Burren Action Group	27
Burren Walking Holidays	171
Byrne Paula	240
Caher Fruits	66
Calypso Productions	175
CAMP	140
Carmichael Centre for Voluntary Groups	89
Cashel Credit Union Ltd.	163
Cassidy, Diana	246
Castlebar Credit Union Ltd	163
Castleblayney Trust	212
Castlepook	244
Catalyser Collective	177
Celtic Spirit-Culture Weeks	171
Centre for Adult Continuing Education	210
Centre for Natural Therapies	235
Cerbral Palsy Ireland	127
Chernobyl Children's Project	89
Chinese Medical Centre	232
Chinese Traditional Massage,	232
Chiro Centre, The	232
Christopher Southgate and Associates	141
Chrysalis Holistic Centre	235
Clean Technology Centre	31
Clinic of Oriental & Traditional Chinese Medicine	247
Clonmel Organic Growers	66
Cloona Health Centre	238
Co-operative Development Society	164
CODEMA	106
COFORD	70
Cohu, Anthony	141
Coisceim Natural Therapy Centre	233
Coleman, Tom	238
Colin Glen Trust	27
College of Integrative Acupuncture	229
College of Naturpathic Complementary Clinic	233
Columban Mission	93
Comhlamh	89
Community Action Network Ltd	209
Community Environmental Services	30
Compassion in World Farming	71
Connaught Waste Recycling Co. Ltd	127
Connemara Safari	171
Connolly, Bonnie	241
Connolly, Margaret	231
Conservation Technology Ltd.	127
Conservation Volunteers Ireland	27
Conservation Volunteers Northern Irl.	30
Continuing Education Centre	236
Cooleenbridge Steiner School	213
Cork City Energy Agency	105
Cork County Council	125
Cork County Energy Agency	105
Cork Cycling Campaign	109
Cork Floats	235
Cork LETS	162
Cork School of Shiatsu	246
Cork Waldorf Steiner Initiative	213
Cornucopia Vegetarian & Vegan Restaurant	50
Cosgrove & Son Good Food Shop	46
Cottage, The	173
Craft Granary, The	174
Craniosacral Therapy	232
Crann (Dublin & East branch)	69
Crann (Offaly)	69
Creative Activity for Everyone (CAFÉ)	176
Croft, Andrew	145
Croí	236
Crookstown Mill	171
Cuba Solidarity Cultural Committee	91
Cussens Cottage	171
Daintree	125
Dances of Universal Peace	243
Dancing the Rainbow	176
David Healy & Associates	30
Debt and Development Coalition	89
DEFY Development Education for Youth	93
Demeter Standards Ltd.	65
Department of Agribusiness & Rural Development	209
Design By Nature	67
Development Studies Centre	93
Development Studies Library	93

Dingle Craft Village	174
Direct Action Against Apathy	188
Dispensary: Medicinal Herbs	238
Divine Challice School, The	245
Donaghmede Homoeopathic Clinic	240
Donegal Energy Action Team	106
Donegal Organic Farm	65
Downhill Hostel, The	173
Doyle, Catriona	236
Dr. Anthony J. Walsh	245
Drogheda Acupuncture Clinic	229
DU Greens Society	27
Dublin City Agenda 21	209
Dublin Co-housing Group	211
Dublin Cycling Campaign	109
Dublin Food Cooperative Society Ltd	48
Dublin Healthy Cities	209
Dublin Institute of Technology	209
Dublin Meditation Centre	242
Dublin Society for Prevention of Cruelty to Animals	32
Dulra Magazine	188
Dunamaise Beekeepers Association	70
Dungarvin Alternative Health Clinic	229
Dunlop, Gillian	239
Dunne, Ruth	239
Dunstar Ltd	106
E.F.Energy (Developments) Ltd.	107
Earth Education Centre, The	31
Earth Wisdom Foundation	211
Earthwatch Magazine (Friends of the Earth Ireland)	188
Earthwatch/Friends of the Earth Ireland	27
East Connacht Energy Agency	105
East Timor Solidarity Group	93
Eco Co-op	164
Eco Cottage (Eco Booley)	145
Eco Cottage (Eco Booley)	172
Eco Cottage (Tourism Development) Project	171
Eco-Community Architect	141
ECO-UNESCO	31
Eco-village at Burdautien	210
Ecobaby Limited	214
Ecological Design Association	139
Ecological Solutions	126
Ecological Trades Community	164
Ecology Society NUI Galway	27
Ecoseeds	164
Ecowater-Karden Distributors	49
Eden Plants	65
El Salvador Awareness	89
EMC	189
Energy Action Ltd.	109
Energy Engineering Group	105
Energy Management Programme, The	233
Energy Research Group UCD	143
ENFO	31
EnviroNature Recovery Associates	28
Environmental Action Alliance EAA	28
Environmental Education for Schools and Organisations	31
Environmental Efficiency Consultants (Ireland) Ltd.	30
Environmental Efficiency Consultants (Ireland) Ltd.	109
Environmental Management Services	30
Environmental Protection Agency	27
ERDA	107
ERM Environmental Resources Management	33
Esperanto-Asocio de Irlando	93
Ethical Investment Co-Operative, The	163
F. H. Wetland Systems	126
F.H. Wetland Systems	126
Fairtrade Mark (Ire)	92
FEASTA	162
Federation of Irish Beekeepers Association (F.I.B.K.A)	71
Fehily Timoney & Co.	141
Felix Eco Art	176
Feng Shui Design	145
Fingal North Dublin Beekeepers Association	70
Florence Garden Nursing Home	244
Focus Ireland, RD+E Division	212
Food For Thought	45
Forest Friendly Floors Ltd	143
Foyle Basin Council	209
Foyle Regional Energy Agency, Energy Advice Centre	109
Friends of Animals	33
Friends of the Irish Environment	28
Fruit Hill Farm	66
Full Spectrum Lighting Ltd.	144
Future Forests Ltd.	70
Future Wind Partnership Ltd.	107
Gaia Ecotecture	140
Gaia Essences	236
Galway Energy Agency Ltd.	106
Galway Metal Co. Ltd	127
Galway One World Centre	95
Garristown Organics	66
Garry Gleeson Associates	143
Gay Community News	188
Genetic Concern	48
Gentle Wind Project	244
Georgian House and Garden	144
Georginas International College of Therapy	241
Gillen, Maureen	245
Gingerbread Ireland	214
Glencree Reconciliation Centre	90
Glynn, Joseph	162
GOAL	90
Going For Green	33

Golden Energy Arts	229	Interior Alignment	145
Golden Energy Arts	246	International Centre for Development Studies	95
Good Food Store, The	46	Into the Wilderness	172
Gorta	90	IOFGA (Irish Organic Farmers & Growers Assoc.)	65
Gortbrack Organic Farm	66	Ionad 'Buail Isteach' na Gaeilge	212
Gortrua Organic Farm	67	Irish Aid Advisory Committee	90
Gortrua Organic Farm	172	Irish Antivivisection Society	33
Grail Movement in the British Isles	243	Irish Association of Medical Herbalists	238
Grainey, The	45	Irish Basketmakers Association, The	175
Green Building Digest	139	Irish Brewing Co., The	49
Green Lodge	172	Irish Council Against Blood Sports	32
Green Party Comhaontas Glas	28	Irish Council for Civil Liberties	90
Greencastle Organic Farm	65	Irish Doctors Environmental Association	28
Grove of Sinann, The	243	Irish Earthworm Company	68
Grow Green Products	68	Irish Eco-Village Information Network	210
Growing Awareness	48	Irish Ecological Design Association	139
Guangming	232	Irish Garden Plant Society	67
Hagel Healing Farm	238	Irish Health Culture Association	241
Hands on Furniture Ltd.	174	Irish Landscape Institute	139
Happen	140	Irish Mexico Group	90
Harbour View Hostel	172	Irish Peatland Conservation Council	28
Haricots Wholefood Restaurant	50	Irish Reflexologists Institute	244
Harvest Moon Centre	235	Irish School of Homoeopathy Ltd.	239
Harvey, Sue	232	Irish Seaweed Industry Organisation	68
Harvey-Paper Animal Bedding	125	Irish Seed Savers Association	69
Healing House, The	235	Irish Shen Therapy Association	246
Healing Oasis, The	235	Irish Society of Homoeopaths	239
Health Therapies Clinic	245	Irish Wildlife Trust	28
Healthy Buildings Consultancy	143	Irish Wind Energy Assoc.	105
Healy, Dennis	66	Irish Womens' Environmental Network	28
Helen, Sweeney	239	Irish Yoga Association	246
Heneghan's Guest House	172	ISPCC	212
Herb Garden, The	66	JANUS	236
Herr Ltd.	126	Jason Harris Design Services	67
Herr Ltd.	127	Jeffrey, David	239
Hoey Environmental	106	Jesuit Centre for Faith and Justice	91
Holistic Therapy Centre	234	Jesuits for Debt Relief and Development	90
Hollies Sustainable Village, The	210	John O'Keeffe & Associates	139
Home Birth Association	213	Just Forests	70
Home Education Network (HEN)	213	Kaempfe, Sabine	239
Hopsack, The	46	Kealamine Organic Farm	67
Horkan, Maura	231	Keating, Ellie	241
Hyperborea	176	Keating, Mary	229
I.H.C.A	242	Keep Ireland Open	29
IBC Computer and Internet Co.	189	Kelly, Angelina	238
Icon Architecture and Urban Design	140	Keras Wholefoods	45
Inishowen Beekeepers Association	70	Kerry Counselling Centre	231
Inishowen Community Organic		Ki Massage Therapy	242
Farm Co-op Society Ltd.	69	Killary Lodge	172
Inishowen Environmental Group Co-Op Society Ltd.	28	Klee Paper	125
Inniu School and Healing Centre	242	KMK Metals Recycling Ltd.	128
Inspioraid	174	Krystyna Pomeroy - Paper craft	174
Institute of Clinical Hypnotherapy	240	L'Arche Kilkenny	164
Interculture	96	Lagan Valley Permaculture	67

Lagerway the Windmaster	108
LaLeche League	213
Landscape Alliance Ireland	29
Larkin, Catherine	145
Latin America Solidarity Centre LASC	93
Leadlines Stained Glass	174
Lettercollum House	50
Letterkenny Acupuncture & Herbal Clinic	229
Lifespring Group	230
Limerick Civic Trust	144
Linda Heffernan Acupuncture Practice	229
Living Earth Apprenticeships	236
Living Landscapes	67
Living Water Workshop, The	236
Lovebites Organic Caterers	50
Lynch, Seamus	229
Maam Children's Playscheme	212
MacCuirc, Eoin	241
Macrobiotic Association	48
Macroom Disrict Environmental Group	29
Mad Jabooba Stuff	174
Magic Badger, The	140
Malin Head Hostel	172
Maynooth Chiropractic Clinic	232
Mayo Energy Agency	106
McGrane, Jamie	243
Meanwell Wholefoods	45
Medical Herbalist	238
Meitheal Bhreannan	162
Meitheal na Mart	163
Merlin Agri-Environmental Consultancy	67
Metamorphic Technique, The	242
Metamorphosis	242
Methan O'Gen	126
Midland Development Education Project	95
Midwives Association of Ireland	213
Miggin, Emily	242
Mike Hall Electronics	107
Mike Keegan Design	140
Milmorane Basketry	174
Mitchell, Mary	240
Mollaghan, Mary	245
Moran, Jaya	145
Mountaineering Council of Ireland	172
Moville/Greencastle Environmental Group	29
Muintir na Coillte - The Coppice Association of Ireland	70
Muintir na Tire	209
Narmada Organics	66
Narrow Water Lime Service	143
National Committee for Development Education	95
National Environmental Education Centre	31
National Windpower Ireland Ltd.	107
Natural Healing Centre	244
Natural Healing Centre, R.Byrne	235
Natural Health	229
Natural Instincts	176
Natural Medicine Centre	232
Natural Technology Systems	144
Naturally Aromatherapy	230
Nature Art Workshop Centre	176
Nature Store	230
Nature's Gold	51
Neantog Organic Farm	65
Nevin, Martina	230
New Delight Cafe/Restaurant, The	50
Newell, Philip	237
NICERT	107
Nicro-Metals Ltd.	128
Nine Acre Organic Farm	67
NJBA Arcitects & Urban designers	139
NODE Network	95
Noodle House Pasta	47
Nordic Natural Energy and Technology	243
Noreen, Barry	242
North Wall Women's Centre	210
North West Organic and Producers Group (NWOPG)	65
Northern Ireland Animal Rights Campaign	33
Northside Exchange & Trading System	163
Nuala Woulfe Beauty Salon Ltd.	230
O'Connor Carmel	145
O'Connor, Aileen	244
O'Reilly, Pauline	239
O'Riordain, Yvonne	245
O'Tooles Organic Butchers	47
Odessy Healing Centre	234
Ogoni Solidarity Ireland (OSI)	91
On the Case	48
One World Centre for Northern Ireland	95
Organic Butcher, John Downey	47
Organic Centre	69
Organic Trust Ltd	65
Organico Healthfood Shop	45
Otto's Creative Catering	45
Outhouse	211
Oxfam Ireland	90
P.Carney Ltd	127
Pandji Natural Therapies, International	234
Pantry, The	46
Papermachie Craft	174
Partnership Ireland-Africa	96
Patagonia	176
Paul O'Connor Architects	140
Peace & Neutrality Alliance	93
Pegasus Healing Centre	240
Pesticides Trust, The	71
Peter Schneider Solar Energy	108

Peterse, Ineke and Theo	173
Petra Berntsson Paintmaker & Designer	143
Phoenix, The	173
Pink House	173
Positive News	188
Pranic Healing Chakra	243
Public Communications Centre	189
Pure H2O	49
Quality Sea Veg.	47
Rachel Bevan Architects	139
Railway Ahead	109
Rainbow Wholefoods	46
Rath-Art	176
Rathmines Clinic of Natural Medicine	233
Reedbed Technologies Ltd J. Dolan. Eco Vill.	231
Regenius Health Care & Clinic	233
Register of Qualified Aromatherpists, Ireland	230
Renewable Energy Information Office (Cork)	105
Renewable Energy Information Office (Dublin)	105
Rhiannon Clinic, The	233
Richard Webb & Associates	141
Roaring Water Bay	47
Roaring Water Bay	68
Rogers Engineering	127
Room For Healing	246
Rosie Devitt Essences	244
Rural Innovation Centre, The	69
Rural Resource Development Ltd	203
S.O.L.D Save Our Lough Derg	29
Sandycove Health Clinic	233
Schumacher Ireland Initiative	162
Self Help Development International	91
Shamrock Health Clinic	233
Shankhill Swapskills	163
Shoselish Holistic Centre	235
Silver Lining Co.	127
Silvercrest Clinic	231
Simple Simon	45
Simply Water Ltd.	49
Slí an Uisce	210
Sligo LETS	162
Solaris	107
Solearth Ecological Architecture	140
Sonairte-The National Ecology Centre	32
Source Magazine	188
Southside Partnership	209
Space Kraft	176
Speedwell Trust, The	213
Spillane Insulations Ltd.	144
Square Wheel Cycleworks	109
St Canices Kilkenny Credit Union Ltd.	163
Stanton, Cathy	246
Stress Elimination Technology Ltd.	243
Stress Management Consultants	245
Studenski, Elizabeth	145
Suaimhneas	233
Sunflower Recycling	127
Sunyata Holiday & Retreat & Herbal Clinic	173
Sure Engineering (Europe) Ltd.	108
Sustainable Housing	143
Sustainable Northern Ireland Programme (SNIP)	209
Sustainable Projects Ireland Ltd.	211
Tao School of Tai Chi	246
TBW GMBH	126
TCD Environmental Society	30
TCD Once World Society	91
Teach Ban	48
Techne Associates	189
Telework Ireland	164
Temple Of Design, Mary Guinan	183
The Triad	92
Therapeutic Dietitian	51
Thermonex	143
This World Services	32
Three Rock Institute	32
Tidy Northern Ireland	31
Tipperary Energy Agency Ltd	106
Tipperary Litter and Tourism Initiative	173
Tipperary Rural and Business Development Institute	210
Tir an Droichid	211
Tir na nOg Holistic Centre and Hostel	173
Tir na nOg Oils	238
Tobin, Rosaleen	245
Tools for Solidarity	91
Traditional Chinese Medical Centre	233
Traditional Farm Hostel	173
Traidcraft	92
Treacy, Nicole	238
Tree Council of Ireland, The	70
Treoir	214
Trinity Greens	29
Triscle Heating	109
Triskel Flower Farm	174
Trocaire	91
Tuile Teanga	211
Tullamore One World Group	95
Ulster Architectural Heritage Society	144
Undercurrents	189
Unicorn Restaurant	50
Unlimited Body Harmony	234
Van Eyken, Lilian	239
Vegan Veg	66
Vegetarian & Vegan Guide to Ireland, The	49
Vegetarian & Vegan Information Group	48
Vegetarian Society of Ireland	48
Vegetarian/Vegan Bed&Breakfast	50
Victim Support	214

Vinceremos Wines and Spirits Ltd	49
VOICE	30
Voluntary Service International	91
Volunteer Resource Centre	29
Walker, Anne Homoeopath	240
Walnut Books	188
War on Want	92
Waste Working Group	125
WasteWorks	126
Well and Good	45
Well Distribution	237
Well Woman Centre	247
West Cork Beekeepers Association	70
Wetlands Advisory Service, The	125
Wexford Hypnotherapy Clinic	240
Wholefoods Wholesale Ltd.	45
Wicklow Planning Alliance	29
Wildfowl and Wetlands Trust, The	29
Wind Tower Manufacturing Ltd.	107
Wind Water Solar Energy Systems	108
World Development Centre	91
Wray, Gillian	240
Yellow Brick Road	236

NOTES

Registration Form for Source Book

If you offer a service or product in Ireland that helps people to live in a more environmentally sustainable, socially just or healthy, way, a listing in the Source Book will prove invaluable.

Name of Organisation or Business _____

Contact Name _____

Address _____

_____

Town/City _____

County/ Region _____

Telephone _____

Fax _____

E-Mail _____

Website Address _____

Area of activity _____

Include a thirty-word description of your activity. _____

Are you interested in advertising in this publication?
☐ Yes ☐ No

Can you facilitate a workshop or present a talk on your area of activity.
☐ Yes ☐ No

Would you consider taking a stall or a stand at any future events.
☐ Yes ☐ No